CONTENTS

1

PRINCIPLES OF CRYSTAL ARCHITECTURE

Mineralogy is the study of minerals. Petrology is the study of rocks. Minerals and rocks, which make up the crusts of the rocky planets and moons, are naturally occurring crystalline materials created independently of human conscious design. Atomic particles that compose crystalline materials are arranged in an orderly and repetitive pattern in three dimensions over large atomic distances. In a liquid or a glass, atomic constituents—atoms, ions, molecules, radicals, and so on—are distributed without long-range order, although local atomic order may very well exist. In any mineral or other crystalline substance, atomic positions are ordered and, in principle, predictable. This characteristic is important, because crystal structure, more than any other factor, determines the unique, characteristic physical properties of minerals. Composition is also important. For instance, trace chemical impurities give distinct colors to otherwise colorless minerals such as quartz and corundum. Physical properties include everything from hardness and density to the way in which a mineral behaves in a beam of visible light or X rays.

Mineral Chemistry A specific mineral species has a definite chemical composition that can be expressed by a chemical formula. A range of substitution of one element for another is allowable, but it must be possible, after analysis, to write a precise formula, which fits into a general formula for a mineral species, for any given mineral sample.

Principles of mineralogy apply equally to ceramics, to metallurgy, to materials research, and to synthetic crystals for gemologic, industrial, and assorted electronic uses. Strictly speaking, however, a mineral is a crystalline substance that is a product of natural inorganic processes. For consistency, regard water as molten ice, with ice crystals the commonest mineral observed at high elevations and latitudes. By the same token, native mercury can occur as crystals in polar regions where temperatures are frequently below its melt point of $-39°C$.

Noncrystalline materials of natural inorganic origin, such as lechatelierite (lightning-fused beach or desert sand), are called mineraloids. Note: Process of formation, not composition, makes this distinction between mineral and nonmineral. Natural crystalline hydrocarbons, such as abelsonite [nickel porphyrin] and flagstaffite [*cis*-terpin hydrate], are valid mineral species. Biologically produced crystalline materials, such as uroliths (kidney stones), are not minerals in a strict sense unless they have inorganically produced analogs. In gallstones of calcite and cholesterol, the first is a mineral and the second is not.

Synthetic crystals have physical properties identical to their natural counterparts. Synthetic ruby and sapphire may be called synthetic minerals, but a crystalline material must have at least one inorganic natural occurrence for it to be admitted to the realm of minerals, even though many such substances are given mineral-like names.

Mineral Names Many kinds of names are used in mineralogy. Each mineral species has a mineral name; there are approximately 3000 presently known species. All mineral samples having the same crystalline structure and chemical composition belong to the same mineral species. A mineral species has unique chemical and physical properties. An example is common quartz, which varies little in its composition and structure. Small structural defects and chemical impurities in quartz give rise, however, to its wide variety of colors and appearances and an equally wide assortment of varietal names, such as amethyst and citrine. But these and other varietal names do not denote separate mineral species because fundamental structure and composition are the same.

Minerals having the same crystalline structure are members of a mineral group. Calcite [$CaCO_3$], siderite [$FeCO_3$], rhodochrosite [$MnCO_3$], and magnesite [$MgCO_3$] are isostructural, and all belong to the calcite group of minerals. Chemical compositions of mineral samples may be restricted to essentially that of an end member, as with calcite, or they may extend to all intermediate compositions between end members, as with siderite and rhodochrosite. Current practice accords species status to end members only and a series name to samples of intermediate chemical composition. Thus, olivine [$(Mg,Fe)_2SiO_4$] is a series name for all mineral compositions between end members forsterite [Mg_2SiO_4] and fayalite [Fe_2SiO_4]. A major exception to this practice is the plagioclase series of feldspars where intermediate composition ranges are accorded separate mineral names (Fig. 2-26). Mineral species status may be accorded a chemical end member even though mineral samples of pure end-member composition may be rare or even nonexistent in nature; the garnet (group name) pyrope (species name) is rarely more than 70% $Mg_3Al_2Si_3O_{12}$.

The status of mineral species names is arbitrated by the Commission on New Minerals and Mineral Names of the International Mineralogical Association, an organization of national mineralogical societies. Members of this commission arbitrate among conflicting names for the same mineral species, and sanction characterizations and names for some four dozen new minerals discovered annually. These names should be submitted to the Commission by the scientific investigators of a purported new mineral in advance of publication.

History of Mineralogy In the past, minerals have been studied and classified from many different perspectives. More than 3000 years ago there was already considerable knowledge about minerals, especially in terms of their uses, both physical (such as building materials) and magical (such as amethyst to cure hangovers). No distinction was then made between naturally occurring materials and things made from minerals (ceramics) or extracted from minerals (metals). By the 10th century, alchemists and others were well-versed in mineral color, hardness, and density, especially in distinctions between precious stones and their imitators. Interest in mineralogy in Europe surged, beginning with the 16th century, as a result of a sharp increase in mining activity, but focus was still on physical properties of minerals (see Chap. 4).

Emphasis in mineral studies shifted abruptly toward the end of the 16th century to identification and classification on the basis of crystal shape—geometrical crystallography (Chap. 3). Another change in emphasis came at the beginning of the 19th century with the development of methods of quantitative chemistry and the resulting chemical analysis and classification of minerals. A new view of mineralogy, as well as of physics and chemistry, began in 1912 when W. Friedrich and P. Knipping, laboratory assistants to Max von Laue, produced evidence at Laue's instigation that crystalline materials diffract X rays (Sec. 1-3). This discovery made possible the determination of crystal structure (Chap. 2). Principles of crystal structures are thus the starting point in this book for a study of mineralogy.

1-1 ATOMIC MODELS

Minerals are composed of atoms, ions, molecules, and polyanions. Atomic particles consist of subatomic particles—electrons, protons, and neutrons. An electron has a single negative charge and nearly negligible mass. A

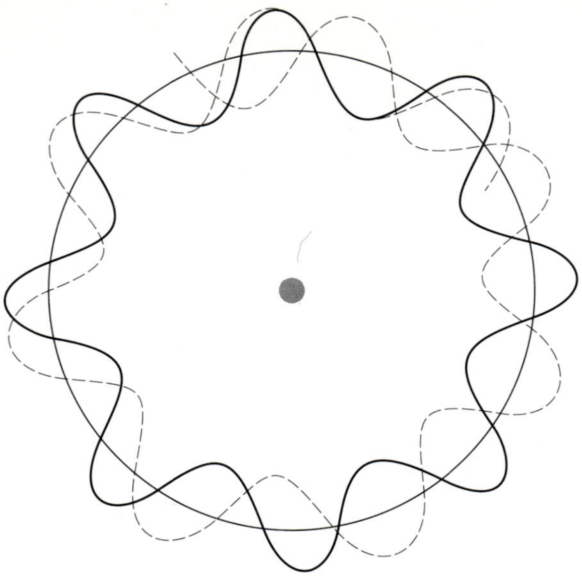

FIGURE 1-1 Schematic standing electron wave in an *s* orbital about an atomic nucleus (solid wave). If this wavelength were slightly different (dashed wave), it would be out of phase with itself and destroyed by wave interference. The next highest energy state occurs when exactly that quantum of energy necessary to add one full wavelength to this standing wave is added to this electron.

proton has a single positive electrostatic charge and a mass 1836 times that of an electron. A neutron has approximately the same mass as a proton but no charge. Neutrons and protons constitute atomic nuclei, which make up most of the mass, but little of the volume of atoms. Electrons occur outside a nucleus and make up the bulk of the volume occupied by an atom. When an atom loses or gains one or more electrons, it becomes an ion. Ionic diameter is on the order of 0.1–0.2 nm (1–2 Å), whereas nuclear diameter is on the order of 0.01 pm (0.0001 Å).

Niels Bohr first described atoms by analogy with our solar system, the sun representing an atomic nucleus and planets representing orbiting electrons. Subsequent research revealed that electrons are confined to certain three-dimensional orbitals that are separated by discrete energy gaps (Fig. 1-1). Packets of energy corresponding to these gaps are called quanta. Since there are four kinds of energy gaps, each electron in an atom is assigned four quantum numbers that label and characterize orbital electrons.

Quantum numbers are defined in the following manner. The principal quantum number n is related to the volume of a given electron orbital and refers to the angular momentum of an orbital electron, which can have values 1, 2, 3, . . . ; the azimuthal quantum number ℓ indicates that certain electron orbitals are nonspherical, and has values 0, 1, 2, . . . , $n - 1$; the magnetic quantum number m refers to orientation of an electron orbital in space and has values 0, ± 1, ± 2, . . . , $\pm \ell$; and the spin quantum number s refers to the sense of rotation of an electron and has values $\pm 1/2$. Wolfgang Pauli's exclusion principle states that in an atom no two orbital electrons can have the same four quantum numbers.

Another variance from the solar-system model of atoms comes from orbital shapes. Atomic s orbitals ($\ell = 0$) are spherical shells, but all other electron orbitals ($\ell > 0$) have strong directional components (Fig. 1-2). Orbital shape has a strong influence on what kind of chemical bond an atom may form (Sec. 1-2).

Numeration Element number 1, hydrogen (H), consists of one proton with one orbital electron. Quantum numbers of this electron are $n = 1$, $\ell = 0$, $m = 0$, and $s = 1/2$. Isotopes of hydrogen may also contain one or two neutrons. All isotopes of hydrogen have the same chemical properties, since these properties depend only on the number of protons present. These isotopes of hydrogen are given separate names: deuterium (D) for nuclear mass 2 (one proton plus one neutron), and tritium (T) for nuclear mass 3.

Descriptions of nuclear and electronic structure become hopelessly unwieldly in their repetition without some simplifying notation. Periods of a periodic chart of chemical elements are determined by a principal quantum number n. Electron shells and orbital electrons may be designated by capital letters: K for $n = 1$, L for $n = 2$, M for $n = 3$, N for $n = 4$, O for $n = 5$, P for $n = 6$, and Q for $n = 7$. Within each period, s refers to electrons with $\ell = 0$, of which there are two in each period. The letter p denotes electrons with $\ell = 1$, six per period. The letters d and f refer to electrons and orbitals with ℓ values of 2 and 3, respectively.

A convenient notation retains the principle quantum number to indicate an electron shell and uses the letters s, p, d, or f to designate an appropriate subshell. Thus, Li has two electrons in its 1s shell and one in its 2s, which may be indicated as $1s^2 2s^1$. Table 1-1 summarizes this notation.

Element Properties A periodic chart of chemical elements (Fig. 1-3; Prog. 1-1) is more than a mere tabulation or exercise in numeration. A periodic chart is a classification of chemical elements on the basis of their chemical properties. These chemical properties are in turn based on configurations of outer electron orbitals in an atom or ion.

A neutral atom is one that has the same number of orbital electrons as protons; in an ion these numbers differ. Beyond H the number of neutrons in an atom is the same as or somewhat greater than the number of protons. All atoms of a given element contain the same number of protons. Atoms with the same number of protons but differing numbers

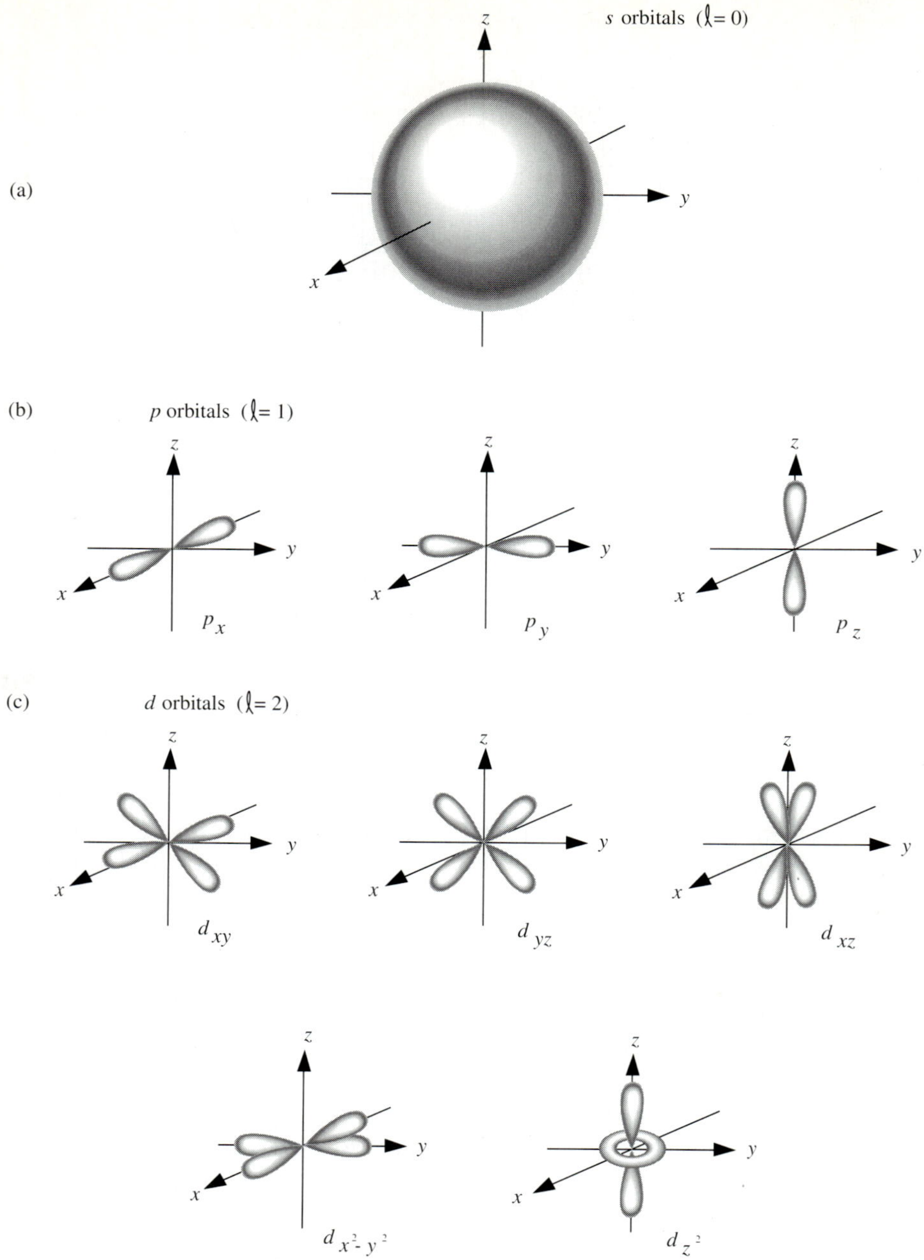

FIGURE 1-2 Shapes of orbitals. Orbitals represent surfaces where the probability of finding an orbital electron decreases both inward and outward from this surface. (a) *s* orbitals are spherical shells. (b) *p* orbitals are "dumbbell-shaped" surfaces; from left to right: p_x, p_y, and p_z. (c) *d* orbitals surfaces: d_{xy}, d_{yz}, d_{xz}, $d_{x^2-y^2}$, and d_{z^2}.

Differentiated by f Electrons
INNER TRANSITION ELEMENTS

Differentiated by d Electrons
TRANSITION ELEMENTS

Differentiated by p Electrons
NONMETALS

Differentiated by s Electrons

														III b	IV b	V b	VI b	VII b		VIII b		I b	II b	III a	IV a	V a	VI a	VII a	Noble gases	I a	II a
																														1 H 2.1	2 He
																														3 Li 1.0	4 Be 1.5
																								5 B 2.0	6 C 2.5	7 N 3.0	8 O 3.5	9 F 4.0	10 Ne	11 Na 0.5	12 Mg 1.2
																								13 Al 1.5	14 Si 1.8	15 P 2.1	16 S 2.5	17 Cl 3.0	18 Ar	19 K 0.8	20 Ca 1.0
														21 Sc 1.3	22 Ti 1.5	23 V 1.6	24 Cr 1.6	25 Mn 1.5	26 Fe 1.8	27 Co 1.8	28 Ni 1.8	29 Cu 1.9	30 Zn 1.6	31 Ga 1.6	32 Ge 1.8	33 As 2.0	34 Se 2.4	35 Br 2.8	36 Kr	37 Rb 0.8	38 Sr 1.0
														39 Y 1.2	40 Zr 1.4	41 Nb 1.6	42 Mo 1.8	43 Tc 1.9	44 Ru 2.2	45 Rh 2.2	46 Pd 2.2	47 Ag 1.9	48 Cd 1.7	49 In 1.7	50 Sn 1.8	51 Sb 1.9	52 Te 2.1	53 I 2.5	54 Xe	55 Cs 0.7	56 Ba 0.9
57 La 1.1	58 Ce 1.1	59 Pr 1.1	60 Nd 1.1	61 Pm 1.1	62 Sm 1.1	63 Eu 1.1	64 Gd 1.2	65 Tb 1.2	66 Dy 1.2	67 Ho 1.2	68 Er 1.2	69 Tm 1.2	70 Yb 1.2	71 Lu 1.2	72 Hf 1.3	73 Ta 1.5	74 W 1.7	75 Re 1.9	76 Os 2.2	77 Ir 2.2	78 Pt 2.2	99 Au 2.4	80 Hg 1.9	81 Tl 1.8	82 Pb 1.8	83 Bi 1.9	84 Po 2.0	85 At 2.2	86 Rn	87 Fr 0.7	88 Ra 0.9
89 Ac 1.1	90 Th 1.3	91 Pa 1.5	92 U 1.7	93 Np 1.3	94 Pu 1.3	95 Am 1.3	96 Cm 1.3	97 Bk 1.3	98 Cf 1.3	99 Es 1.3	100 Fm 1.2	101 Md 1.3	102 No 1.3	103 Lr	104																

← f → | ← d → | ← p → | ← s →

FIGURE 1-3 Periodic chart of the chemical elements. Electronegativities are in arbitrary units based on C = 2.5 and F = 4.0 (from Linus Pauling, reference at chapter end). Values change slightly for different oxidation states: Fe^{2+} = 1.8, Fe^{3+} = 1.9, Cu^{+} = 1.9, Cu^{2+} = 2.0; Sn^{2+} = 1.8; Sn^{4+} = 1.9.

TABLE 1-1 Electron Distribution and Quantum Notation

Shell	Subshell	Number of orbitals	Maximum electrons	
K (n = 1)	1s (ℓ = 0)	1	2	2
L (n = 2)	2s (ℓ = 0)	1	2	8
	2p (ℓ = 1)	3	6	
M (n = 3)	3s (ℓ = 0)	1	2	18
	3p (ℓ = 1)	3	6	
	3d (ℓ = 2)	5	10	
N (n = 4)	4s (ℓ = 0)	1	2	32
	4p (ℓ = 1)	3	6	
	4d (ℓ = 2)	5	10	
	4f (ℓ = 3)	7	14	
O (n = 5)	5s (ℓ = 0)	1	2	50*
	5p (ℓ = 1)	3	6	
	5d (ℓ = 2)	5	10	
	5f (ℓ = 3)	7	14	
P (n = 6)	6s (ℓ = 0)	1	2	72*
	6p (ℓ = 1)	3	6	
	6d (ℓ = 2)	5	10	
Q (n = 7)	7s (ℓ = 0)	1	2	98*

*Maximum possible electrons for each completed shell; this number is not realized in nature.

of neutrons are isotopes of a chemical element. Basic chemical properties of elements depend on configurations of outer atomic electrons—valence electrons—that are available to form chemical bonds in minerals. Although properties of elements are determined by the outermost electrons, most of an atom's electrons are much closer to its nucleus (Fig. 1-4).

Elements may be grouped together on the basis of their outermost electron configurations, upon which many chemical (mineralogic) properties depend. The first group, the noble gases, consists of atoms that have (once He is passed) a complete octet of *s* and *p* electrons. Since this configuration is particularly stable, these elements are not geochemically reactive and tend neither to lose nor to gain electrons in geochemical reactions, although some crystalline noble-gas fluorides are not difficult to synthesize.

Atoms in which valence electrons occupy shells of highest energy constitute a second type of element. These atoms have incomplete *s* or *p* orbitals. Elements with mostly unfilled *s* and *p* orbitals are metallic, but progressively across a periodic chart elements become nonmetallic with increased number of *p* electrons. This group of elements tend to gain or lose sufficient electrons in geochemical reactions to result in ions with the preceding or following noble-gas configuration. Ions S^{2-}, Cl^{-}, K^{+}, and

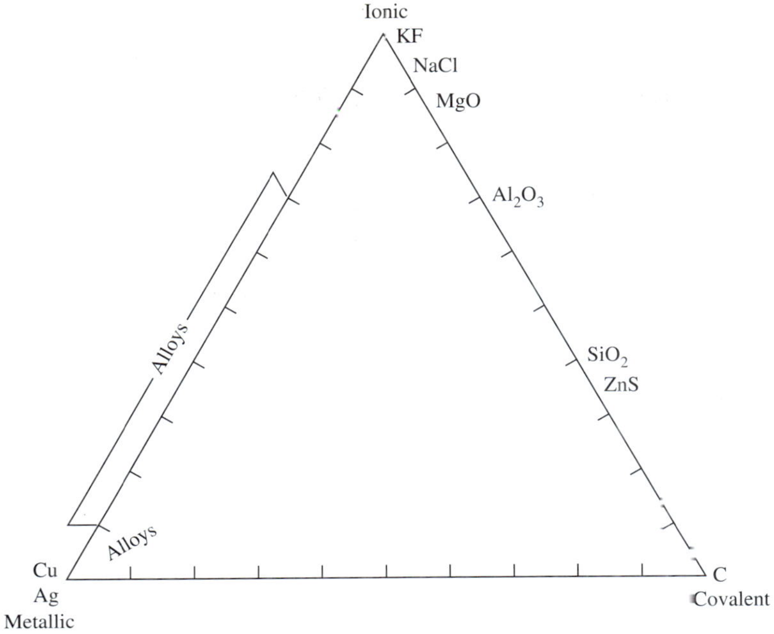

FIGURE 1-5 Types of chemical bonds with examples. Each apex represents an idealized chemical bond type. Crystals with bonds of intermediate character are plotted along triangle edges or interior. Minerals with more than one kind of chemical bond plot as more than one point. Thus, forsterite [Mg_2SiO_4] has both Mg—O and Si—O bonds.

attraction between positively charged ions (cations) and negatively charged ions (anions) holds these ions together in a crystal. Detailed X-ray diffraction studies have shown that in crystals such as halite [NaCl], electrons are largely transferred from Na to Cl to give each nearly monovalent ion (Na^+ and Cl^-) a noble-gas electronic configuration (Fig. 1-4).

Purely electrostatic attraction is nondirectional so each cation tends to surround itself with as many oppositely charged anions as the relative sizes of cations and anions permit (Sec. 1-4). Predominantly ionic bonds tend to form between ions just before and just after noble-gas elements in the periodic table; they never form between similar elements. Ionic bonding creates no molecules. Minerals with ionic bonding have high melting points and conduct electricity only by ion migration at temperatures near their melting points (Table 1-2).

Covalent Bonds In a covalent bond, atoms involved attain a more stable electronic configuration, again commonly that of a noble gas, by sharing one or more electrons among them. In this idealized case no ions result from bonding atoms. Because of the specific locations of the overlapping

TABLE 1-2 Properties Associated with Bond Type

Name	Nature of bond	Directionality
Ionic (Heteropolar) (Electrovalent)	Electrostatic attraction between charged particles (ions) formed by gain or loss of electrons by atoms	Nondirectional, never between similar units
Covalent (Homopolar)	Sharing of electron pairs between ions	Directional, commonly between similar units
Metallic	Positive nuclei in electron "gas" with electrons not localized	Nondirectional
van der Waals	Weak forces caused by induced dipoles resulting from juxtaposition of molecules	Nondirectional

orbitals of shared electrons, covalent bonds tend to be strongly directional; bonding occurs in some directions and not in others. Covalent bonds thus tend to be stronger than ionic bonds. Covalent bonds may occur between atoms of the same element or between similar elements. Molecules and polyanions may form. Crystals with covalent bonding are electrical insulators and generally have a short liquid range between melting and boiling (Table 1-2).

Metallic Bonds With both an idealized ionic bond and an idealized covalent bond, valence electrons are localized in the resulting crystal structures. In a metallic bond, however, valence electrons are free to move from atom to atom. An idealized metal may be conceived as positive ions bathed in an electron "gas" that always preserves local electrostatic neutrality. Directional forces are weak, and no molecules form. Because valence electrons are free to move from metal ion to metal ion throughout a metallic substance, metals are good conductors of electricity. And because light of any wavelength will excite these valence electrons, metals are opaque to light (Sec. 5-1). Minerals with predominantly metallic bonds have variable strength and hardness and have a long liquid range between melting and boiling (Table 1-2).

Weak Bonds Two other chemical bonds, much weaker than the three already described, contribute to mineral structures and properties. In

Electron density between atoms	Cation coordination	Mineral properties
No discrete groups or molecules	Commonly >VI, efficient packing	Mechanically strong; hard; high m.p.; colorless; high thermal expansion; ionic conductor
Commonly causes discrete molecules, organic solids	<IV, poor packing due to directional forces	Fairly strong; fairly hard; low m.p.; short liquid range; colorless; low expansion; insulators
No discrete units	>VI, commonly XII, perfect packing	Variable strength and hardness; long liquid range; opaque; moderate expansion; conductor
Does not cause discrete units	XII	Weak; very soft; very low m.p.; very high expansion; insulators

some crystals, H^+ ions are attracted to two strongly electronegative anions. These H^+ ions form bridges called hydrogen bonds. Such H^+ ions may be midway between anions or, more commonly as in ice [H_2O], substantially closer to one than to another.

Juxtaposition of atomic particles causes an atomic nucleus to be displaced from the center of its electron cloud. This induced dipole is polarized with slight electrostatic charges on opposite sides. The resulting weak forces of electrostatic attraction are van der Waals bonds. These forces, although much weaker than hydrogen bonds, influence crystal structures and mineral properties; the soapy feel of talc [$Mg_6(Si_8O_{20})(OH)_4$] results because weak van der Waals bonds break easily, permitting small flakes of talc to glide over one another.

Real Bonds Real chemical bonds in minerals often have characteristics of two or more of these bond types. Idealized bonds may be plotted as four corners of a tetrahedron with real bonds located within (Fig. 1-5). Thus, real Cu—Cu bonds in copper plots near the idealized metallic bond apex, those of Na and Cl in halite near the idealized ionic bond apex, and the C—C of diamond near the idealized covalent apex. Other bonds plot along edges, faces, or within this tetrahedron.

The degrees to which each idealized bond type contributes to chemical bonds in real minerals may be determined by detailed analysis by X-ray diffraction and by other analytical techniques. A degree of ionic versus covalent character of a bond, however, may be estimated from electronegativities (X) of combining elements. An element is electronegative if it readily accepts valence electrons and electropositive if it readily donates electrons in chemical reactions. Elements immediately preceding noble gases in a periodic chart of chemical elements are the most electronegative, and those immediately following are the most electropositive (Fig. 1-3; Prog. 1-1).

The greater the difference in electronegativities between combining elements ($X^- - X^+$), the greater is the degree of ionic character in any chemical bond between them. Although several empirical relationships between electronegativity and percent ionic character have been proposed, none is entirely satisfactory. In general, a difference in electronegativity greater than approximately 1.8 indicates a chemical bond that is predominantly ionic in character. Mineralogically important Si—O bonds are about 40% ionic and 60% covalent in character.

Most minerals, especially complex silicates, have more than one kind of chemical bond in their structures because they have more than two kinds of elements or because, as in graphite, one element has two kinds of bonds (see Fig. 4-5). Minerals such as halite have only one kind of chemical bond. In minerals with more than one kind of chemical bond, structural patterns are governed by the strongest chemical bonds present. Most physical properties of these minerals, such as hardness and cleavage, are determined by the weakest bonds present. Mica, for example, cleaves into thin sheets because of strong bonds within these sheets and weak bonds between them.

1-3 PROPERTIES OF IONS

Even though Si—O bonds are less than 40% ionic, most minerals have chemical bonds that are sufficiently ionic in character to permit use of an idealized ionic bond model to describe their structures and other properties. For this reason, ions and ionic bonds are treated in some detail. Other bonding models are introduced wherever ionic concepts are inadequate to describe mineral phenomena.

Ionic Charge Atomic particles that do not have the same number of electrons as protons are known as ions: they are called cations if they have lost electrons to acquire a positive charge, and anions if they have gained electrons to acquire a negative charge (Prog. 1-2). Radicals (anionic molecules, such as CO_3^{2-}) may be treated as ions.

Because atomic size is determined in part by electrostatic attraction between a positively charged nucleus and its surrounding negatively charged electron cloud, ionization changes effective sizes of atomic particles. Since cations have lost electrons, they are smaller than their neutral atoms. Anions are correspondingly larger.

Electrostatic charge on an ion depends on its electronic structure and its chemical and structural environment. In atoms, noble gases with two *s* electrons and six *p* electrons have a stable electronic configuration (Sec. 1-2). In minerals, the halogens F and Cl always occur with a -1 charge as F^- and Cl^-, which have a noble-gas electronic configuration. Neutral halogen atoms have a configuration of two *s* electrons and five *p* electrons. In acquiring an additional electron by chemical reaction, these halogen elements attain the stable noble-gas electronic structure of eight outer electrons.

Similarly, Na^+ and other alkali metals attain a noble-gas electronic configuration upon losing one valence electron. The $+2$ ions of alkali earths and -2 ions of group VI elements likewise have noble-gas electronic configurations.

Neutral transition elements have two incomplete outer electronic shells. They have two *s* electrons but no *p* electrons, and their *d* shells are incomplete. The first three or four transition elements in each period form ions from which all *d* and both *s* electrons have been stripped. These elements also have ions with noble-gas configurations. The remaining transition elements retain some of their *d* electrons after ionization. These remaining electrons interact with electrons of surrounding anions, giving resultant chemical bonds nonionic characteristics.

Neutral rare-earth elements have three incomplete outer electronic shells. In minerals, these elements almost uniformly lose their two *s* electrons plus either a 5*d* or a 4*f* electron. Two actinide rare earths, Th and U, have half-lives long enough to be mineralogically significant and generally acquire a noble-gas electronic configuration, although other valence states of U do occur in minerals.

For many discussions, ions and polyanions are treated as though they were hard spheres. This treatment is valid to a first approximation. Ionic size, however, is influenced by its environment; for instance, if squeezed by increasing pressure, an ion becomes smaller. Furthermore, the ionic strength of its nearest neighbors influences ion size. Electron distribution for Na^+ is shown in Fig. 1-4. Note that electron density is quite low throughout most of the volume of any ion. For this reason measured sizes of ions vary, depending on environment.

Atomic Evidence Ionic properties that determine kinds of crystalline compounds into which an element will go are, in order of importance, ionic size, electronic charge, and polarizability; the last property is a measure of deformability of an electron cloud by the electrostatic field of a neighboring ion. Although we have discussed relationships between ionic charge and electronic configuration and have referred to ionic size, we need now to see how these properties of atomic particles are known.

That is, what laboratory experiments have been performed to substantiate such statements? (In any scientific discussion, only one type of definition is useful—an operational definition. A distinction that cannot be related to observation of a measurable property or reaction and that cannot be universally verified is not a valid distinction and is of little use in any science.)

Although discussion of an atomic theory of matter goes back at least to Greek philosophers of the 5th century B.C., no solid experimental basis for it was provided until the 18th century. In 1785, A. L. Lavoisier showed that no change in mass occurred during a chemical reaction; that is, product mass equals exactly reagent mass. In 1799, Louis Proust observed that different samples of a substance contain its elementary constituents in the same proportions. Other contemporary experiments revealed that every time 1 g of hydrogen gas reacted with 8 g of oxygen, 9 g of water resulted. By 1805, John Dalton had sufficient data to state a hypothesis that elements consist of atoms, that all atoms of one element are identical, and that compounds result from combination of a certain number of atoms of one element with a fixed number of atoms of another element. This law of constant proportions described what was observed in many chemical reactions. But this idea of atoms remained hypothetical until atoms themselves could be studied, about a century later.

X-ray Evidence In 1895, Wilhelm Roentgen reported a new kind of radiation, which, like light, traveled in straight lines and affected photographic emulsions, but it was invisible. Because the nature of this newly discovered radiation was unknown, Roentgen called it X radiation. The nature of X radiation remained a mystery until 1912 when P. P. Ewald, a graduate student, discussed with Max von Laue the idea that crystals consisted of regularly spaced atoms. The two reasoned that if X rays were electromagnetic radiation and that if crystals consisted of regularly spaced atoms that might act as scattering centers, then a crystal should diffract X rays. Note the two "ifs" in this reasoning. At that time, there was only indirect evidence that X rays might be a kind of electromagnetic radiation and only indirect evidence that crystals might consist of atoms. This lag of 17 years between the discovery of X rays and Laue's reasoning indicates just how speculative atoms and radiation theories were at that time. (For many major scientific advances, a discovery is 90% asking the right question and 10% answering it.) Laue's laboratory assistants, W. Friedrich and P. Knipping, then placed a crystal of copper sulfate between an X-ray source and a photographic plate; spots caused by diffraction appeared when they developed that plate. Those spots were the first direct evidence of orderly arrays of atoms, not just their existence, in crystals.

Charge Evidence Direct evidence of ionic mass and electronic charge resulted from experiments done in the 1930s with a mass spectrometer.

This instrument works because an electric current traveling in a magnetic field exerts a force at right angles to the direction of current flow and to the direction of magnetic flux. A moving ion constitutes just such an electric current.

Without going into spectrometer design and construction, what kind of direct evidence confirms the existence of ions? A vapor consisting of ions can be produced by heating a substance in a vacuum. Since ions are electrostatically charged, they may be accelerated by an electric field. If high-velocity ions pass through a magnetic field, their paths are bent by this field in a fashion that is related to their mass and charge. By considering geometry of a mass spectrometer, velocity of ions, strength of magnetic fields, and amount of deflection from a straight path that an ion suffers, we can compute an exact charge-to-mass ratio for a given particle. This information, when combined with results from previously mentioned experiments on combining weights and X-ray diffraction, reveals not only the existence of atoms and ions but their individual charges and masses as well.

Ionic Size Any discussion of X-ray diffraction would make it appear that the size of an ion in a crystal is one of its easier properties to measure accurately. This appearance is true for size values that are approximately accurate, but, when great precision is required, values for ionic sizes become elusive. Ionic size depends not only on electronic structure but on chemical environment. Different crystalline environments alter the apparent sizes of ions.

As you can see from any structure model (see Chap. 2), ions in a crystal appear to be stacked in layers. Viewed from different directions, different sets of planes or layers appear in these models. X-ray diffraction measures the distance between these layers (see Chap. 5). Although this measurement does not yield a unique radius of either cation or anion, it does yield a precise value for the sum of those radii. Clearly, this sum is different for halite [NaCl] and for sylvite [KCl]. But these same measurements can be made for other alkali halides having the same structure. Given a sufficient number of sums of ionic radii (interplanar spacings), we can now assign an internally consistent set of individual ionic radii to each alkali and halide ion.

An ion is not actually a rigid sphere, however (Fig. 1-4). The distance between ions in a crystal is an exact balance of attractive forces between ions of opposite charge and repulsive forces between adjacent ions. In the halite structure (Fig. 2-2), each ion is surrounded by six ions with opposite charge. If, instead, each ion were surrounded by four or by eight ions of opposite charge, attractive forces between these ions would be somewhat different. Interionic distances would then be affected, and ionic sizes would also be different. For example, Mg^{2+} has a radius of 80 pm (0.80 Å) when surrounded by six O^{2-} ions, its commonest occurrence in silicate minerals. In a crystalline environment of four neighboring O^{2-} ions, the right radius is 66 pm (0.66 Å), whereas with eight neighbors its radius is 97 pm (0.97 Å) (see Table 1-3).

Minerals shrink with increased pressure and expand upon heating (see Chap. 5). With compression or expansion, interplanar spacings change due to changes in ionic radii; cationic and anionic radii do not generally change by the same amount.

So far in this section (see Fig. 1-2 for electron orbital shapes), ions have been visualized as perfect spheres. This sphericity is reasonably accurate for ions with noble-gas electronic configuration and electronic charge of 2 or less. With highly charged cations or cations with incomplete outer shells, however, there is always a directional component to chemical bonds (Fig. 1-2); that is, the bonds have some covalent characteristics. This covalency, too, will affect measured sizes of ions. Measuring ionic size in one crystalline environment will not always predict its size in another one, where the ionic-covalent character of a bond may be different.

Ionic radii given in Table 1-3 are based on the work of Whittaker and Muntus. Other sets of ionic radii, including those of V. M. Goldschmidt, Linus Pauling, Shannon and Prewitt, and L. H. Ahrens, have also been published. Each set gives slightly different values for ionic radii because, since measurement is necessarily indirect, different kinds of experimental data may be used to calculate them. When using ionic radii for any single problem, all radii should come from the same source since they are internally normalized and consistent only unto themselves; they cannot be mixed.

Ionic Trends Certain trends and relationships among ionic radii are obvious (Table 1-3; Progs. 1-1, 1-2). Within a single period, ions with the same electronic configuration become progressively smaller with increasing atomic number and electronic charge. Decrease in size, for instance, from element 11, Na^{+} (110 pm, 1.1 Å), to element 16, S^{6+} (37 pm, 0.37 Å), is quite regular, as you should expect from descriptions of atomic structure. Numbers of electrons remain constant, whereas nuclear charge increases and attraction on each electron increases across this period. Anions that have exactly the same electronic structure, on the other hand, grow with increase in valence charge. Increase in size from element 9, F^{-} (125 pm, 1.25 Å), to element 8, O^{2-} (132 pm, 1.32 Å), results from the fact that the latter has one less proton in its nucleus and, therefore, less nuclear attraction for the same numbers of electrons.

Within each group (column) of a periodic chart, ions with the same kind of outermost electronic configuration and the same charge increase in size with increase in atomic number. An increase in ionic radii from element 11, Na^{+} (110 pm, 1.10 Å), to element 55, Cs^{+} (178 pm, 1.78 Å), should be expected, considering electron shells added to atoms with each additional period.

TABLE 1-3 Ionic Radii (pm) of Ions by Coordination Number (CN)

Ion	III	IV	VI	VIII	X	XII
Ag	—	—	123	138	—	—
Al	—	47	61	—	—	—
As	—	42	58	—	—	—
B	10	20	—	—	—	—
Ba	—	—	144	150	160	168
Be	25	35	—	—	—	—
C	—	—	—	—	—	—
Ca	—	—	108	120	136	143
Cd	—	88	103	115	—	—
Ce^{3+}	—	—	109	122	—	—
Ce^{4+}	—	—	88	105	—	—
Cl^{-}	—	167	172	—	—	—
Co^{2+}	—	65	83	—	—	—
Co^{3+}	—	—	69	—	—	—
Cr	—	—	70	—	—	—
Cs	—	—	178	182	189	196
Cu^{2+}	—	—	81	—	—	—
F^{-}	122	123	125	—	—	—
Fe^{2+}	—	71	86	—	—	—
Fe^{3+}	—	57	73	—	—	—
Hg	—	104	110	122	—	—
I^{-}	—	—	213	197	—	—
K	—	—	146	159	167	168
La	—	—	113	126	136	140
Li	—	68	82	—	—	—
Mg	—	66	80	97	—	—
Mn^{2+}	—	—	91	101	—	—
Mn^{4+}	—	—	62	—	—	—
Mn^{6+}	—	35	—	—	—	—
Mo^{4+}	—	—	73	—	—	—
Mo^{6+}	—	50	68	—	—	—
Na	—	107	110	124	—	—
Ni	—	—	77	—	—	—
O^{2-}	128	130	132	134	—	—
P	—	25	—	—	—	—
Pb	—	—	126	137	—	157
Ra	—	—	—	156	—	172
Rb	—	—	157	168	174	181
S^{6+}	—	37	—	—	—	—
S^{2-}	—	156	172	178	—	—
Sb^{3+}	—	85	—	—	—	—
Sb^{5+}	—	—	69	—	—	—
Sc	—	—	83	95	—	—
Se^{6+}	—	37	—	—	—	—
Se^{2-}	—	188	—	190	—	—
Si	—	34	48	—	—	—
Sn	—	—	77	—	—	—
Sr	—	—	121	133	140	148
Ta	—	—	72	77	—	—
Th	—	—	108	112	—	—
Ti	—	—	69	—	—	—
U^{4+}	—	—	—	108	—	—
U^{6+}	—	56	81	—	—	—
V^{3+}	—	—	72	—	—	—
V^{5+}	—	44	62	—	—	—
W^{4+}	—	—	73	—	—	—
W^{6+}	—	50	68	—	—	—
Y	—	—	98	110	—	—
Zn	—	68	83	98	—	—
Zr	—	—	80	92	—	—

Radii of transition ions are for the high-spin state—that is, all *d* electrons as unpaired as possible. (Data from E. J. W. Whittaker and R. Muntus, "Ionic radii for use in geochemistry," *Geochim. Cosmochim. Acta* 34 (June 1970): 952–953.

Lanthanide contraction is an interesting reversal of size trends established in other parts of the periodic chart. Because additional electrons in lanthanides go into the 4*f* shell, which is interior to each ion as defined by locations of 5*s* and 5*p* orbitals, each added nuclear charge exerts progressively greater attraction on outer electrons, resulting in each succeeding rare-earth ion being smaller than the previous one. This lanthanide contraction causes ions of the third transition series to be only slightly larger than those of the second transition series in spite of added electron shells of the intervening period. One result of this similarity in size is that third-transition ions may readily substitute for second-transition ions in crystal structures.

Note that few cations are substantially larger than 100 pm (1 Å) and that most common anions are considerably larger than 100 pm. In most minerals, therefore, more volume is occupied by anions than by cations. Crystal structures may be viewed as periodic arrays of spherical anions, with cations inhabiting intervening spaces. Since O^{2-} constitutes more than 90% of the volume of the earth's crust, crustal minerals may be regarded as masses of closely packed O^{2-} ions, with small cations filling the interstitial voids.

Polarizability A third factor that determines how a particular ion behaves in a crystal structure is its polarizability. Unfortunately, ionic polarizability is not as easily defined as ionic size and charge. An ion is highly polarizable if its apparent size or shape strongly depends on its crystalline environment. In general, large ions, monovalent ions, and ions with non-noble-gas electronic configurations tend to be polarizable. If an ion tends to behave rigidly as a sphere of constant size in many different crystalline environments, it has low polarizability. Small cations with high electronic charge and noble-gas electronic configurations have low polarizabilities.

1-4 PACKING OF SPHERICAL IONS

Preceding discussions on ionic properties lead to an observation that ions in crystalline structures may be treated, to a first approximation, as small, hard spheres. Different ions fit together in minerals, depending largely on their relative sizes; hence, ways in which space can be filled with spheres of different sizes must be considered.

Closest-Packed Layers Consider filling a volume with ions of one kind—that is, rigid spheres all of one size. For example, one most efficient arrangement exists for racking balls on a pool table. This arrangement is

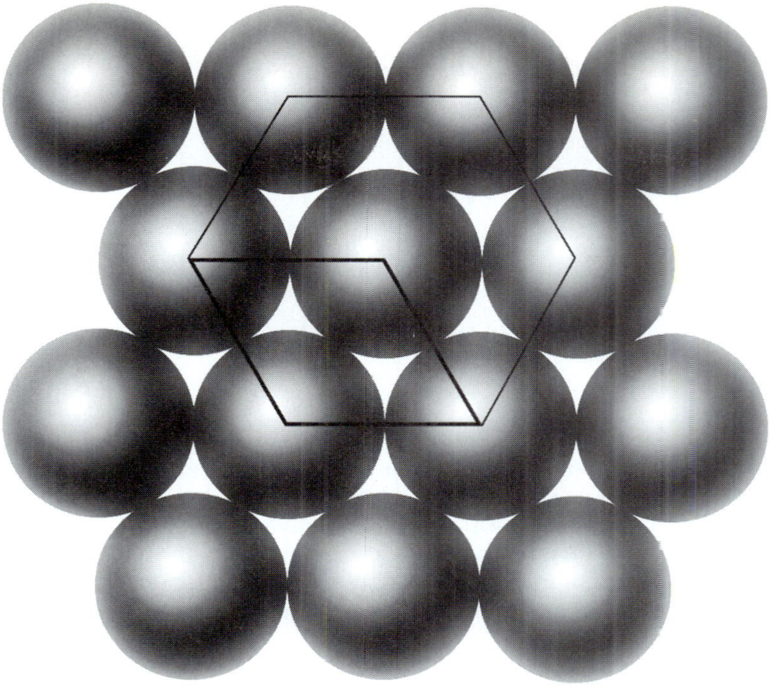

FIGURE 1-6 A closest-packed layer of spheres. Each sphere is surrounded by six spheres (light line) and six void spaces. A unit cell of this layer (dark line) contains one sphere and two void spaces.

a hexagonal, two-dimensional array (Fig. 1-6; Prog. 1-3) and should be so familiar, even to those of you who have never shot pool, that a detailed analysis of spatial properties of a closest-packed layer is warranted. (Things most familiar often bring the most surprises when looked at in detail.) Each sphere is surrounded by six other spheres. Each space between spheres (void) has three spheres about it. If this void is imagined to be divisible, one third of each void space may be assigned to each adjacent sphere. In addition to six spheres about each sphere, six void spaces surround each sphere. Since six voids surround each sphere and three spheres surround each void, twice as many void spaces exist in this closest-packed layer as there are spheres.

The radius of the largest small sphere that could fill one of these voids without separating the large spheres from mutual contact is 0.155 times the radius of these large spheres. If the large spheres represent anions, then the largest cation that could exactly fill space between them would have a radius equal to 0.155 times that of these anions regardless of anionic radius.

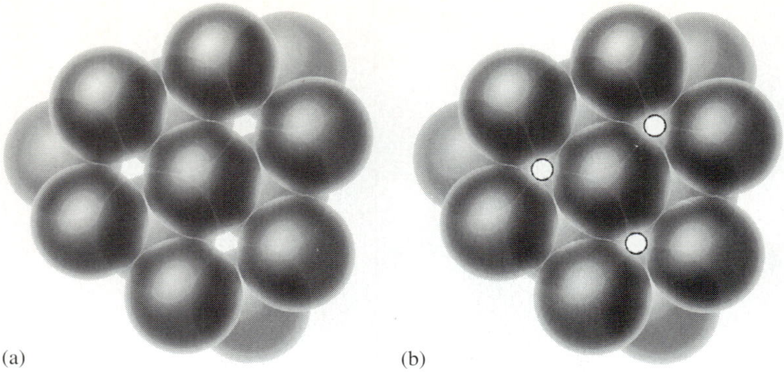

(a) (b)

FIGURE 1-7 Closest-packed layers of spheres. Each sphere of a second layer rests over a trigonal planar void space in the first layer. There are two options for placing a third layer of spheres. (a) Placing a third layer over the first layer and repeating this pattern with additional layers produces a succession . . . ABABABA. . . , called hexagonal close packing (HCP). (b) Placing spheres of a third layer over the common trigonal planar voids in both layers and repeating this pattern with additional layers produces a succession . . .ABCABCA. . . , called cubic close packing (CCP).

Closest-Packed Volume A succession of closest-packed layers stacked one upon another represents the most efficient way in which hard spheres can fill a volume. "Most efficient" here means the highest possible sphere-to-void ratio—the least amount of space not filled by spheres. Examine closely two layers in a stack of closest-packed layers, and notice two kinds of three-dimensional void spaces between these layers (Fig. 1-7; Prog. 1-3). Where a sphere of the upper layer rests directly above a trigonal void of the lower layer or where a sphere of the lower layer lies directly under a trigonal void of the upper layer, a void between layers is surrounded by four spheres—a tetrahedral void. Where trigonal voids of each layer are aligned, the resulting space between layers is surrounded by six spheres—an octahedral void. Lines connecting centers of surrounding spheres determine the geometric shapes assigned these void spaces (Fig. 1-8; Prog. 1-4).

Add a third layer to our stack of two closest-packed layers to produce yet another interlayer of tetrahedral and octahedral voids between these layers of spheres. First, place this third layer with its spheres directly over spheres of the first layer. This placement aligns octahedral interlayer voids between the second and third layers directly over octahedral interlayer voids between the first and second layers. Continuing in this fashion, with odd- and even-numbered layers offset and all even- and all odd-numbered layers aligned, we develop a closest-packed volume of spheres closely resembling the periodicity of ions in many pure metals. Designate this sequence . . . ABABA. . . .

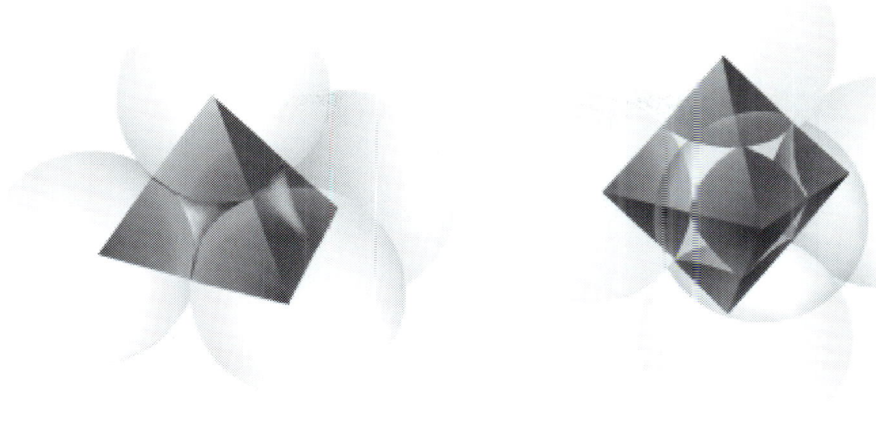

(a) (b)

FIGURE 1-8 Three-dimensional voids in closest-packed spheres. (a) Interlayer void created by one sphere of a second layer over three spheres in a first layer has four spheres around it—a tetrahedral void. (b) Interlayer void created by three spheres of second layer over three spheres of a first layer has six spheres around it—an octahedral void. Both voids are named for the geometric shape produced by lines connecting centers of surrounding spheres.

A second option in placement of a third layer, however, fills space just as efficiently, but produces a different pattern. Placing spheres of a third layer directly over interlayer octahedral voids between the first and second layers causes the third layer to be offset from both the second and the first layers. Continuing in this fashion, every third layer in our stack is aligned with the same efficiency of packing as when every second layer was aligned. Designate this sequence . . . ABCABCA. . . . Clearly, second- and third-layer alignment may be mixed in various ways, but resulting patterns of spheres and voids are less commonly found in structures of real minerals.

These two kinds of simple repetitions of layers in groups of two or of three are distinguished on a basis of the symmetry of the pattern of spheres (see Chap. 3). A pattern of two closest-packed layers alternating infinitely has hexagonal symmetry and that of three such layers has cubic symmetry, leading to their designations as hexagonal close packing (HCP) and cubic close packing (CCP), respectively (Fig. 1-7). A CCP array of spheres is more commonly described as face-centered cubic (FCC) (Fig. 1-9).

Patterns in which a sphere's neighboring void spaces are arranged depend on whether a sphere is in HCP or CCP array. In both cases, each sphere is surrounded by 12 other spheres in direct contact with it—3 below, 3 above, and 6 in the same plane. In both arrays, each sphere

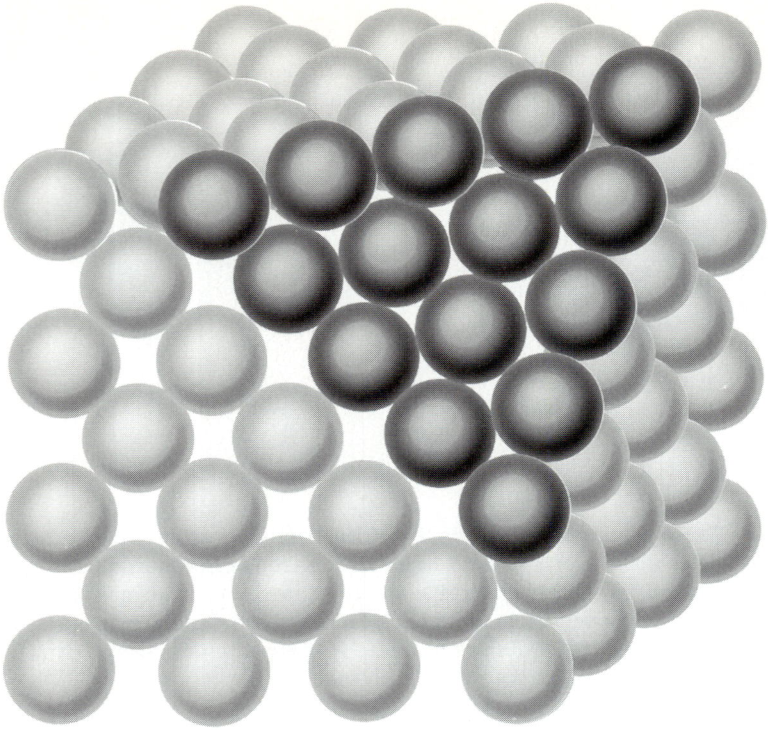

FIGURE 1-9 Identity of face-centered cubic (FCC) with cubic close packing (CCP). Dark spheres represent a closest-packed layer that truncates a cube corner.

is surrounded by six octahedral interlayer voids, making octahedral interlayer voids equal the surrounding spheres in number. And in both arrays, eight tetrahedral voids surround each sphere, making twice as many of these voids as surrounding spheres. The patterns of void spaces, however, are different. In HCP, octahedral voids are aligned at right angles to planes of closest-packed layers in such fashion that adjacent octahedral voids share three spheres in common between them (Fig. 1-10; Prog. 1-4). Tetrahedral voids are paired between octahedral voids, with additional ones directly above and below each sphere. In CCP no such pairing occurs, so octahedral and tetrahedral voids alternate throughout this structure.

Many native metals crystallize in one of these two closest-packed arrays, and many ionic minerals have anions arranged in one of these arrays, with cations located in some of their tetrahedral and octahedral interlayer voids. Not all cations, however, are of exactly the right size to fill either tetrahedral or octahedral interlayer voids, so many anion arrays differ from closest-packed structures.

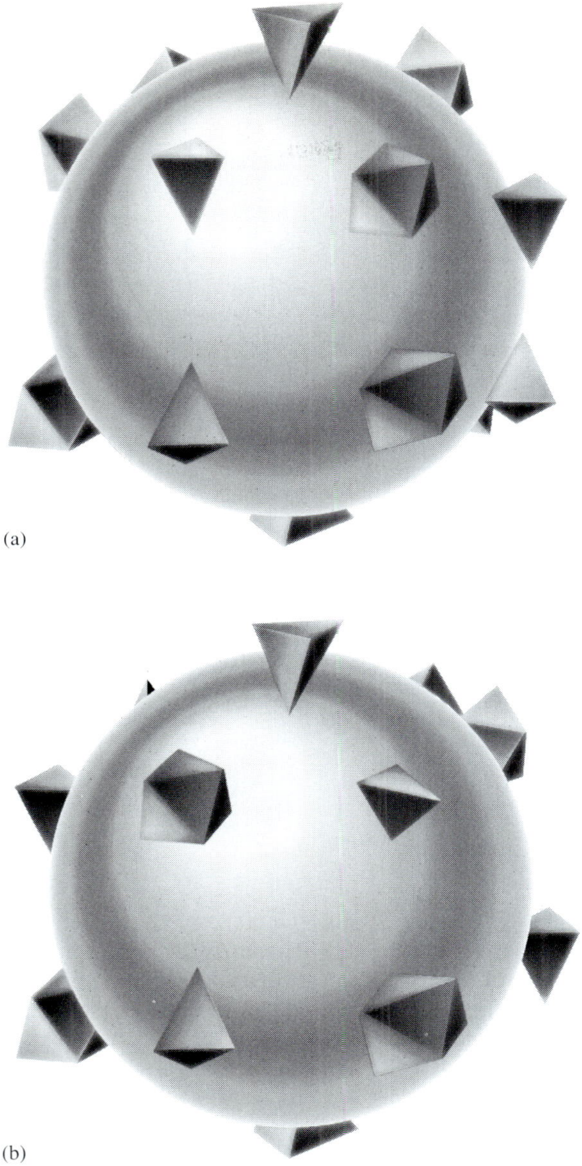

(a)

(b)

FIGURE 1-10 Schematic representation of void distribution in closest-packed structures. Each sphere is surrounded by six octahedral voids and by eight tetrahedral voids. (a) In hexagonal close packing, octahedral and tetrahedral voids are each aligned vertically. (b) In cubic close packing (FCC, Fig. 1-9) octahedral voids alternate with tetrahedral voids in directions at right angles to closest-packed layers.

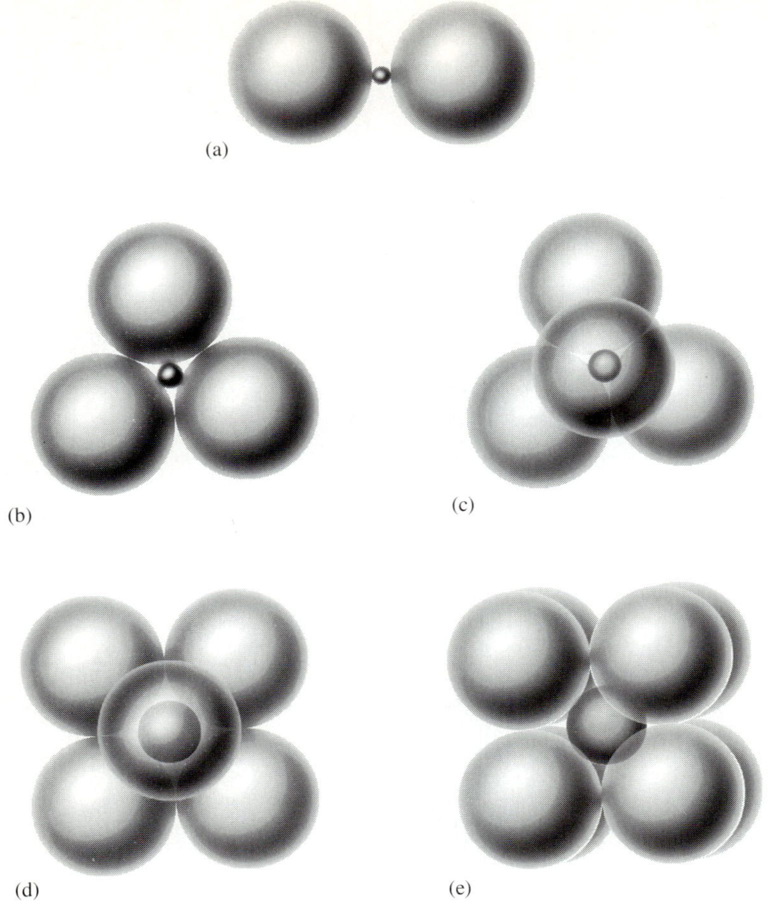

FIGURE 1-11 Coordination polyhedra. (a) Small sphere with radius less than 0.155 of large spheres coordinates two large spheres as in molecular CO_2. (b) Small sphere with radius 0.155 of large spheres coordinates three large spheres in a trigonal planar group such as CO_3^{2-} polyanion. (c) Small sphere with radius 0.225 of large spheres coordinates four large spheres at corners of a tetrahedron as in SiO_4^{4-} group. (d) Small sphere with radius 0.414 of large sphere coordinates six large spheres at corners of an octahedron as in AlO_6^{9-}. (e) Small sphere with radius 0.732 of large spheres coordinates eight large spheres at corners of a cube as in CsCl. If two kinds of spheres are the same size, each is surrounded by 12 spheres to resemble closest packing.

Radius Ratio Except for native elements, minerals are made of different kinds of ions—that is, spheres of different sizes. The number of large anions that can surround a central cation depends on the size of each; the smaller a cation with respect to an anion, the fewer the anions that can come into mutual contact with this cation. The number of anions

TABLE 1-4 Radius Ratios (r^+/r^-) and Their Coordination Numbers

r^+/r^-	CN	Configuration	Example
<0.155	II	Linear	CO_2
0.155–0.225	III	Trigonal planar	CO_3^{2-}
0.225–0.414	IV	Tetrahedral	SiO_2
0.414–0.732	VI	Octahedral	NaCl
0.732–1.000	VIII	Cubic	CsCl

surrounding a central cation is the coordination number (CN) of the cation. This relationship is best expressed as a radius ratio, a numerical result of dividing cation radius by anion radius (r^+/r^-).

Theoretical coordination numbers, based purely on radius ratio and geometry, are given in Fig. 1-11 and Table 1-4 (Prog. 1-5). Since many minerals are compounds of various cations with oxygen, Table 1-5 compares theoretically predicted coordination numbers based on a hard-sphere model with those actually found in minerals. Most ions that deviate from predicted coordination are those with O^{2-} radius ratio close to the boundary between two theoretical coordinations. This table shows that our hard-sphere model is, indeed, a good approximation for many minerals.

Many apparent discrepancies in Table 1-5 disappear if ionic polarizability and formation of partially covalent bonds are taken into account. In general, larger ions are more polarizable than smaller ones. The most abundant large ion in minerals is O^{2-}. Pressure squeezes ions together in a crystal structure, making them effectively smaller, with large O^{2-} being shrunk more than most cations. Thus, as minerals form at different, but higher, pressures, the cation coordination number with O^{2-} increases.

TABLE 1-5 Theoretical (T) and Observed (O) Cation Coordination Number

Cation	r (pm)	r^+/r^- (O^{2-})	CN(T)	CN(O)
Ca	108	0.82	VIII	VI
Ca	120	0.94	VIII	VIII
Na	110	0.84	VIII	VI
Na	124	0.93	VIII	VIII
Fe^{2+}	86	0.65	VI	VI
Mg	80	0.60	VI	VI
Fe^{3+}	73	0.55	VI	VI
Ti	69	0.52	VI	VI
Al	61	0.46	VI	VI
Al	47	0.36	IV	IV
Be	35	0.27	IV	IV
Si	34	0.26	IV	IV
S	20	0.15	III	IV

Commonly, those ions with coordination numbers greater than those predicted by geometry alone are found in minerals formed at high pressure.

A minimum radius ratio represents an exact fit in which all anions touch one another, with a cation exactly filling a void space. If a cation is too small for a perfect fit, the next smaller anion coordination will be stable. A cation with a radius slightly too large for a perfect fit merely separates its surrounding anions from mutual contact.

Crystal Structures In addition to seeking principles underlying crystal architecture, crystallographers and mineralogists desire descriptions of specific crystal structures (Chap. 2). You can describe crystal structures by selecting a small volume, or unit cell, of a structure in which all chemical elements and their geometrical relationships are included. After giving locations of each ion in this unit cell, an entire structure may be envisioned as an infinite repetition of this unit cell in three dimensions. This procedure is relatively simple for structures such as halite or fluorite, which are chemically simple and have a high degree of geometrical symmetry. It becomes quite complex and unwieldly for structures with large unit cells and many ions.

A second way of describing crystal structures states the kind of array in which its anions are found, such as HCP or CCP, and in which of its voids the cations are located. This kind of description is adequate for a structure like corundum [Al_2O_3], where O^{2-} ions are in approximately HCP.

A third way of describing crystal structures utilizes the geometry of anions coordinated by a cation—a coordination polyhedron (Fig. 1-11). Visualize a coordination polyhedron as a geometric shape created by lines connecting anionic centers about a cation. The simplest coordination polyhedron is a trigonal plane such as is found in the polyanions CO_3^{2-} and BO_3^{3-}. If one anion is common to two different polyhedra, that anion is shared by the two polyhedra. In geometric terms, polyhedra may share corners (Fig. 1-12).

The smallest three-dimensional polyhedron is a tetrahedron, for example, SiO_4^{4-} and SO_4^{2-}. Corner sharing makes possible dimers, rings, chains, sheets, and frameworks of silica tetrahedra (Fig. 1-12).

A central cation may be surrounded instead by six anions at the corners of an octahedron. If two anions are common to two adjacent polyhedra, edges are shared. If three anions are common to adjacent polyhedra, faces are shared. Edge-sharing and face-sharing octahedra, however, tend to be distorted due to mutual repulsion by central cations. A coordination number of 8 generates a cubic polyhedron that may share corners, edges, or even faces.

Many of these polyhedra do not represent the most efficient filling of space, as do the two closest-packed configurations. Two fairly common,

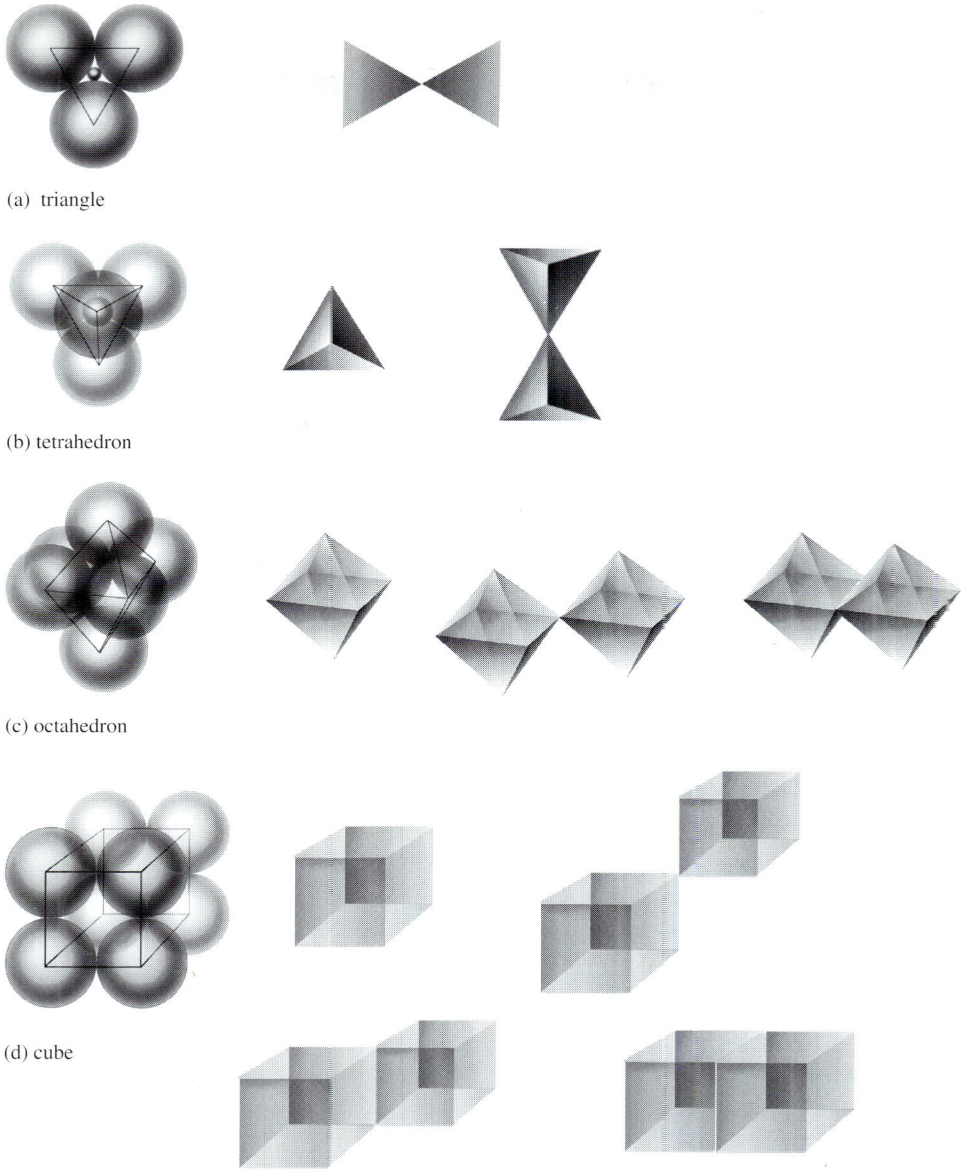

FIGURE 1-12 Shared polyhedral elements. When a sphere is common to two coordination polyhedra, it is shared. (a) Trigonal planar groups may share corners. (b) Tetrahedra may share corners. (c) Octahedra may share corners or edges. (d) Cubes may share corners, edges, or faces.

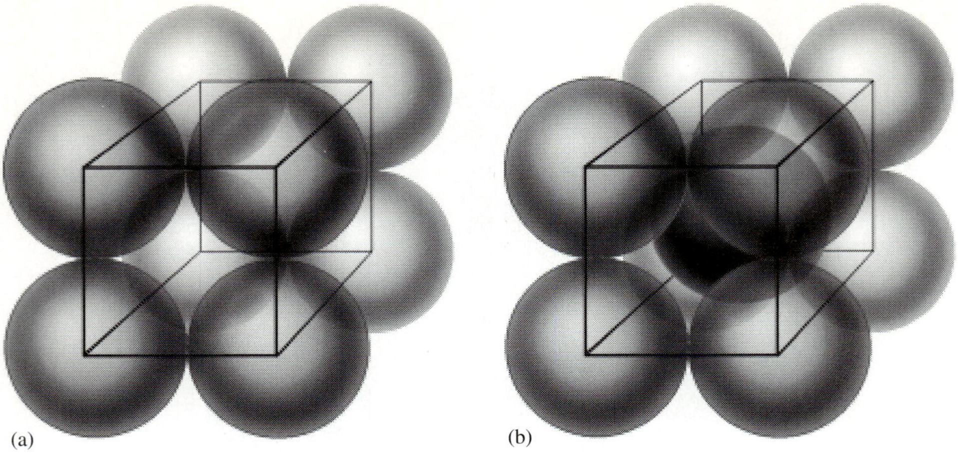

FIGURE 1-13 (a) Primitive cubic (PC) array of spheres with one complete sphere per unit cell (solid line). (b) Body-centered cubic (BCC) array of spheres with two spheres per unit cell as in native iron.

less efficient arrays are primitive cubic (PC) and body-centered cubic (BCC) (Fig. 1-13).

Pauling's Rules After studying crystals and crystal structures, Linus Pauling formulated a set of rules about them. Although not rigorously derived nor universally applicable, especially not to sulfides, ionic minerals mostly display characteristics of these rules:

> *A coordination polyhedron of anions is formed about each cation, the cation-anion distance being determined by the radius sum and the ligancy of the cation by the radius ratio.* [Ligancy is the same as CN.]
> *In a stable ionic structure the valence of each anion, with changed sign, is exactly or nearly equal to the sum of the strengths of the electrostatic bonds to it from the adjacent cations.*
> *The presence of shared edges and especially of shared faces in a coordinated structure decreases its stability; this effect is large for cations with large valence and small ligancy.*
> *In a crystal containing different cations those with large valence and small coordination number tend not to share polyhedron elements with each other.*

If crystal structures are thought of as anions in some approximation of a close-packed array, only three sizes of void spaces exist for cations to fill. Substitution of one cation for another is common, but substituting ions are generally similar in size and charge to the ones replaced. In silicates, however, the Si—O bond is predominantly covalent and, therefore, strongly directional; hence, silicate structures tend to be determined by the manner in which the silica tetrahedra share corners. This strong directionality leaves room for a wide variety of cation sites and makes silicate mineralogy more interesting than that of purely ionic minerals.

1-5 DEVIATION FROM PERFECTION

Idealized crystal structures were invented as a conceptual means of simplifying a vast array of crystal structure data. Certain deviations from these idealized perfect structures occur in such a regular and systematic fashion that they, too, have been idealized somewhat. For instance, one ion may proxy for another without radically altering a mineral's original structure. Two important examples of such substitution common in rock-forming minerals are Fe^{2+} for Mg^{2+} and Al^{3+} for Si^{4+}.

Chemical Substitution The most important factor governing the substitution of one ion for another in a crystal structure is their relative size. In ionic structures, radius ratio determines a stable coordination polyhedron. Any size difference that would change the cation coordination of a site would prevent successful substitution. For example, with O^{2-}, Al^{3+} has a radius close to the border between octahedral and tetrahedral coordination. The radius of Si^{4+}, on the other hand, is well below the range of allowable sizes for octahedral coordination. For this reason Al^{3+} commonly substitutes for Si^{4+} in silicate structures, but Si^{4+} almost never substitutes for Al^{3+} in octahedral sites.

Ionic charge is the most important factor in determining chemical characteristics of ions in aqueous solution. In minerals, where coupled substitution is possible, deficiencies in electronic charge balance may be compensated elsewhere in a crystal. Thus, size permitting, a charge difference of 1 or, less commonly, 2 may occur in ionic substitution.

Table 1-6 lists some common ionic substitutions found in minerals together with their coordination numbers and ionic radii. Similarity in size permits Mg^{2+} to substitute readily for Fe^{2+}, and difference in size prevents it from readily substituting for Ca^{2+}. Proximity in size between Ge^{4+} and Si^{4+} and between Ga^{3+} and Al^{3+} accounts for the fact that Ge and Ga minerals are so rare, even though these elements are more abundant in the continental crust than W, Hg, and Ag, which form less rare minerals (Fig. 7-1). The elements Ge and Ga simply "hide" in minerals containing abundant Si and Al.

Temperature and pressure of mineral formation affects the extent or percentage of ionic substitution. High temperatures increase the tolerance of crystal structures for foreign ions. High pressures may shift maximal substitution either way, depending on relative polarizabilities of all ions involved.

A crystal (solid) solution series exists when two or more end-member compositions are soluble in one another to degrees ranging from a few

TABLE 1-6 Common Ionic Substitution Pairs

Ion	CN	Radius (pm)	Ion	Radius (pm)
Mg	VI	80	Fe^{2+}	86
Al	IV	47	Si	34
F	VI	125	O	132
Ba	IX	155	K	163
Ge	IV	48	Si	34
Ga	VI	70	Al	61
Hf	VIII	91	Zr	92
Mn^{4+}	VI	62	Fe^{3+}	73
Mn^{2+}	VI	91	Fe^{2+}	86
La–Lu	VIII	126–105	Ca	120
Na	VIII	124	Ca	120

percent to 100%. Complete substitutional crystal solution is exemplified by the olivine series, where all compositions between 100% forsterite [Mg_2SiO_4] and 100% fayalite [Fe_2SiO_4] may exist. An example of partial substitution is the solubility of Fe^{2+} in sphalerite [ZnS with a structure based on CCP], which may incorporate up to 50 mole% FeS even though no terrestrial isostructural FeS end member exists.

Interstitial crystal solutions, in which ions fill voids in a crystal structure, include variable amounts of H^+ in quartz and many different ions in zeolite minerals. Omission crystal solutions involve systematic absence of one ion coupled with a valence change. Pyrrhotite (pyrrhotine) almost never occurs as pure FeS (structure based on HCP); there are almost

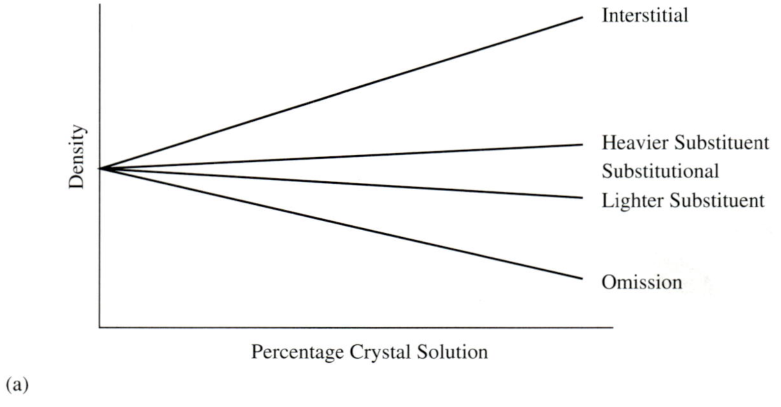

FIGURE 1-14 Influence of crystal solution on density. (a) Interstitial crystal solution increases crystal density by adding mass per unit volume. Omission crystal solution decreases density by subtracting mass per unit volume. Substitutional crystal solution either increases or decreases density, depending on whether a substituent ion is heavier or lighter than the substituted ion.

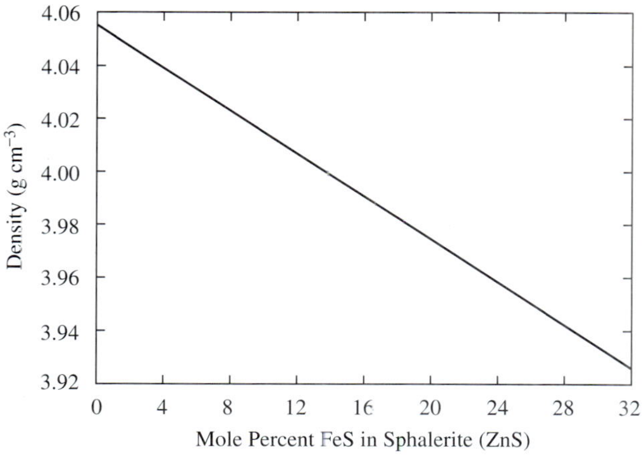

(b)

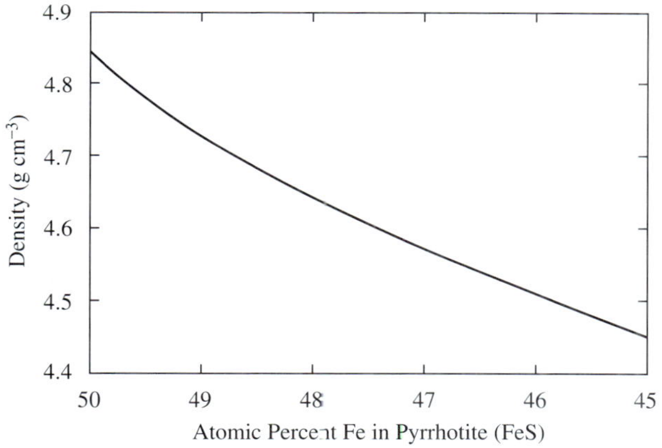

(c)

FIGURE 1-14 continued (b) Density of sphalerite as a function of Fe^{2+} (atomic weight 55.85) replacing Zn^{2+} (atomic weight 65.37). (c) Density of pyrrhotite as a function of omission of Fe^{2+} from the crystal structure.

always measurably more S ions than Fe ions in this structure (Fig. 1-14). Electrostatic neutrality is maintained since some Fe ions are ferric.

Interstitial crystal solutions increase in density as the amount of solution increases, because more matter occupies the same volume. Omission crystal solutions tend to decrease in density with increased omission. In substitutional crystal solutions, relative atomic mass and ionic size determine direction and amount of density changes (Fig. 1-14).

Perfect crystals exist only in a crystallographer's or mineralogist's mind. Actual crystalline materials contain a little of everything in anything. Many reagent-grade compounds on chemical stockroom shelves are less than 99% of what is listed on container labels. Alkali halide

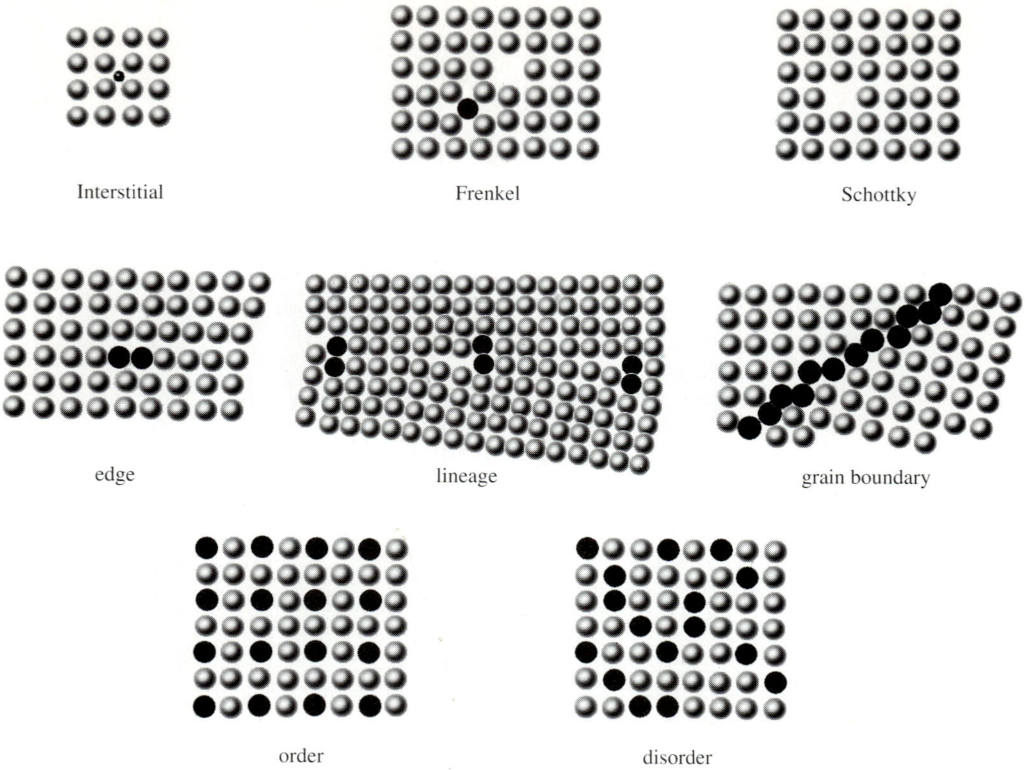

FIGURE 1-15a Defects in crystal structures. ***Top row:*** **Interstitial, vacancy coupled with interstitial (Frenkel), and vacancy (Schottky).** ***Middle row:*** **Edge dislocation, series of edge dislocations to produce a lineage, and a grain boundary.** ***Bottom row:*** **Order and disorder.**

crystals, available from specialty sources, are five nines pure (99.999%). These high-grade materials may have more than 10^{18} foreign ions per mole (remember that Avogadro's number is 6×10^{23} atoms per mole).

Physical Defects Ionic substitution may be thought of as one kind of defect—a chemical defect—in an ideal crystal. In addition, many physical defects exist in real crystals. In general, a physical defect describes an ion that is out of place in a crystal structure, such that some chemical bonds are weakened or missing altogether. Some defects depend on past history and may be increased by repeated stressing or decreased by annealing. Other defects, however, are temperature-dependent. Complete absence of defects, therefore, can occur only at absolute zero, a thermodynamically unattainable temperature.

FIGURE 1-15b Screw dislocation; units of a structure spiral around a line of dislocation.

Point defects, including interstitials and omissions, characterize disturbed crystal volumes where the disturbance decreases radially from a point in a structure. Interstitial defects (Fig. 1-15, Table 1-7) are the same as interstitial crystal solutions. Atoms of carbon in steel, for instance, are interstitials. In addition, an ion may be simply displaced from its regular structural site to another nearby site where it appears as an interstitial. Another kind of point defect is the same as omission crystal solution where an ion is missing completely. Any electronic charge imbalance so created may be neutralized if an oppositely charged ion is also missing nearby, by change in oxidation state of a nearby ion, or by some other structural adjustment.

No crystal structure is free of point defects; percentages of misplaced ions is a function of temperature. Additional point defects may be caused by radiation damage to a structure. Amethystine and smokey quartz owe their colors to such defects (Chap. 5). Under stress, point defects may migrate—an ion moves into a vacancy, thereby creating a new vacancy. They then tend to pile up at grain boundaries and influence physical properties as in work hardening of metals.

Whereas a point defect is a disturbance of a crystal structure that decreases, in effect, concentrically from a point, a line defect involves an entire row of ions with some kind of bonding irregularity. Where a plane of ions extends only partly into a crystal and terminates, the terminal line is an edge defect (Fig. 1-15, Table 1-7). At an edge defect, some bonds are extended and weakened while others are compressed. In a screw dislocation, planes of ions do not close upon themselves but continue as a spiral. All ions in such a spiral are in otherwise normal crystalline environments except those at a spiral axis, which is a line of defect.

Line defects are important to crystal growth (Chap. 7). Since adding ions to a step on a growing crystal face is energetically easier than starting a new layer, screw dislocations facilitate crystal growth. Many galena [PbS] crystals have visible screw dislocations displayed on their cube faces.

Plane defects occur where an entire sheet of ions has an irregular crystalline environment. A lineage (Fig. 1-15, Table 1-7) occurs where a series of edge dislocations appear at regular intervals. As a result, a structure on one side of a lineage is slightly tilted with respect to the other side. Additional tilting of the two sides results in a true grain boundary with all ions at this interface in an irregular crystalline environment. Not all angles of tilt are energetically equal, however; some angles have less ionic mismatch than others. One type of stacking fault occurs in a close-packed structure if a layer is missing from CCP or a CCP layer intrudes into HCP.

Disorder in a structure is a three-dimensional defect (Fig. 1-15, Table 1-7). Two different ions may be similar enough to be distributed randomly in a particular coordination polyhedron in a crystal structure with but small addition of energy to the system. This disorder is typical of minerals

TABLE 1-7 Types of Imperfections in Crystals

Defect	Description
Point defects	
Interstitial	Extra atom forced into structure
Schottky	Atom missing from site
Frenkel	Atom missing from site and interstitial nearby
Line dislocations	
Edge	Row of atoms marking the edge of a structural plane extending partway in a crystal
Screw	Row of atoms about which a structural plane appears to spiral
Plane defects	
Stacking fault	Boundary between two parts of closest packing with alternate packing sequences
Lineage	Boundary between two regions that are slightly tilted to one another because of a series of edge dislocations
Grain boundary	Boundary between two crystals
Volume defects	
Disorder	Two or more chemical elements randomly distributed over a single structural site

of appropriate chemistry at high temperatures. Slow cooling, however, may permit formerly randomly located ions to take up periodic structural positions and become ordered. Order-disorder effects are important in Al^{3+} and Si^{4+} distribution in tetrahedral sites of feldspar minerals.

All minerals deviate from ideality in some respect or other. The amount and kind of defect that may exist in a particular mineral species may be typical of that mineral and actually aid in its characterization and identification. Some mineral colors result directly from defects and only occur when those defects are present (Chap. 5).

1-6 IONIC CONFIGURATIONS

Some general statements concerning crystal chemistry of minerals have been made, and some principles set forth. Before applying these ideas to specific mineral structures (Chap. 2), you need to appreciate certain generalizations about how ions organize themselves in various arrays.

Isomorphism Many minerals have the same order and structure in the arrangement of their constituent ions. These resemblances range from exactly analogous to generally similar structures. Minerals in which structure is exactly analogous and in which each ion in one mineral has a counterpart in an identical environment in another are isotypes. Minerals with structures basically similar, but in which not all ions in one mineral have counterparts in another, are isostructural. Examples include many derivative structures (Fig. 1-16, Table 1-8). If two minerals have the same general internal structure, closely similar external morphology (shape), and similar X-ray diffraction patterns, they are isomorphous. Our structural classification of minerals results directly from these similarities.

In addition to demonstrating similarities among apparently different minerals, studies of isostructural crystals have importance in experimental mineralogy. Silicate minerals are somewhat difficult to work with in the laboratory, but some relationships among silicate minerals may be studied by proxy by experimenting with isostructural matter or model structures.

Two kinds of models are in current, general use in experimental mineralogy. In a size model, radius ratios are the same in both structures. Thus one can predict much about the crystal chemistry of BaSe by studying that of periclase [MgO]. A charge model is one in which ionic charges are in a simple ratio. Thus, LiF is a charge model of periclase, and BeF_2 is a charge model for silica [SiO_2].

Derivative structures are those in which anions are in the same configuration as in a parent structure, but in which cations are different. A half-breed derivative has two cations of different valances replacing a single ionic species in a parent structure, the average charge being the same in both instances (Table 1-8). When corundum [Al_2O_3] is taken as a parent structure, replacement of half the Al^{3+} by Fe^{2+} and half by Ti^{4+} yields ilmenite [$FeTiO_3$] as a half-breed derivative. A stuffed derivative has a cation of lower ionic charge replacing one of higher charge with electrostatic neutrality maintained by stuffing an interstitial ion into the parent structure. Albite [$NaAlSi_3O_8$] is a stuffed derivative of coesite [SiO_2], with Al^{3+} replacing Si^{4+} in one quarter of its tetrahedra and a Na^+ stuffed among these tetrahedra.

Polymorphism A given chemical compound may exist in more than one crystal structure; such structures are polymorphs. Diamond and graphite, for example, both have chemical formula C. Different polymorphs of the same chemical composition are given different mineral names (Fig. 1-17). Kyanite, sillimanite, and andalusite all have chemical composition Al_2SiO_5. Numbers of polymorphs that may coexist stably are limited, as proven in Sec. 6-2. In general, at a given pressure and temperature, one polymorph is stable and all others are not, with any unstable polymorphs attempting to invert to this stable structure. Each polymorph is a phase, as are each liquid and gas in a system. Melting, crystallization, vaporization, and polymorphic transformations are phase changes or phase transformations. A phase diagram shows stability relationships among phases, commonly as a function of pressure and temperature (Fig. 1-17). Consider these diagrams as stability maps in pressure-temperature space.

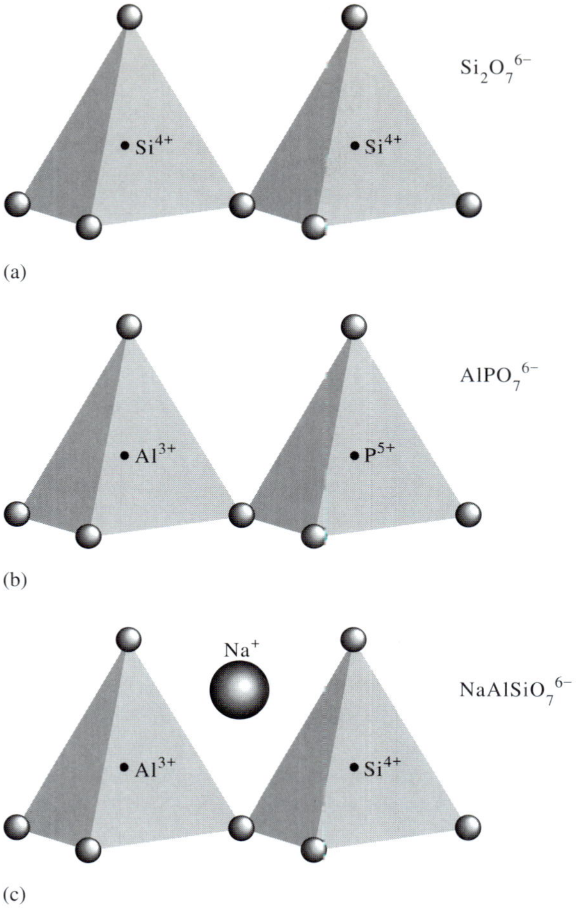

FIGURE 1-16 Derivative structures. (a) Parent structure of $Si_2O_7^{6-}$. (b) Half-breed derivative with coupled substitution of Al^{3+} and P^{5+} for $2Si^{4+}$. (c) Stuffed derivative with Al^{3+} and Na^{+} replacing Si^{4+}.

Phase transformations may be classified according to ease or difficulty with which they occur—that is, according to rates of reaction. Rapid phase transformations occur too quickly to be studied except by dynamic methods. High-temperature quartz, for example, inverts to low-temperature quartz almost instantaneously on cooling to 573°C, and nothing can stop it from doing so. When a high-pressure or high-temperature phase can be collected in the field, the transformation from the high-temperature or high-pressure phase to the low-pressure or low-temperature phase is sluggish and quenchable. Diamond jewels never spontaneously invert to graphite, even though the latter is the stable phase of these two polymorphs

TABLE 1-8 Examples of Derivative Structures

		Coupled substitution		
	Si	Si	O_4	Quartz
	Al	P	O_4	Berlinite
	Al	Al	O_3	Corundum
	Fe	Ti	O_3	Ilmenite
		Stuffed derivatives		
	Si	Si	Si_2O_8	Coesite
K	Al	Si	Si_2O_8	Sanidine
Na	Al	Si	Si_2O_8	Albite
Ca	Al	Al	Si_2O_8	Anorthite

at surface temperature and pressure. Phases in the earth's mantle that invert rapidly will not be found at the surface as minerals.

Dilational phase transformations require change in primary coordination about a cation. At high pressures, cation coordination of halite is 8, but on pressure release it goes back to 6. A displacive transformation occurs when primary coordination about a cation remains constant, but second-nearest neighbors change. An example of a displacive transformation is the high-low inversion of quartz at 573°C. Silica remains in tetrahedral coordination, but angles between silica tetrahedra change. In some volcanic rocks, quartz crystals retain high-temperature shapes after their internal order has inverted to its low-temperature structure.

Not all phase transformations involve structural changes. Above 585°C, magnetite [$FeOFe_2O_3$] lacks permanent magnetization (magnetic order), whereas below that temperature (its Curie point) it becomes permanently magnetized (magnetically ordered), most conspicuously as lodestone. Inversion of magnetite through its Curie point is an example of a nonstructural transformation. Paleomagnetic studies are possible because magnetite's ferrimagnetic character exists only below its Curie point.

Quenched Instability Sluggish and quenchable transformations that permit high-pressure and high-temperature polymorphs to be preserved for collection include constructive, polytypic, and order-disorder transformations. Main chemical bonds are broken and reformed in reconstructive transformations. The calcite-aragonite [$CaCO_3$] reconstructive transformation, for instance, changes the coordination of O^{2-} around Ca^{2+} from 6 to 9. Meteorite-impact shock pressures on quartz cause the primary

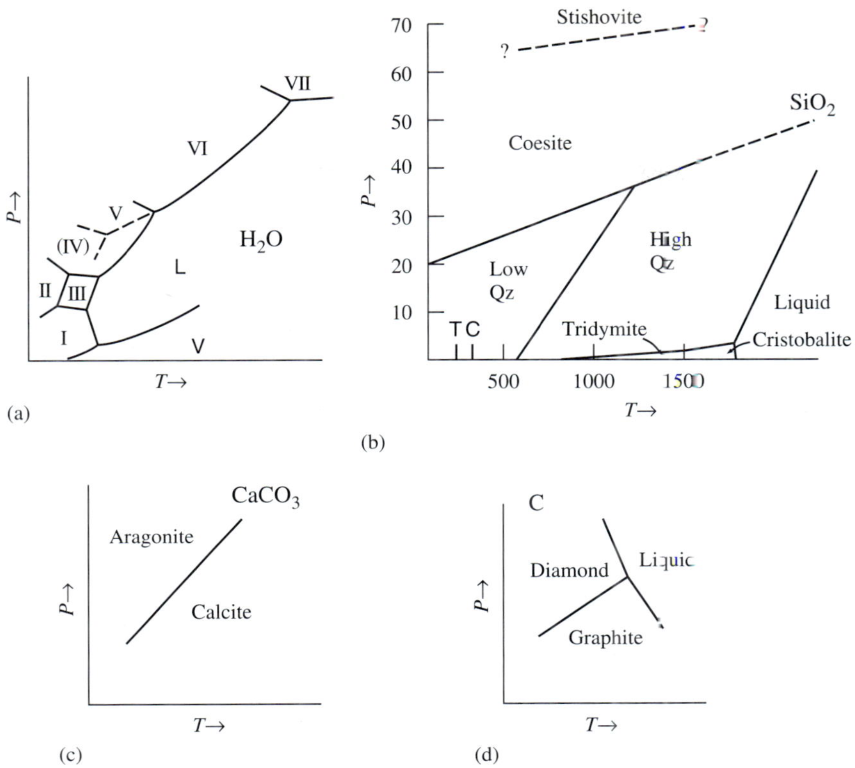

FIGURE 1-17 Polymorphism. Each area represents pressures and temperatures where each phase is stable (or metastable). (a) Six stable and one metastable (IV) crystal structures of ice. (b) Crystal structures of silica. (c) Crystal structures of calcium carbonate. (d) Crystal structures of carbon. Other common examples of polymorphism include kyanite, sillimanite, and andalusite [Al_2SiO_5] (Fig. 4-1); diaspore and boehmite [AlO(OH)]; sphalerite and wurtzite [ZnS] (Fig. 2-3); and cinnabar and metacinnabar [HgS].

coordination of O^{2-} around Si^{4+} to change from 4 to 6, forming the mineral stishovite.

Polytypy—one-dimensional polymorphism—occurs when two polymorphs differ only in the stacking of identical two-dimensional sheets. Layered silicates, including clays and micas, are notorious for their variety in stacking their layers. Kaolinite, dickite, and nacrite [$Al_2Si_2O_5(OH)_4$] differ only in the pattern of stacking their identical layers; they are called polytypes.

Some silicate minerals hold fascinating variation because of the possibility of order and disorder in the substitution of Al^{3+} for Si^{4+} in tetrahedral coordination. For example, two kinds of disorder may occur in the alkali feldspars [$(Na,K)AlSi_3O_8$]. At temperatures near their melt points both Na and K are distributed randomly, and Al replaces Si in one quarter of the tetrahedra at random. At near-surface temperatures, Na and K separate into the mineral species albite and microcline, as separate mineral species, with tetrahedral Al ordered periodically in each species. Perthites (bits of albite in microcline) and antiperthites (bits of microcline in albite) contain these two minerals intimately trapped in the process of separating from a single crystal into two crystals.

At intermediate temperatures, there are different degrees of ordering in feldspars. For example, an ordered half of the tetrahedra may contain Si only while the other half contains Si and Al in equal amounts but randomly distributed.

Phase diagrams are maps of pressure-temperature-composition (PTX) space showing areas of stability of mineral phases for different chemical compositions (Fig. 1-17). At boundaries of stability fields, two phases are equally stable. Triple points mark where three stability fields meet at a fixed temperature and pressure; all three phases are equally stable there and may coexist in equilibrium (see Sec. 6-2).

1-7 NONCRYSTALLINE AND CRYPTOCRYSTALLINE MATTER

Glass Volcanic glass is a noncrystalline material. Glass lacks long-range order but has short-range order. Its short-range order results from all Si^{4+} being in tetrahedral coordination and Al^{3+} in both tetrahedral and octahedral coordination, just as in minerals with long-range order. In addition, it has domains of isolated silica tetrahedra, of silica dimers, of silica chains, and of silica frameworks, just as in silicate minerals in igneous rocks (Table 2-2). These domains may have profound influence on nucleation and crystal growth (Sec. 7-1) and on resultant igneous rock textures (Sec. 7-2). Yet it is a glass and has the properties of glass and not those of a mass of mineral grains. In a relatively short geologic time, leaching, hydration, and devitrification cause minerals to crystallize from volcanic glass.

Colloids Precipitation of dissolved silica under certain conditions yields a colloidal material (dispersed particles in the nanometer size range) rather than distinct crystals. Modern silica gels, for example, form in an alkaline environment when seasonal variations in alkalinity of natural waters range from a pH greater than 9, where silica is somewhat soluble, to less than 9, where it is quite insoluble. As water pH drops below 9, colloidal silica accumulates as a gel. Partial dehydration of silica gel yields opal, an aggregate of submicroscopic spherules, which may or may not be individually crystalline, and up to 9% nonstructural water. Further dehydration and recrystallization may yield chalcedony, a cryptocrystalline variety of silica. A material is cryptocrystalline if individual crystals or grains cannot be resolved with an optical microscope; it is microcrystalline if they can.

Metamictization A metamict mineral is one in which crystal structure and long-range order have been broken down by nuclear irradiation. In crystals containing essential U or Th or nonessential U or Th in sufficient amounts for sufficient time, radioactive decay destroys crystallinity partly by alpha-particle bombardment and partly by drastic changes in size and charge of daughter ions (Fig. 4-9). Most thorite [$ThSiO_4$] and zircon [$ZrSiO_4$] with impurity Th or U are metamict or partly metamict. A mineral may become amorphous to X rays when as few as 20% of its ions have been displaced. Crystallinity can be restored, in many instances, merely by heating the metamict mineral to temperatures between 500 and 900°C.

Radioactive emission of alpha particles may cause visible effects in minerals enclosing radioactive grains such as thorite, zircon, or monazite [$REPO_4$] (RE refers to rare earths). Colored aureoles—pleochroic halos—result from alpha bombardment of host minerals, including micas, tourmalines, chlorites, and fluorite.

Pseudomorphism In natural processes at or near the earth's surface, one mineral may replace another one while retaining the external form of the original crystal. A paramorph results when a phase transformation occurs in a well-formed crystal. Low-temperature quartz with crystal faces that, for reasons of symmetry, could only develop on high-temperature quartz is a paramorph. Calcite [$CaCO_3$] with crystal faces that could only have formed on aragonite is another example. Pseudomorphs involve chemical changes while preserving old external forms. Crystals of native copper that have the crystal form of cuprite [Cu_2O] result from a change in oxidation state and a loss of oxygen. Crystals of gypsum [$CaSO_4 \cdot 2H_2O$] with the external forms of anhydrite [$CaSO_4$] have gained H_2O. Goethite [$FeO(OH)$] in the form of pyrite [FeS_2] has undergone changes in oxidation state and exchange of ions with its environment.

Secondary material in a pseudomorph need not be a single mineral species. Leucite [$(K,Na)AlSi_2O_6$], which crystallizes in some volcanic rocks, becomes unstable on cooling and may invert to pseudoleucite, an intergrowth of sanidine [$KAlSi_3O_8$] and nepheline [$Na_3K(AlSiO_4)_4$], while maintaining its original crystal shape.

1-8 THERMOCHEMISTRY

One aim of the study of earth materials—rocks and minerals—is to determine how they formed and under what conditions they formed. In recent years this study has become progressively more quantitative and has relied on thermochemistry for information on rock origin through mineral analysis.

Thermochemistry is a theoretical branch of chemistry, including mineral chemistry, that treats reactions and energetically stable reaction products. It shows the relationships among the basic properties of matter such as temperature (T), pressure (P), volume (V), internal energy (E), entropy (S), and composition. The absolute internal energy content of a system is unknowable. Therefore, thermochemistry deals only in the change in energy, ΔE or dE, that takes place when a system changes from one state to another. The symbol Δ is used to indicate a finite change, and the symbol d is used to indicate an infinitesimally small change.

In general, ΔE is the sum of different kinds of energy transfer between a system and its surroundings. The kinds of change-of-state mechanisms include heat, pressure-volume work (expansion and contraction), electrical work, work resulting from the gain or loss of matter to the system, work resulting from change in surface area of material in the system, and work against a gravitational, electric, or magnetic field. A virtually unlimited number of energy transfer mechanisms contribute to ΔE.

The inclusion or exclusion of a mechanism of energy transfer in the evaluation of ΔE depends on the nature of the problem being addressed. An engineer designing a new electrical storage battery is concerned with electrical work, whereas a sedimentologist studying the nucleation and growth of clay minerals is interested in the energy change resulting from the increase in size of the clay mineral crystallites. If a study focuses on a system that gains or loses material—an open chemical system—then primary attention is directed toward the energy change due to the gain or loss of materials.

In mineral chemistry, it is often permissible to neglect many of these kinds of energy transfer and to consider only two, pressure-volume work and heat. Such a simplification is possible only if the system does not gain or lose material (a closed chemical system), and if the value of the other energy transfer mechanisms is very small compared with pressure-volume work (w) and heat (Q).

System-State-Equilibrium-Reversibility Before proceeding with a more detailed discussion of energy change and transfer, we consider four important thermochemical concepts: system, state, equilibrium, and reversibility.

A system is any part of the universe chosen for study; it can be chosen to be complex or simple. It can be real or hypothetical. An isolated system is one that cannot interact with its surroundings in any way. A closed system can exchange heat and work with its surroundings, but cannot exchange matter. An open system can exchange heat, work, and matter with its surroundings.

State is used to indicate the condition of the sample of matter—the system—under study. The state of a system is defined by its state properties, which include temperature, pressure, density, mass, index of refraction, velocity of sound, internal energy, entropy, atomic spacing, and so on. These state properties are called *extensive* if they are divided when a system is divided (e.g., mass) and *intensive* if they are not divided when a system is divided (e.g., density).

Thus, a material is identified (defined in the words of thermochemistry) as quartz, say, by measuring some of its state properties (e.g., density and index of refraction) at room temperature and pressure. The quartz sample can be changed to a second state by changing any of its state properties, for example, by heating (a temperature change) or compressing (a volume change) it. From a thermochemical point of view, the quartz in the second state is not the same material as that in the initial sample. Many of its state properties have different values. If the state properties return to their original values, the quartz is indistinguishable from the original quartz and is, therefore, in the same state as the original sample.

An equilibrium system is one that does not change in any way with time and, furthermore, has *no tendency* to change with time. Consider an ordinary coffee cup with a marble inside. The system is the cup and marble. Further stipulate that cup and marble are always in contact and that friction can be ignored. The state properties of the cup-marble system are position (x), measured by the horizontal distance from some arbitrary point, say the center of the cup bottom, and gravitational potential energy, which depends on the vertical height of the marble above some arbitrary point, say the bottom of the cup. The equilibrium state for the cup-marble system occurs when the marble occupies the very lowest position in the cup. It will occupy this position forever unless the system is disturbed by some mechanism from outside.

All other positions in the cup are some distance above the bottom and have a potential energy higher than the equilibrium state. If the marble occupies one of these positions, it moves spontaneously (Δx) to the lowest point and the energy of the system is decreased (ΔP_G). The equilibrium state is that state with the lowest energy and is called the state of stable equilibrium (Fig. 1-18). (Metastable and unstable equilibria both satisfy the definition of equilibrium given here, but are not the states of lowest energy in the system.)

The criteria of equilibrium of a system at constant temperature and pressure is that $\Delta E = 0$. During a chemical reaction, two processes occur: (1) the reactants combine to form products, and (2) the products react with one another in a reverse manner. As the overall reaction proceeds, the speed of the forward reaction slows as the reactants are consumed, and the reverse reaction speeds up as the products increase in amount. Eventually the forward and reverse reactions proceed at the same rate, and no *net* change occurs in the system. The system is then said to be in chemical equilibrium.

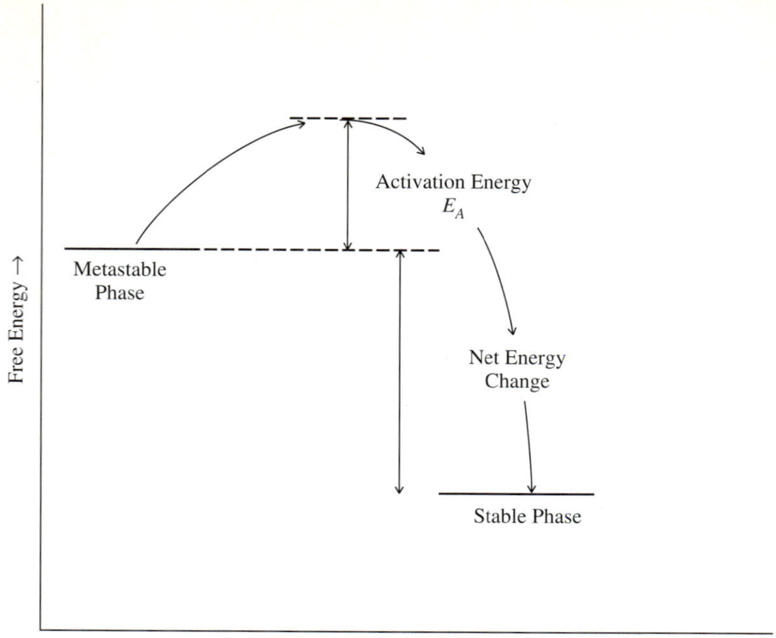

FIGURE 1-18 Stable and metastable equilibria. The energy level on the left is the metastable one; the one on the right is stable. A metastable state has no tendency to change until outside activation energy is supplied.

The notion of reversibility is closely related to the concept of stable equilibrium. Whereas equilibrium refers to a condition of the system, reversibility refers to a process involving the system. Consider a sample of quartz in an equilibrium state and allow the state properties to change so that the quartz reaches a second equilibrium state. If the change from one equilibrium to another is carried out in infinitesimally small steps, such that an infinitesimal change in conditions can reverse the direction of change, the process is reversible.

Phrases such as "initial state" and "from one state to another" are used to discuss the change in system properties during some process. The standard state is an arbitrarily chosen reference state against which all other states can be compared. Standard-state conditions are often specified to be 25°C and one atmosphere pressure, but the choice is arbitrary.

***P-V* Work and Heat** Mechanical work (w) is defined as the product of a force (f) and the distance (Δx) through which it travels; thus, for a constant force, $w = f\,\Delta x$. Pressure (P) is defined as force (f) per unit area (A), so $P = f/A$. Therefore, $w = f\,\Delta x = PA\,\Delta x$. The product of area A and change in distance Δx is the change in volume (ΔV). Furthermore, $w = f\,\Delta x = -PA\,\Delta x = -P\,\Delta V$. The negative sign is added in order to distinguish, by sign, whether the work is done *on* the system (+) or *by* the system (−). If the system expands (increases in volume), work is done by the system and the energy of the system decreases; by convention, the sign is negative. If the system is compressed (work done on the system), the volume decreases ($-\Delta V$), the work done on the system is $w = -P(-\Delta V)$, and the energy of the system increases by the amount $P\,\Delta V$. When the change is infinitesimal, $w = -P\,dV$.

Heat is the mechanism of energy exchange between a system and its surroundings caused by temperature difference only. Heat added to a system increases the energy of the system and has a positive sign; heat given off by the system decreases the energy of the system and has a negative sign. Heat and work are not state properties because their value depends on the path of the process as a system changes from an initial state to a second state.

The property of matter called entropy was deduced more than a century ago from the study of a hypothetical heat engine, the Carnot engine. It was shown that the sum of the amount of heat gained and lost by a material divided by temperature is zero when the substance is changed from its initial state to a second state and then returned to its initial state, provided the changes are carried reversibly and isothermally. This is expressed mathematically as $\Sigma\, q_r/T = 0$, where q_r is the infinitesimal amount of energy transferred as heat between the system and its surroundings. Entropy (S) is defined as $dS = q_r/T$ in a cyclic reversible process, and $\Delta S = Q_r/T$ is a finite amount of heat exchanged at constant temperature in a reversible manner.

Reversible processes are carried out in infinitesimally small steps and, therefore, require infinite time. Spontaneous processes, such as those that occur in nature, are irreversible. In this case $dS > q/T$. The entropy of a system always increases during a spontaneous (irreversible) process; the entropy of the universe is increasing. A process where $dS < q/T$ is impossible. Entropy is a state property of matter, and it has a value of zero at absolute zero temperature (0 K) provided the matter is homogeneous and is in internal equilibrium.

Derived Energies The relationship among internal energy and the equivalents of heat and work is given by the equations $dE = T\,dS - P\,dV$ (infinitesimal changes) and $\Delta E = T\,\Delta S - P\,\Delta V$ (finite changes) at constant temperature and pressure.

It is useful, for convenience in derivations and calculations, to define a new set of quantities in terms of the five basic properties of matter: T, P, E, V, and S. Three are

Enthalpy	$H = E + PV$
Helmholtz free energy	$A = E - TS$
Gibbs free energy	$G = E + PV - TS$

For infinitesimal changes, these equations can be written

$$dH = T\,dS + V\,dP,$$
$$dA = -S\,dT - P\,dV,$$
$$dG = -S\,dT + V\,dP.$$

The Gibbs free energy, or just free energy, is often used in mineral chemical calculations because temperature and pressure are the independent variables. They are relatively easy to measure in nature and in the laboratory. At equilibrium, dG and ΔG are zero. The free energy of a system is the sum of all the chemical potentials (μ_i) times the number of moles (n_i) of each component i: $\Sigma\ \mu_i n_i$. Under equilibrium conditions, chemical potentials of each component are uniform throughout a system.

Fugacity and Activity For an operational notion of fugacity and activity, think of them as ideal pressure and concentration, respectively. They are related to free energy, real pressure, and concentration in the following manner.

The free-energy change in a system due to an infinitesimal change in the equilibrium temperature and pressure is given by the equation $dG = -S\,dT + V\,dP$. At constant temperature ($dT = 0$), this equation reduces to $dG = V\,dP$. For an ideal gas, $PV = nRT$, where n is the number of moles of gas and R is the gas constant. Thus, $V = nRT/P$, so $dG = nRT(dP/P) = nRT \ln dP$. Integrating gives

$$\int_{G^\circ}^{G} dG = nRT \int_{P^\circ}^{P} \ln P dP,$$
$$G - G^\circ = nRT \ln(P/P^\circ),$$

where P° is a standard or reference pressure and G° is then the free energy of the system at pressure P°; that is, G° is the standard-state free energy. Note that the choice of a standard state is completely arbitrary and is simply a reference to which another set of conditions can be compared. Then G is the free energy of the system at any other pressure (at constant temperature). If P° is chosen as 1 atm, then

$$G = G^\circ + nRT \ln(P/1) = G^\circ + nRT \ln P.$$

A general chemical gas reaction can be written in the form

$$a\mathrm{A} + b\mathrm{B} + \cdots = \cdots + y\mathrm{Y} + z\mathrm{Z},$$

where a moles of reactant A and b moles of reactant B, and so on, produce y moles of product Y and z moles of product Z, and so on. The free-energy change, ΔG, for this reaction is the free energy of the products minus the free energy of the reactants:

$$\Delta G = (G_\mathrm{Y} + G_\mathrm{Z}) - (G_\mathrm{A} + G_\mathrm{B}),$$

where G_Y is the total free energy of component Y, G_Z is the total free energy of component Z, and so on.

$$
\begin{aligned}
G_Y &= G_Y^\circ + yRT \ln P_y = G_Y^\circ + RT \ln P_Y^y, \\
G_Z &= G_Z^\circ + zRT \ln P_z = G_Z^\circ + RT \ln P_Z^z, \\
G_a &= G_A^\circ + aRT \ln P_a = G_A^\circ + RT \ln P_A^a, \\
G_b &= G_B^\circ + bRT \ln P_b = G_B^\circ + RT \ln P_B^b.
\end{aligned}
$$

The change in free energy in this standard state, ΔG_R for the reaction, is the difference in the standard free energies of the products and reactants:

$$
\begin{aligned}
\Delta G_R^\circ &= (G_Z^\circ + G_X^\circ + \cdots) - (G_A^\circ + G_B^\circ + \cdots), \\
\Delta G_R &= \Delta G_R^\circ + RT(P_Z^z P_X^x / P_A^a P_B^b) = 0
\end{aligned}
$$

at equilibrium and constant temperature. The pressures are those of each ideal gas at equilibrium. The quantity $P_Z^z P_X^x / P_A^a P_B^b$ is called the (pressure) equilibrium constant K_1. It can be calculated from the relation

$$\Delta G = \Delta G^\circ + RT \ln(P_Z^z P_X^x \cdots / P_A^a P_B^b \cdots) = 0$$

as $\Delta G^\circ/RT = -\ln K_1$. The equilibrium constant is in terms of pressure; however, other concentration units can also be computed.

Most common gases at pressures less than a few atmospheres and at temperatures greater than a few hundred degrees Celsius are close to ideal. Thus, total air pressure is the sum of the partial pressure of N_2 plus the partial pressure of O_2 plus the partial pressure of Ar plus the partial pressure of H_2O, and so on. But in many reactions of geochemical interest, real gases do not obey the ideal gas law; therefore, a special quantity called fugacity (f) was invented for convenience in calculations. The formal definition of fugacity is $dG = nRT\, d \ln f$ at the limits where $f/P \rightarrow 1$ as $P \rightarrow 0$. Fugacity becomes identical with pressure as pressure approaches zero. Fugacity may be thought of as a partial or corrected pressure and is expressed in the same units as pressure. Pressure is related to fugacity by the fugacity coefficient α, so $f = P\alpha$. In general, α is not constant because it changes with temperature, pressure, and composition of the system.

To deal with equilibria involving solids and liquids as well as gases, a quantity called the activity, a, was invented to make computation more convenient. Activity is defined as $a = f/f^\circ$ or, for ideal gases, $a = P/P^\circ$, where f (or P for ideal gases) is the fugacity and f° (or P° for ideal gases) is the standard-state fugacity, usually 1 atm for gases; thus, in most gases, $a = f$, and $a = P$ for ideal gases.

For solids and liquids, f is the vapor fugacity and f° is the vapor fugacity in the standard state. Many solids and liquids have very low vapor fugacity, and the substitution of vapor pressure for vapor fugacity is a very close approximation. The relation between free energy G and activity a is given by the equation $G = G^\circ + RT \ln a$ for one component.

For a reaction among solids, liquids, or gases, such as $aA + bB + \cdots = yY + zZ + \cdots$, the equation

$$\Delta G = \Delta G^\circ + RT \ln(a_Y^y a_Z^z \cdots / a_A^a a_B^b \cdots)$$

shows the relationship among products and reactants. At equilibrium,

$$\Delta G = 0 = \Delta G^\circ + RT \ln(a_Y^y a_Z^z \cdots / a_A^a a_B^b \cdots),$$

and the quantity $a_Y^y a_Z^z \cdots / a_A^a a_B^b \cdots$ is called the chemical equilibrium constant K: $\Delta G = 0 = \Delta G^\circ + RT \ln K$.

The activity of a pure solid or liquid is unity. This is so because the standard state for a pure substance is usually chosen as the pure substance at 1 atm total pressure. Standard-state fugacity (f°) is the vapor fugacity (f_1, or vapor pressure for ideal gases, most solids, and many liquids) at 1 atm total pressure. If the pressure on the pure substance is 1 atm, then $f_1 = f^\circ$ and, from the defining equation, $a = f_1/f^\circ = 1/1 = 1$.

The standard state for a solution is usually chosen in the same way as for pure solids or liquids (25°C, 1 atm). For dilute solutions, the activity (a_1) of the solvent is equal to the mole fraction (x_1) of solvent. In more concentrated solutions, $a_1 \neq x_1$, but they are related by the activity coefficient γ; that is, $a_1 = \gamma_1 x_1$. In general, γ does not have a unique value but depends on the temperature, pressure, and composition of the system. In most geochemical calculations involving fresh water, the activity of the water is often assumed to be unity because fresh water contains, on average, 120 ppm of dissolved material. On the other hand, seawater, which contains 35,000 ppm of dissolved material, must have γ evaluated experimentally in order to compute the activity of the water.

The activity of the solute may be expressed in different ways. One way is based on the observation that the vapor pressure of the solute above a solution is proportional to its concentration in the solution at infinite dilution. Ideal solutions obey proportionality throughout their concentration ranges: $f_2 = k_2 x_2$, where k_2 is the proportionality constant and x_2 is the solute mole fraction. Rewriting gives $x_2 = f_2/k_2$. The solute standard state is chosen as a hypothetical solution where $x_2 = 1$, $f_2^\circ/k_2 = 1$, and $f_2^\circ = k_2$. Activity is given by the defining equation $a_2 = f_2/f_2^\circ$, and, thus, $a_2 = f_2/k_2$, which equals x_2. Note that this relationship holds only when the solute vapor fugacity is proportional to the amount of solute in solution. This proportionality does not hold for many solutions. In this case, activity is related to mole fraction by the activity coefficient γ_2, so $a_2 = \gamma_2 x_2$. The value of γ_2 depends on the temperature, pressure, and composition of the system.

pH and Eh It is often convenient to discuss geochemical processes occurring in natural water in terms of pH and Eh. Equilibria involving acids and bases involve the activity of the hydrogen ion (H^+). Pure water (H_2O) dissociates into hydrogen ions (H^+) and hydroxyl ions (OH^-). For each formula weight (mole) of H_2O at 25°C and 1 standard atmosphere, there are 10^{-7} ions of H^+ and 10^{-7} ions of OH^- (10^{-7} = 0.1 ppm). The pH is defined as the negative logarithm of the activity (or concentration if ideal) of the hydrogen ion. The reason for the odd definition of pH can be seen by considering a reaction involving the hydrogen ion, such as the dissociation of water (H_2O) into H^+ and OH^-: $H_2O = H^+ + OH^-$. The equation for the free energy of this reaction is

$$\Delta G = \Delta G^\circ + RT \ln(a_{H^+}^{-7} a_{OH^-}^{-7} / a_{H_2O}).$$

The activity of water (a_{H_2O}) is unity, so this expression could also be written

$$\Delta G = \Delta G^\circ + RT \ln a_{H^+}^{-7} + RT \ln a_{OH^-}^{-7}$$

Note that the negative logarithm of hydrogen ion activity ($a_{H^+}^{-7}$) is 7, the pH of pure water. It may help to think of pH as a measure of a liquid's ability to supply H^+ to bases and to accept H^+ from acids.

Because of other dissolved ions, ordinary stream waters have pH values ranging from 5 to 6.5; acid streams and lakes, less than 4; oceans, from 8.1 to 8.3; and playa lakes in arid regions, greater than 9. A general pH range for the earth's natural waters is 4 to 9.

The term Eh is the oxidation potential. It describes the oxidation or reduction properties of a chemical environment. Natural waters have a great range of oxidation potentials. Water in equilibrium with oxygen in air is oxidizing; it tends to strip electrons from cations. Iron in such an environment tends to occur in its highest oxidation state, Fe^{3+}, in solution and in minerals. Groundwater percolating through decomposing organic matter tends to be reducing, and iron, for example, occurs in the ferrous, Fe^{2+}, state in solution and in minerals. Oxidation potential is a quantitative measure of the oxidizing or reducing conditions of such systems.

Consider the ordinary lead-acid battery used in an automobile. When such a cell is fully charged, it is capable of doing electrical work—sounding the horn, starting the engine, and the like. The process is one of converting chemical energy into electrical work as well as heat and *P-V* work. The amount of electrical work (w_e) performed is the product of electromotive force ($\mathcal{E}$) (or voltage) and the amount of electricity (I) flowing in the circuit: $w_e = -\mathcal{E}I$. The negative sign is used to keep electrical work consistent with *P-V* work. The quantity I is the product of the number of equivalents (i.e., moles) of electrons that flow and the amount of electricity per equivalent of electrons, $\mathcal{F}$, called the Faraday constant: $I = n\mathcal{F}$, so $w_e = -n\mathcal{E}\mathcal{F}$.

The overall chemical reaction that occurs as electricity flows is

$$Pb + PbO_2 + 4H^+ + 2SO^{2-} = 2H_2O + 2PbSO_4$$

where metallic lead and solid lead oxide react with hydrogen ions and sulfate ions to produce water and lead sulfate. However, at the positive battery terminal the reaction is

$$PbO_2 + 4H^+ + SO_4^{2-} + 2e^- \rightarrow PbSO_4 + 2H_2O$$

Lead oxide reacts with hydrogen ions, sulfate ions, and electrons to produce lead sulfate and water. The reaction at the negative terminal is

$$Pb + SO_4^{2-} \rightarrow PbSO_4 + 2e^-$$

Metallic lead reacts with sulfate ions to produce lead sulfate and electrons. The reactions proceed, and the electricity flows when the two terminals are connected by an electrical conductor. The reaction at each electrode is called a half-cell reaction. (Note also that the metallic lead is oxidized by losing two electrons in becoming lead sulfate, and lead oxide is reduced by gaining two electrons in becoming lead sulfate.) In general, any oxidation-reduction reaction can be written in terms of two half-reactions.

The free energy of the reaction (ΔG) is the electrical work done provided that temperature and pressure are constant and the reaction proceeds in a reversible manner: $\Delta G = -n\mathcal{F}\mathcal{E}$. If the reaction takes place under standard-state conditions, then $\Delta G^\circ = -n\mathcal{F}\mathcal{E}^\circ$, where $\mathcal{E}^\circ$ is the electromotive force (voltage) of the cell when the reactants and products are in their standard states.

For a general chemical reaction where $a\text{A} + b\text{B} + \cdots = y\text{Y} + z\text{Z} + \cdots$, the free-energy change is given by the equation

$$\Delta G = \Delta G^\circ + RT\ln(a_\text{Y}^y a_\text{Z}^z \cdots / a_\text{A}^a a_\text{B}^b \cdots).$$

Therefore,

$$\mathcal{E} = \mathcal{E}^\circ - RT/n\mathcal{F}\ln(a_\text{Y}^y a_\text{Z}^z \cdots / a_\text{A}^a a_\text{B}^b \cdots),$$
$$\mathcal{E} = -\Delta G/n\mathcal{F}.$$

At equilibrium $\mathcal{E} = 0$.

Values of $\mathcal{E}^\circ$ have been measured for many combinations of half-cell reactions. The hydrogen half-cell is of particular interest because it is given a value of *zero* by convention. The hydrogen standard cell is gaseous hydrogen in equilibrium with hydrogen ions in solution when both are at 25°C and 1 atm pressure. The $\mathcal{E}^\circ$ values of other half-cells are measured, each in combination with the hydrogen half-cell. The electromotive force for a half-cell reaction, measured against the hydrogen standard cell, is called the oxidation potential, Eh, for the general case when the reactants and products are not in their standard states.

The upper oxidizing limit in terrestrial aqueous systems is the dissociation of water (H_2O) to molecular oxygen (O_2) at 1 atm, hydrogen ions (H^+), and electrons (e^-), a half-cell reaction:

$$H_2O \rightleftharpoons \tfrac{1}{2}O_2 + 2H^+ + 2e^-$$

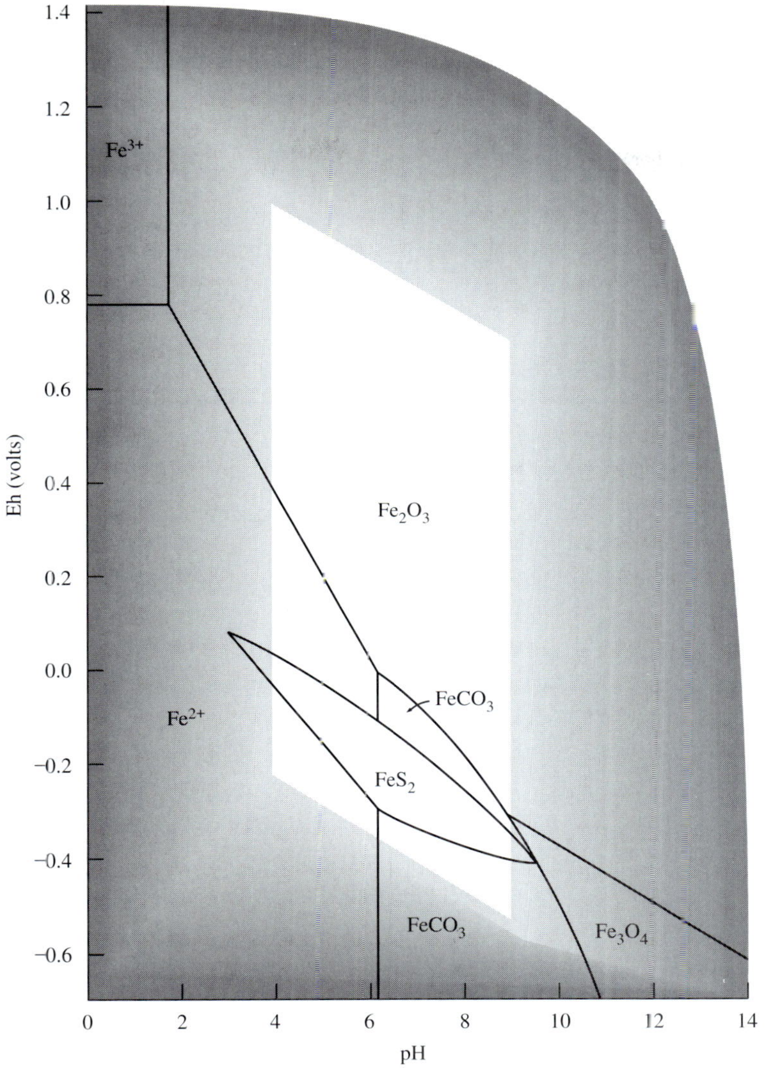

FIGURE 1-19 Eh–pH diagram for dissolved iron (10^{-6} *M*) in an aqueous solution containing carbonate (1 *M*) and sulfur (10^{-6} *M*). Shaded area represents the window for terrestrial limits.

The lower reducing limit for these systems is the reduction of hydrogen ions (H^+) and electrons (e^-) to hydrogen gas (H_2) at 1 atm, a half-cell reaction:

$$H_2 \rightleftharpoons 2H^+ + 2e^-$$

Stability relationships among various related mineral species in terrestrial waters may be shown graphically by plotting Eh versus pH for various minerals and related ionic species (Fig. 1-19). Note that variables other than Eh and pH, such as pressure and the presence and concentrations of other solutes, will influence boundaries of stability fields on this kind of plot.

These thermochemical concepts are used to determine the geologic histories of earth materials and to predict their futures resulting from current geologic processes.

FURTHER READINGS

Bloss, F. D., *Crystallography and Crystal Chemistry*. New York: Holt, Rinehart and Winston, Inc., 1971.

Evans, R. C., *An Introduction to Crystal Chemistry*, 2nd ed. New York: Cambridge University Press, 1964.

Frye, K., *Encyclopedia of Mineralogy*. New York: Van Nostrand Reinhold, 1981.

Kieffer, S. W., and A. Navrotsky (eds.), *Microscopic to Macroscopic: Atomic Environments to Mineral Thermodynamics*. Washington: Mineralogical Society of America, 1985.

Megaw, H. D., *Crystal Structures: A Working Approach*. Philadelphia: Saunders, 1973.

Pauling, L., *The Nature of the Chemical Bond*. Ithaca: Cornell University Press, 1960.

Putnis, A., and J. D. C. McConnell, *Principles of Mineral Behaviour*. New York: Elsevier, 1980.

Wells, A. F., *Structural Inorganic Chemistry*, 4th ed. Oxford, UK: Oxford University Press, 1984.

Wood, B. J., and D. G. Fraser, *Elementary Thermodynamics for Geologists*. Oxford, UK: Oxford University Press, 1978.

2

CRYSTAL STRUCTURES

Since discovery that crystalline materials diffract X rays, a main thrust in mineralogy has been toward elucidation of crystal structures by means of X-ray diffraction. Within months after diffraction experiments were reported by Friedrich, Knipping, and Laue in Germany (Sec. 1-3), the Braggs, father and son, in England reported the structures of sylvite, halite, sphalerite, fluorite, calcite, and diamond.

This method by which an individual crystal structure is determined requires interpretation of its diffraction pattern (Sec. 5-6) in terms of symmetrical properties of crystals. Indeed, crystal symmetry was developed mathematically on the basis of crystal morphology (shape) during the 19th century, well in advance of discovery of X-ray diffraction (see Chap. 3). Before looking at abstract geometrical crystallography, we look first at actual distributions of atomic particles (atoms, ions, molecules, radicals) in space as determined by X-ray diffraction and other methods.

Unit Cell Crystal structures are characterized by three-dimensional repetition of unit cells, parallelopipeds with linear dimensions on the order of 50–150 pm (5–15 Å), although some are considerably larger than this range. Not only are all proportions of essential chemical elements of a mineral contained in its unit cell, but geometric relationships among chemical constituents are included as well. These spatial relationships, treated in Chap. 3, commonly require that a unit cell of a mineral contain more than one formula unit, commonly seen as formula subscripts with a common denominator, such as kaolinite [$Al_4(OH)_8Si_4O_{10}$], or as a multiplier, such as $2[Al_2(OH)_4Si_2O_5]$. Once you select a unit cell (in some instances somewhat arbitrarily), you reveal an entire crystal structure by stacking identical unit cells in parallel orientation in three dimensions.

Classification Principles A useful way of classifying mineral structures is to proceed, first, on the basis of their cation-to-anion ratio and, second, on the basis of their cation coordination number (CN). Geologically important silicate minerals, because of partial covalency of Si—O bonds and polymerization of silica tetrahedra, are treated slightly differently. As indicated by Si:O ratios, silica tetrahedra may share one, two, three, or all four of their corners to form dimers, rings, chains, sheets, and frameworks (see Fig. 2-14). Because of directionality of Si—O bonding, which dominates silicate structures, coordination of other cations may be somewhat irregular. Therefore, we classify silicates according to number of shared tetrahedral corners and patterns of resulting linkages, reflected in part by Si:O ratios.

Graphic Representation Several methods exist for showing graphically spatial relationships of ions in minerals. A simple perspective sketch may adequately represent ion locations in some simple structures. Alternatively, outlines of coordination polyhedra better represent these structures visually either alone or mixed with individual ion locations. Many minerals, especially oxides, halides, and sulfides, have structures in which anions are in an approximate HCP or CCP (=FCC) array (see Fig. 1-7); these are described by stating which close packing exists and which spaces among the anions are filled by specific cations.

Two methods of describing spatial relationships among ions are always complete and precise, but not immediately easy to visualize. First, give a unit-cell edge a value of unity in each crystallographic direction; then give coordinates of each ion as fractions or percentages of each unit-cell edge. Second, project all ion locations onto one face of a unit cell; then give heights above that face in fractions or percentages of the projected unit-cell direction. Crystal structures are described best by whichever method makes them most obvious.

Crystal structures described in this chapter include most common rock-forming minerals and ore minerals. In the rest of this book, you will see how geometric symmetry (Chap. 3), physical properties (Chap. 4), electromagnetic properties (Chap. 5), stability (Chap. 6), and mineral genesis (Chap. 7) all directly relate to crystal structures of mineral species.

2-1 NATIVE ELEMENTS

Of 94 chemical elements occurring in the earth's crust, only a few occur as native elements. Most native transition metals have CCP (=FCC)

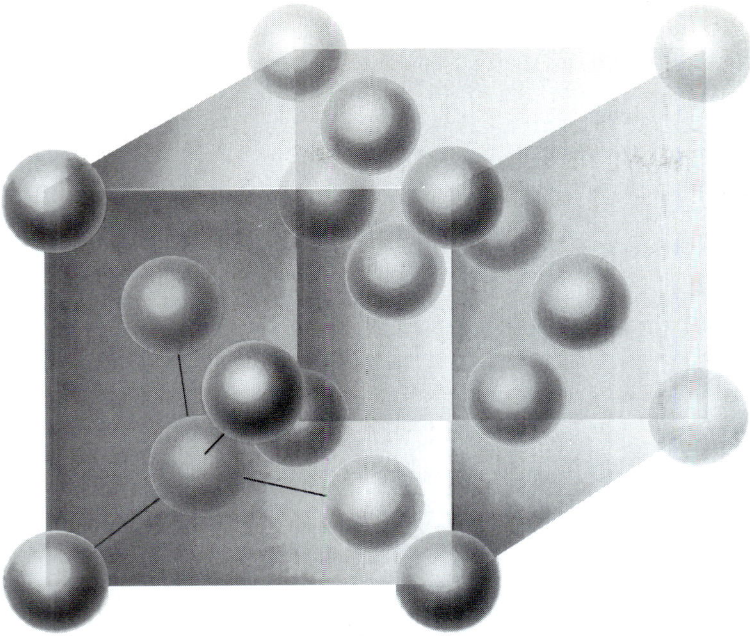

FIGURE 2-1 Diamond structure. Carbon ions are located at each corner of this unit cell cube, at centers of each face, and at approximately ¼ or ¾ along alternate body diagonals of this cube. Tetrahedral *t* bonds (sp^3) of carbon are shown by lines for an interior carbon ion at lower left.

structures (Fig. 1-7). These native metals include copper alloyed with minor amounts of Fe, Ag, Bi, Sn, Pb, or Sb; silver alloyed with up to 10% Au and lesser amounts of Cu; gold with up to 35% Ag; platinum with 10–20% Fe, to 3% Rh and Ir, and lesser amounts of other platinum group elements as well as Cu, Pd, and Os; and lead with traces of Ag. Native iron comes from terrestrial and extraterrestrial (meteoritic) sources. Iron from both sources is in a body-centered cubic array because of overlapping *d* orbitals and is commonly alloyed with Ni—approximately 2% from terrestrial sources, but up to 20% in meteorites.

Around some volcanic fumaroles, native sulfur occurs in crystals composed of molecules of eight-membered rings. Native carbon occurs in two common polymorphs, graphite and diamond. Graphite consists of C ions in sheets of six-membered rings with no strong chemical bonds at right angles to these sheets (see Fig. 4-5). Diamond, a high-pressure polymorph, has C ions in two interpenetrating CCP arrays that are offset so that the C ions of one array are located in the tetrahedral voids of the other (Fig. 2-1; Prog. 2-1; see also Fig. 4-5). (The idealized ionic model is useful here even though C—C bonding is entirely covalent.)

These two polymorphs of carbon present a dramatic example of dependence of physical properties on crystal structure. Diamond, the hardest mineral known, is used as an abrasive; graphite, one of the softest, is used as a dry lubricant. The C—C bonding in diamond forms a rigid, three-dimensional framework. The C—C bonding in graphite is actually stronger (shorter) than in diamond, but is confined to two dimensions with weak bonds between sheets, thus permitting them to slip readily past one another. Electrically, graphite is a conductor, while certain rare diamonds may be doped semiconductors (see Chap. 4).

2-2 ONE-CATION STRUCTURES

Simple mineral structures occur in compounds with a 1:1 cation-to-anion ratio (AX), their electrostatic charges necessarily being equal and opposite. Three major kinds of AX structures are considered.

Halite A halite structure has both ions in a CCP array (Fig. 2-2; Prog. 2-2). (Mineral structures are named for a common mineral species having that structure.) The Cl^- ions at face centers in this structure are shared between two adjacent unit cells; therefore, each face-center ion counts as

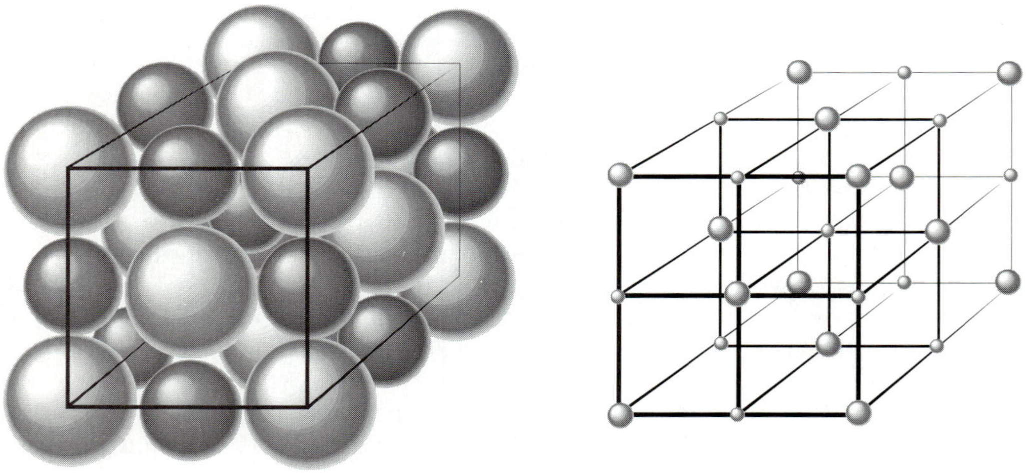

(a) (b)

FIGURE 2-2 Halite structure. Chloride ions are located at corners and face centers of this unit-cell cube. Sodium ions are located midway along unit-cell edges and at the center. (a) Ions depicted approximately to scale. (b) Ion centers shown with assignable bond directions indicated by heavy lines. Both cations and anions are in mutual octahedral coordination. Alternatively, sodium and chloride ion position assignments could be reversed.

half an ion in each adjacent unit cell. Six faces on a cube give a total of three face-centered ions per unit cell. A corner Cl^- ion is shared among eight corner-adjacent unit cells; therefore, each corner ion contributes one eighth to a unit cell. Eight corners on a cube give one Cl^- corner ion per unit cell for a total of four Cl^- ions per unit cell.

Cations lie along centers of edges of this unit-cell cube plus one in its center. Each Na^+ on an edge is shared among four different edge-adjacent unit cells; therefore, each edge-centered ion contributes one quarter of an ion to each corner-adjacent unit cell. Twelve edges on a cube give a total of three Na^+ ions per unit cell that, when added to its center one, yield a total of 4, exactly the same as Cl^- ions. Note that in a halite structure either Na^+ or Cl^- may define corners of this unit cell. (Coincidence of unit-cell corners with atomic particles is a convention, not a necessity.)

Each Na^+ ion in a halite structure is surrounded by six Cl^- ions; it has octahedral coordination. Each Cl^- ion is also in octahedral coordination. You can see a closest-packed layer of Cl^- ions in this CCP structure by removing any corner anion and the next three edge cations, thereby revealing six anions in a closest-packed layer of anions. Approaching this structure from any of its eight corners gives the same result, so four directions of closest-packed layers exist in CCP. Since this halite structure is described in terms of a face-centered cube, this more usual designation for this structural arrangement will henceforth be used.

Examples of minerals crystallizing with halite structure include sylvite [KCl], periclase [MgO], and galena [PbS]. The pyrite [FeS_2] structure may be derived from halite by replacing each Na^+ by Fe^{2+} and each Cl^- by a dumbbell-shaped S_2^{2-} group. Since halite (a chloride) and galena (a sulfide) are isostructural, those properties that depend on structure should be the same in both minerals. Indeed, both minerals commonly grow as cubes and display cubic cleavage when broken.

Zinc Blende Two additional *AX* structures, sphalerite and wurtzite, are named for two polymorphs of ZnS, both close-packed structures. In sphalerite structures, anions are in an FCC (CCP) array with cations filling half the tetrahedral voids (Fig. 2-3). Alternatively, we can view sphalerite derived from the diamond structure by replacing corner and face C ions with S^{2-} and interior C ions with Zn^{2+} (Prog. 2-2). Chalcopyrite [$CuFeS_2$] is a half-breed derivative of sphalerite with Cu^{2+} and Fe^{2+} replacing Zn^{2+} in tetrahedral coordination with S^{2-} (Prog. 2-2). The chalcopyrite unit cell is then twice the height of the sphalerite unit cell. Stannite [Cu_2FeSnS_4] also may be derived from chalcopyrite by replacing half the Fe^{2+} with Sn^{2+} ions.

The wurtzite structure has anions in HCP with cations occupying half its tetrahedral voids (Fig. 2-3b). Enargite [Cu_3AsS_4] has the wurtzite structure with three quarters of Zn^{2+} replaced by Cu^+ and one quarter by As^{5+}. Troilite [FeS] has S^{2-} ions approximating hexagonal close packing

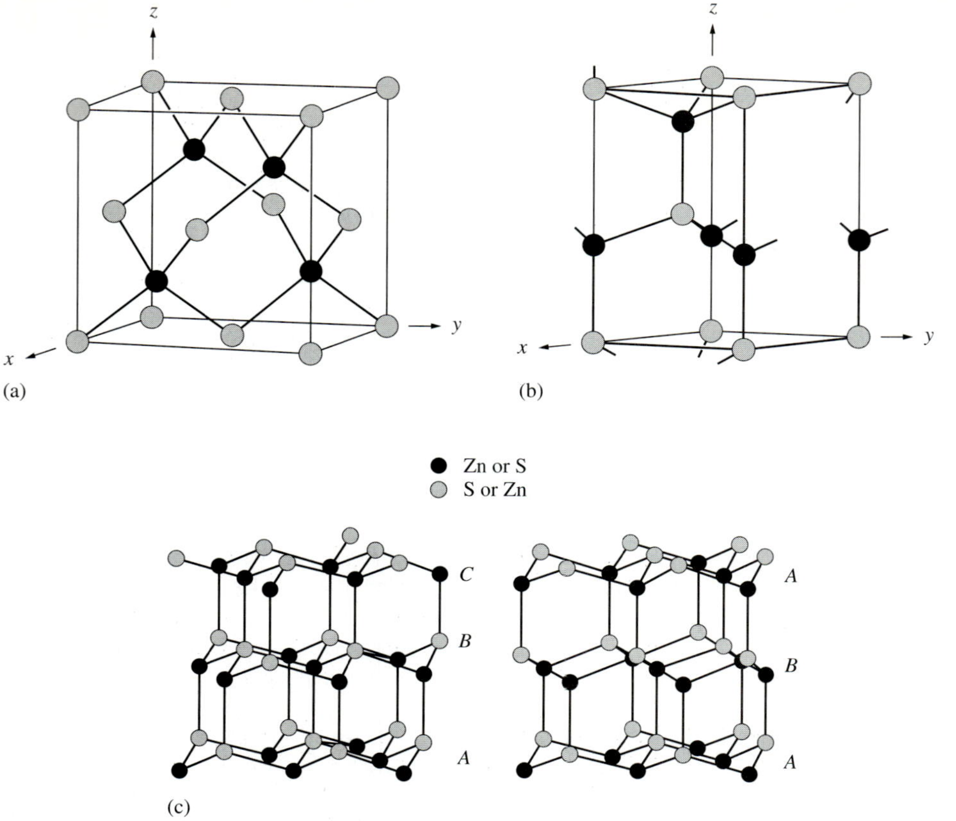

FIGURE 2-3 ZnS structures. (a) Sphalerite structure with S^{2-} ions in a FCC array with Zn^{2+} occupying half the interior corner positions. Compare this structure with diamond (Fig. 2-1). (b) Wurtzite structure. (c) Sphalerite and wurtzite structures compared. Closest-packed layers are parallel to the bottom in both illustrations. Sphalerite structure is based on FCC, whereas wurtzite structure is based on CCP of ions. All ions are in fourfold coordination.

like wurtzite, but with Fe^{2+} occupying octahedral voids. Pyrrhotine (pyrrhotite) [$Fe_{1-x}S$], a terrestrial analog of meteoritic troilite, has varying degrees of iron deficiency with electrostatic neutrality maintained by partial oxidation to Fe^{3+}.

AX_2 Three important crystal structures have a cation-to-anion ratio expressed as AX_2; they are, in order of decreasing cation size, fluorite [CaF_2], rutile [TiO_2], and quartz [SiO_2] with CNs of eight, six, and four, respectively. The fluorite structure (Fig. 2-4) has Ca^{2+} in an FCC array, which yields four cations per unit cell. Eight anions occupy positions along body diagonals of this unit-cell cube. Each cation coordinates eight

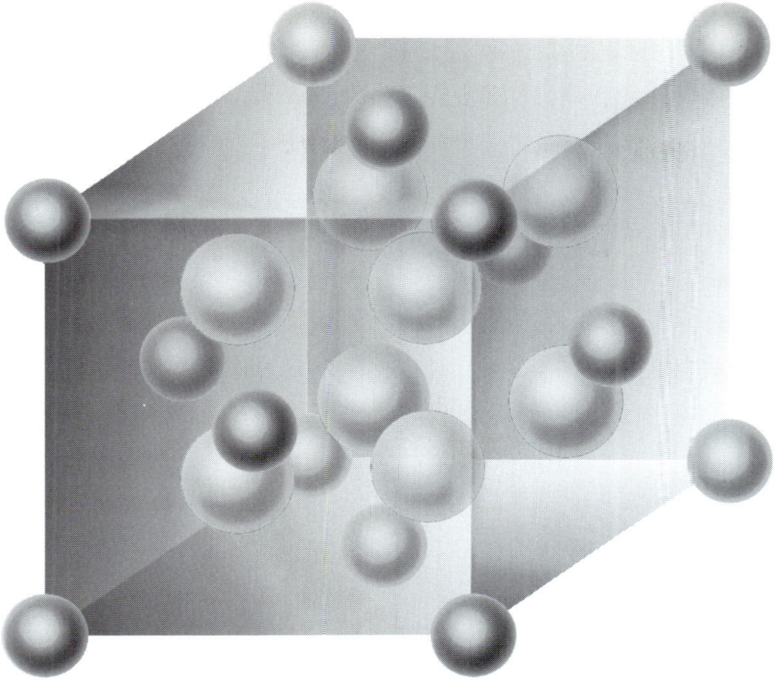

FIGURE 2-4 Fluorite structure. Calcium ions are located at corners and face centers of a unit-cell cube. Fluoride ions are located at approximately ¼ and ¾ along each body diagonal of this cube. Each fluoride coordinates four calcium ions, and each calcium coordinates eight fluorides.

anions, and each anion coordinates four cations. Octahedral cleavage of fluorite parallels closest-packed layers of Ca^{2+} ions in this structure. Uraninite [UO_2], thorianite [ThO_2], and cerianite [CeO_2] have fluorite structures. Cuprite [Cu_2O] has an antifluorite structure; each F is replaced by Cu, and each Ca is replaced by O^{2-}.

Rutile's structure (Fig. 2-5; Prog. 2-3) can be described as having cations arrayed at the corners and center of a flattened cubelike unit cell for a total of two per unit cell. Four anions lie in pairs on two opposite faces, and two more occupy its interior for a total of four. Anions form a distorted octahedron about each cation, a distortion resulting from shared octahedral edges in conformance with Pauling's third rule. Cassiterite [SnO_2], polianite [MnO_2], and stishovite [SiO_2], as well as rutile, have this structure.

The structure of quartz is based on silica tetrahedra, with each cation surrounded by four anions and each anion bonded to two cations. In terms of coordination polyhedra, each tetrahedron shares all four corners with

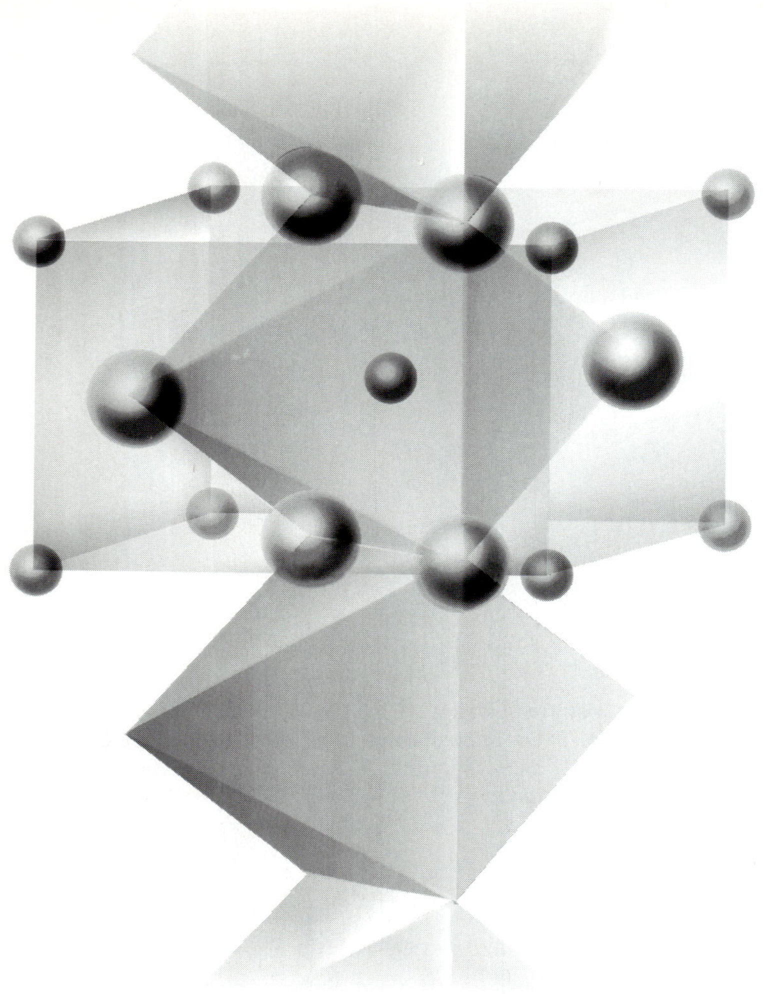

FIGURE 2-5 Rutile structure. Unit cell is a square prism with titanium ions at each corner and at center. Oxygen ions are paired along opposite faces plus two interior to this unit cell. Distorted TiO_6 octahedra share edges to form vertical chains.

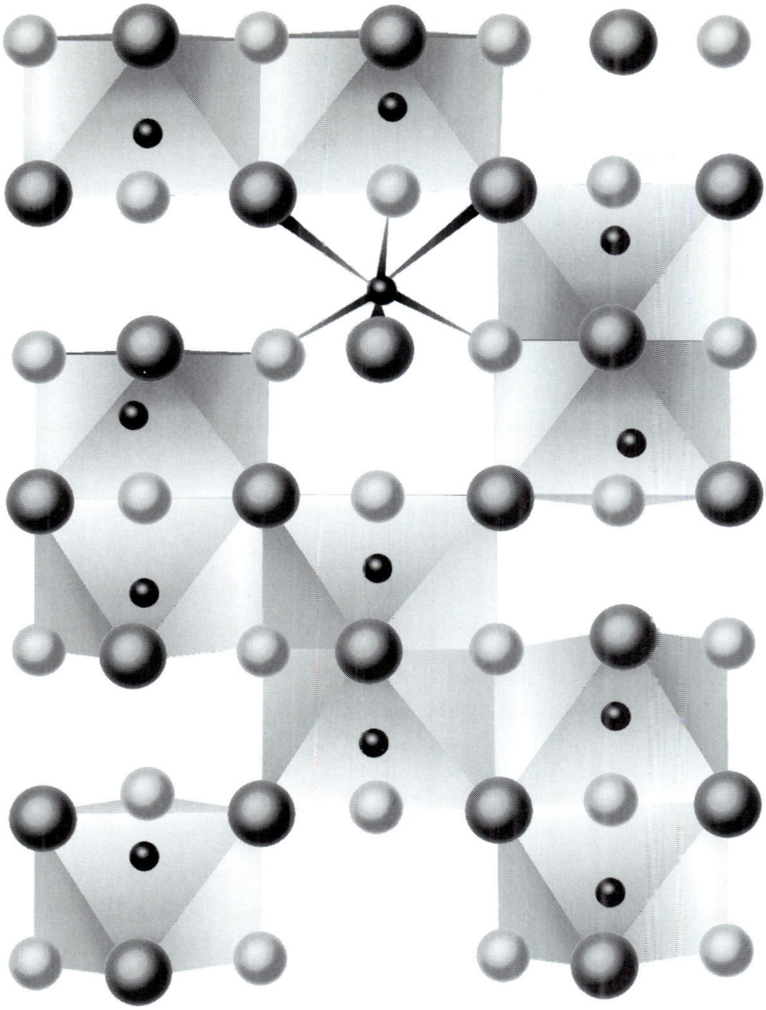

FIGURE 2-6 Corundum structure. Oxygen ions (large spheres) in an HCP array viewed on edge with darkest spheres representing nearest oxygens. Aluminum ions (small spheres) occupy ⅔ of octahedral voids. Assignable bond directions are shown for one octahedron. Note distortion of face-sharing octahedra due to cation-cation repulsion.

adjacent tetrahedra. Although quartz is an oxide, discussion of this all-important mineral is placed with the silicates (Sec. 2-6).

A_2X_3 Sesquioxide means that there are 1½ oxygen ions for each cation; that gives a ratio of 2:3. The structure of corundum [Al_2O_3] is based on an HCP of O^{2-} ions with Al^{3+} filling two thirds of all octahedral voids in

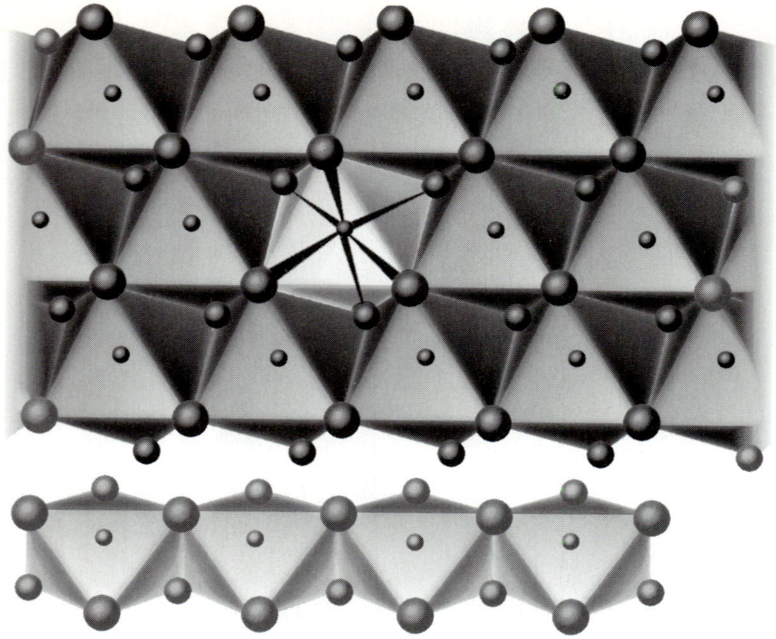

FIGURE 2-7a Brucite structure. Two layers of hydroxyl ions in HCP with magnesium ions filling 3⁄3 of the octahedral voids. *Top:* Plan view with assignable bond directions indicated for one octahedron. *Bottom:* Edge view of brucite structure.

an ordered fashion (Fig. 2-6, Prog. 2-4). Because one third of all octahedral voids are vacant and because adjacent octahedra share faces, O^{2-} ions are distorted slightly from a perfect HCP array. Hematite [Fe_2O_3] has the corundum structure, as do sesquioxides of Cr^{3+} and V^{3+}. Ilmenite [$FeTiO_3$] is a half-breed derivative.

Two additional structures similar to corundum are gibbsite [$Al(OH)_3$] and brucite [$Mg(OH)_2$] (Fig. 2-7; Prog. 2-4). Both these structures are based on two closest-packed layers of $(OH)^-$. In gibbsite, Al^{3+} ions fill two thirds of all available octahedral voids between the two layers, making it a dioctahedral layer unit. In brucite, Mg^{2+} ions fill three thirds of all available octahedral voids, making it a trioctahedral layer unit. In addition to being important minerals in their own right, these dioctahedral and trioctahedral layer units are useful in describing parts of structures of micas and other layered silicates (Sec. 2-5).

The molybdenite [MoS_2] structure is derived from brucite by replacing the closest-packed layers of OH^- with S^{2-} and filling all the octahedral voids with Mo^{4+} (Prog. 2-4). Weak S—S bonding between layers permits

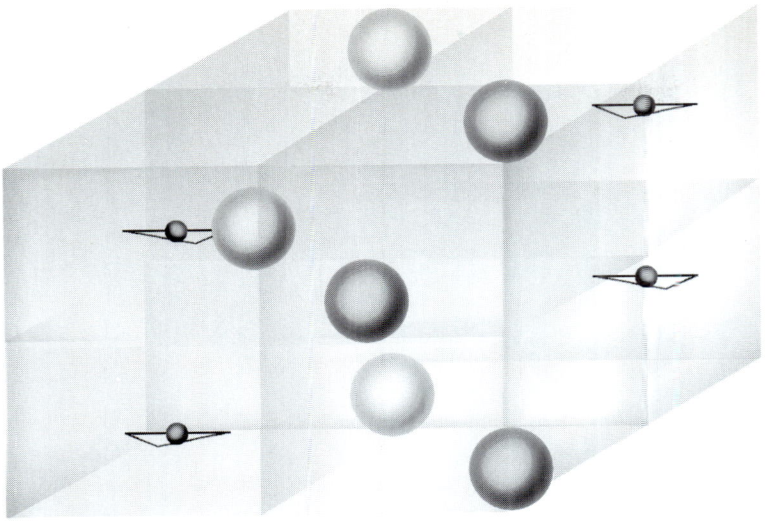

FIGURE 2-8c Aragonite structure with calcium ions represented by spheres and carbonate polyanions by triangles surrounding a central carbon ion.

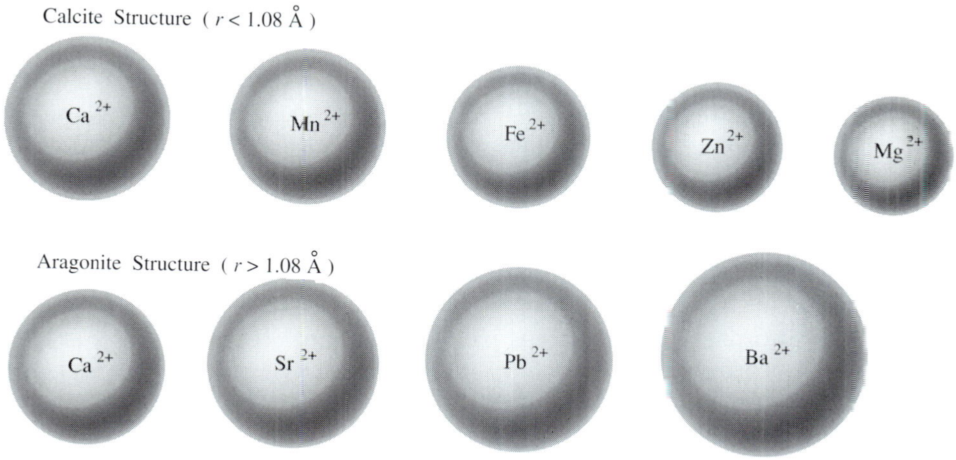

FIGURE 2-8d Cations the size of Ca^{2+} (108 pm, 1.08 Å) and smaller crystallize in calcite structures, the size of Ca^{2+} and larger in aragonite structures.

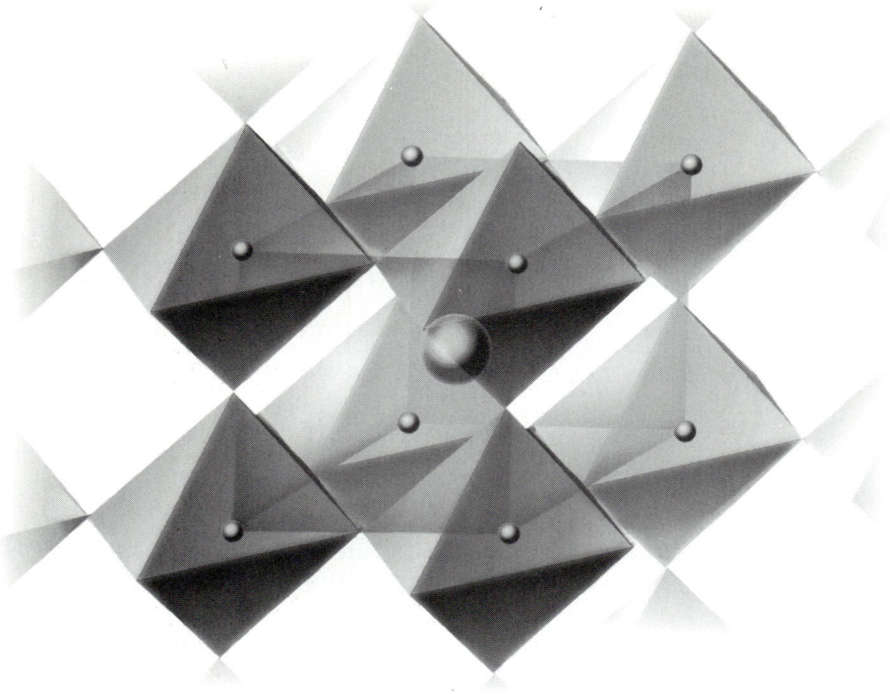

FIGURE 2-9 Perovskite structure. Octahedrally coordinated titanium ions (small spheres) form a three-dimensional, corner-sharing network. Calcium ions fill large spaces within this octahedral framework. A unit cell with corners at each titanium ion is lightly shaded.

Cl^-. The resulting cell is a rhombohedron rather than a cube because of the nonsphericity of CO_3^{2-}. This cell is not a true unit cell, however, since adjacent layers of CO_3^{2-} "point" in opposite directions (Fig. 2-8b). All carbonate minerals with cations smaller than Ca^{2+} crystallize with the calcite structure, including magnesite [$MgCO_3$], smithsonite [$ZnCO_3$], siderite [$FeCO_3$], and rhodochrosite [$MnCO_3$], as well as calcite (see Fig. 2-8d).

Aragonite is a high-pressure or a biogenetic polymorph of $CaCO_3$ with Ca^{2+} surrounded by six CO_3^{2-} polyanions as in calcite, but arranged so that nine O^{2-} ions surround each Ca^{2+} ion (Fig. 2-8c). Alternatively, you may visualize calcite as based on an FCC-based anion array and aragonite as based on an HCP-based anion array. All carbonate minerals having cations larger than Ca^{2+} crystallize in aragonite structures, including strontianite [$SrCO_3$], cerussite [$PbCO_3$], and witherite [$BaCO_3$], as well as aragonite (Fig. 2-8d).

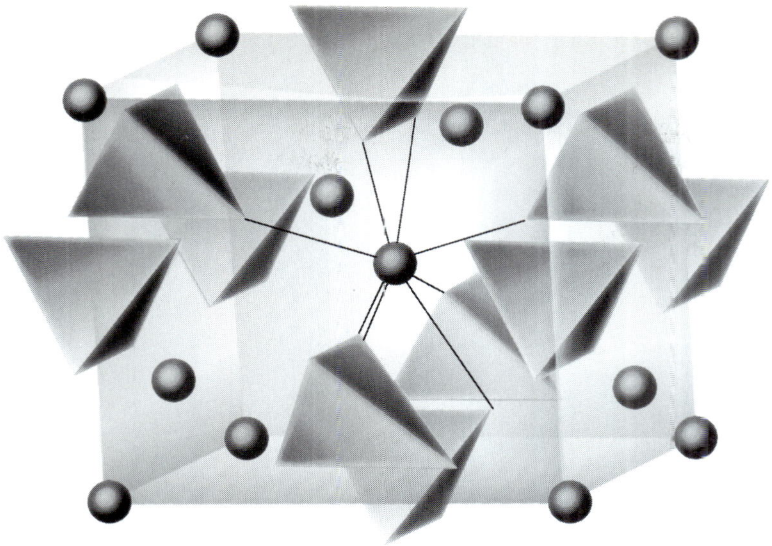

FIGURE 2-10 Zircon structure. Zirconium ions shown as spheres, and SiO_4^{4-} radicals as tetrahedra. Each zirconium ion coordinates eight oxygens from tetrahedra in an irregular cube with four oxygen ions farther from the zirconium than the other four.

Ilmenite structure is a half-breed derivative of the corundum structure with all Al^{3+} between one pair of closest-packed O^{2+} layers replaced by Fe^{2+} and all Al^{3+} in the next pair replaced by Ti^{4+}. (Sulfide half-breed derivatives are covered in the preceding section.) Perovskite (Fig. 2-9) is a framework of TiO_6^{2-} sharing adjacent corners, with Ca^{2+} filling intervening spaces. Although not a common mineral species, magnesium silicate with the perovskite structure may be the most important phase in the earth's mantle. Synthetic crystals with this structure permit electrical superconductivity above the boiling temperature of nitrogen (−195.8°C).

ABX_4 Many ABX_4 structures are half-breed or stuffed derivatives of AX_2 structures. Most of these derivatives are silicates (Sec. 2-6).

The zircon [$ZrSiO_4$] structure has Zr^{4+} in eight-fold coordination with O^- of its silica tetrahedra. The O^{2-} ions about Zr^{4+} are not equidistant: four are a little closer than the other four in a distorted cube (Fig. 2-10). Thorite [$ThSiO_4$], coffinite [$USiO_4$], xenotime [YPO_4], and hafnon [$HfSiO_4$] crystallize with this structure as well as zircon. Huttonite [$ThSiO_4$] and monazite [$CePO_4$] crystallize in a related, but somewhat different, architecture with ninefold coordination about the large cation. Actinide minerals are generally metamict.

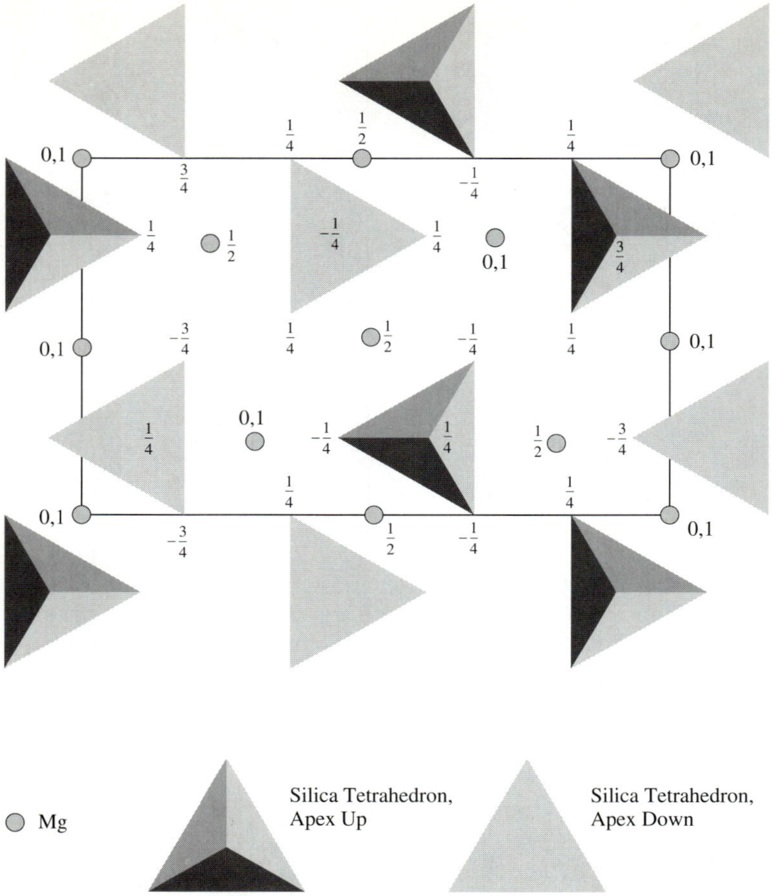

FIGURE 2-11 Olivine structure. This structure is projected onto one face of its unit cell. The SiO_4^{4-} radicals are shown as tetrahedra, half with an apex up and half with an apex down. Fractions represent distances above this projection face of this unit cell as fractions of the length of the projected edge. Oxygen ions are in a distorted HCP array, with magnesium ions occupying octahedral voids and silicon ions occupying tetrahedral voids.

A_2BX_4 Minerals of the olivine and spinel groups have structural formula $A_2^{VI}B^{IV}X_4$, both based on closest packing of O^{2-} ions. Olivine structure is based on distorted HCP of anions, with divalent cations in half the octahedral voids and Si^{4+} in one eighth the tetrahedral voids (Fig. 2-11). An important feature of olivines is chains of edge-sharing octahedra cross-linked by independent silica tetrahedra. Minerals with the olivine structure include forsterite [Mg_2SiO_4], fayalite [Fe_2SiO_4], and tephroite [Mn_2SiO_4]. Complete crystal solutions exist among these minerals, with the name

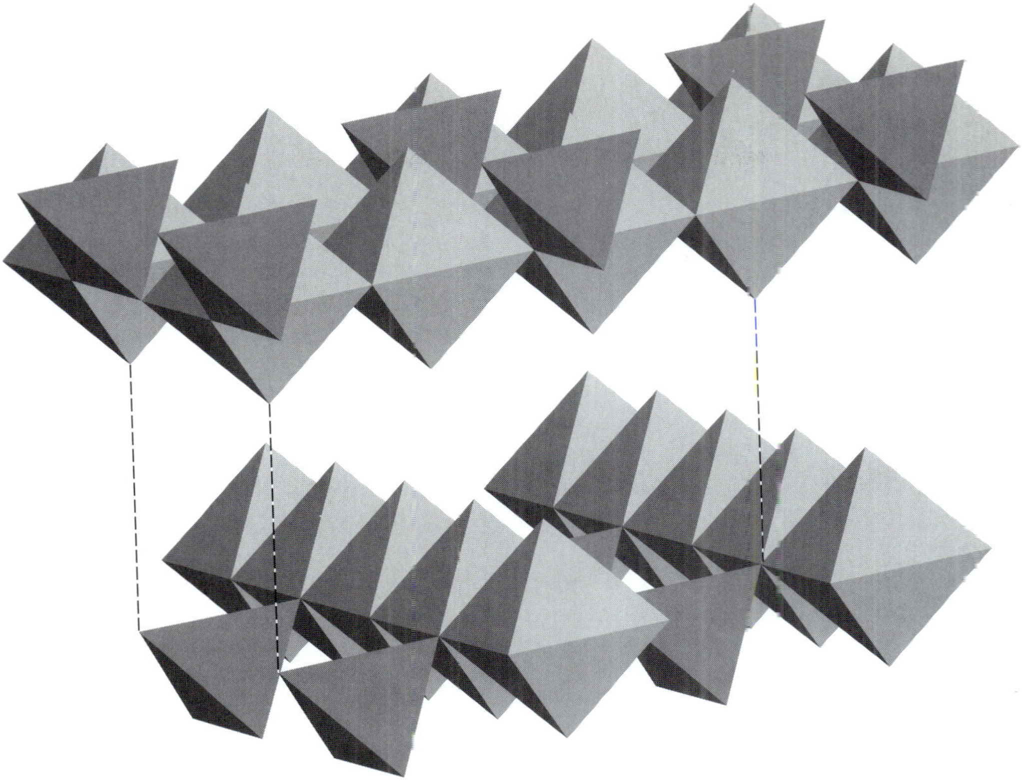

FIGURE 2-12 Spinel structure. Two layers of a spinel unit-cell cube are shown. Bottom layer consists of chains of edge-sharing octahedra running diagonally across a cube face. Octahedral chains are cross-linked by tetrahedra. Second layer of this structure has octahedral chains running diagonally across the cube at right angles to those of its first layer. Dashed lines show shared oxygen ions.

TABLE 2-1 Minerals with Spinel Structure

Normal spinels		Inverse spinels	
Aluminum series		Iron series	
Spinel	$MgAl_2O_4$	Magnetite	$FeFe_2O_4$
Hercynite	$FeAl_2O_4$	Magnesioferrite	$MgFe_2O_4$
Gahnite	$ZnAl_2O_4$	Franklinite	$ZnFe_2O_4$*
Galaxite	$MnAl_2O_4$	Jacobsite	$MnFe_2O_4$
Chromium series		Trevorite	$NiFe_2O_4$
Chromite	$FeCr_2O_4$		
Magnesiochromite	$MgCr_2O_4$		

*Predominantly normal structure.

olivine commonly referring to minerals having forsterite-fayalite compositions in igneous and metamorphic rocks. Monticellite [$CaMgSiO_4$] is a half-breed derivative of olivine.

The spinel structure is based on a slightly distorted FCC O^{2-} array, just as in periclase (Fig. 2-2). Double the length of each edge of periclase to get a unit cell of 32 O^{2-} ions with 32 octahedral and 64 tetrahedral voids (Prog. 2-6). Fill all octahedral voids with Mg^{2+} to get periclase. Fill half the octahedral voids with Al^{3+} and one eighth the tetrahedral voids with Mg^{2+} to get spinel (Fig. 2-12). Since the numbers of octahedral and tetrahedral voids are the same in HCP as in FCC (Fig. 1-10), the major difference is in their distribution and available size ranges for each cation site. In olivines and spinels, two thirds of all ions are in octahedral coordination, and one third are in tetrahedral. A spinel is normal if all *A* ions are in octahedral sites and all *B* ions are in tetrahedral [$A_2^{VI}B^{IV}O_4$] (Table 2-1). It is inverse if half the *A* ions are in octahedral coordination, half the *A* ions are in tetrahedral coordination, and all of the *B* ions are in octahedral coordination [$A^{VI}B^{VI}A^{IV}O_4$]. In general, Cr^{3+} spinels are normal, whereas Fe^{3+} and Ti^{4+} spinels are inverse, although most spinels appear to be intermediate between these two structural states. (Note the convention in Table 2-1 of formulating spinels $B^{IV}A_2^{VI}X_4$. This problem results from two conflicting conventions in mineral formulation. According to one convention, cation charge increases from left to right. In another, cation coordination decreases from lest to right.) Crystal solution among spinel end-member compositions [see Ulmer, G. C., in Frye, K. (ed.), *Encyclopedia of Mineralogy*. New York: Van Nostrand Reinhold, 1981, p. 480] is extensive and complex. Because of their unique ferrimagnetic properties, many new compounds having a spinel structure have been synthesized in recent decades.

2-4 ISLAND SILICATES

Silica tetrahedra are fundamental building blocks of many minerals in the earth's crust and upper mantle. Experimental evidence suggests the presence of octahedrally coordinated silica at depths below 500 km in mantle rocks, but no mineral phase from these depths has yet been recovered at the surface. We may classify silicates on the number and pattern of shared corners, which appear also in Si:O ratios (Table 2-2; Prog. 2-7). As the number of shared corners increases, silicate structures become less like oxides governed by radius ratios and more characteristically silicate with structures governed by tetrahedral linkages. First consider tetrahedral arrangements in finite groups—island silicates (see Fig. 2-13).

The simplest island silicates have independent silica tetrahedra (nesosilicates); they do not share their O^{2-} ions with other tetrahedra. These

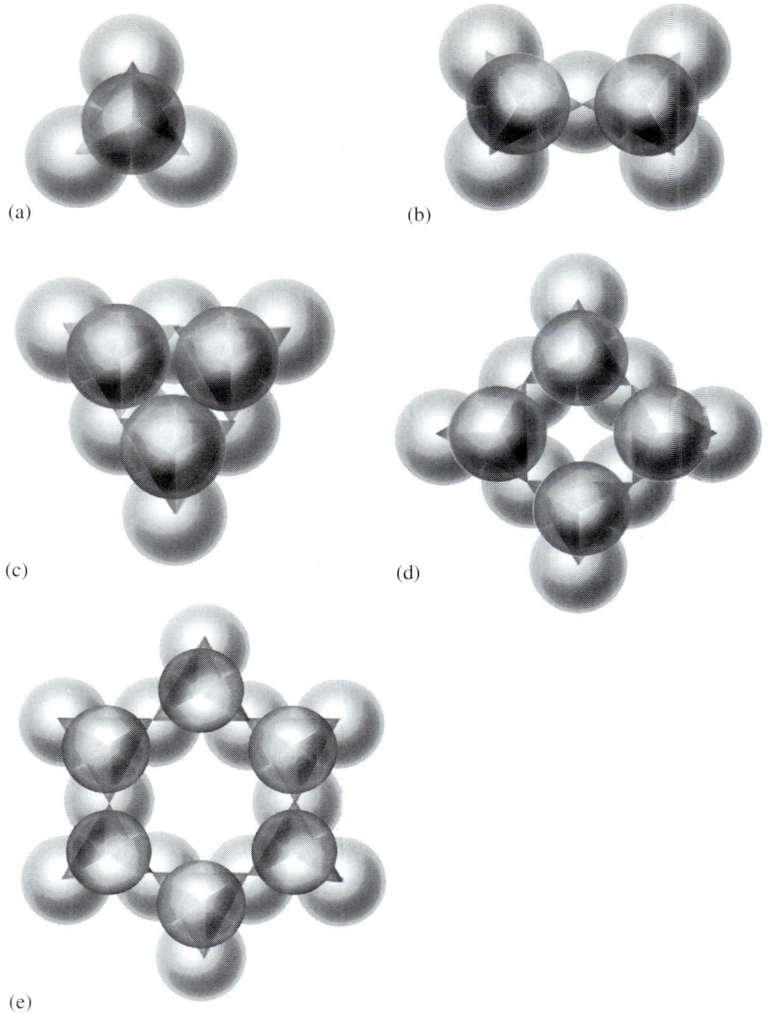

FIGURE 2-13 Isolated tetrahedral groups. (a) Single SiO_4^{4-} tetrahedron depicted with oxygen ions shown as spheres, tetrahedral outline shaded, and silicon ion at center not shown. (b) Two tetrahedra sharing one corner oxygen ion. (c) Three tetrahedra share three oxygen ions to form a three-membered ring. (d) Four tetrahedra share four oxygen ions to form a four-membered ring. (e) Six tetrahedra share six oxygen ions to form a six-membered ring similar to those found in tourmalines.

TABLE 2-2 Classification of Silicate Structures

Structure	Arrangement of tetrahedra
Island	Independent tetrahedra
	Pair of tetrahedra sharing a corner
Ring	Closed rings of tetrahedra sharing two corners (single rings) or three corners (double rings)
Chain	Infinite single chains of tetrahedra each sharing two corners
	Infinite double chains of tetrahedra alternately sharing two and three corners
Sheets	Infinite sheets of tetrahedra each sharing three corners
Framework	Unbounded framework of tetrahedra each sharing all four corners

SiO_4^{4-} tetrahedra bond to cations located between tetrahedra, giving an overall electrostatically neutral structure. These silicates include garnets, olivines, zircon, phenakite, aluminum silicates, sphene, and topaz structures; olivine and zircon are covered in Sec. 2-3.

Garnets Garnets are a group of minerals with numerous hypothetical pure end-member compositions and a wide range of crystal solutions among end members. A general formulation of garnet compositions is $8[X_3^{VIII}Y_2^{VI}T_3^{IV}O_{12}]$, where X, Y, and T represent cations, subscripts represent cation ratios, and superscripts represent cation coordination sites (Table 2-3). Coupled substitutions among these cation sites and O^{2-} replacement by OH^- prevent unique assignment of valence to them. Hydrogarnets result from the substitution $4H^+$—Si^{4+}, resulting in a vacant tetrahedral site surrounded by four OH^- radicals.

Anions in garnets lie roughly in a body-centered cubic array, but the unit cell is rather large (96 anions) and complex. Tetrahedra and octahedra share corners to form a three-dimensional array with large X cations occupying resultant voids in this framework. Synthetic crystals of nonsilicate garnet, such as yttrium aluminum garnet (YAG), are important in electronic devices and imitation gems.

Aluminum Silicates Aluminum silicates [Al_2SiO_5] include the polymorphic minerals sillimanite, kyanite, and andalusite. These minerals all consist of chains of edge-sharing AlO_6^{4-} octahedra that differ only in their cross-linkage by Si^{4+} and the remaining Al^{3+} cations (Fig. 2-14). All chain-linking Si^{4+} cations are in tetrahedral coordination. Cross-linking Al^{3+} cations are also in tetrahedral coordination in sillimanite (the high-temperature polymorph), but they are in octahedral coordination in kyanite (the high-pressure polymorph), thus resulting in a CCP anion array. These remaining Al^{3+} cations are in fivefold coordination in andalusite (the low-pressure polymorph), the only common rock-forming mineral with such an irregular pentahedral coordination.

Shared corners	Repeat unit	Si:O	Example
0	TO_4^{4-}	1:4	Garnets, olivines
1	$T_2O_7^{6-}$	1:3½	Hemimorphite
2	TO_3^{2-}	1:3	Tourmalines
3	$T_{12}O_{30}^{12-}$	1:2½	Osumilite
2	TO_3^{2-}	1:3	Pyroxenes, pyroxenoids
2½	$T_4O_{11}^{6-}$	1:2¾	Amphiboles
3	$T_2O_5^{2-}$	1:2½	Micas, chlorites, talc
4	TO_2	1:2	Feldspars, zeolites

Topaz Anions approach a close-packed array . . . ABAC . . . that is neither cubic nor hexagonal in topaz [$Al_2SiO_4(OH,F)_2$]. Silicon occupies tetrahedral voids and aluminum octahedral voids in this anion array with one third of O^{2-} replaced by variable proportions of monovalent OH^- and F^-. Although physically resembling quartz or feldspar, topaz has a distinctly higher density than either of those minerals because of its efficient filling of space with its closest-packed anions.

Sphene Sphene (titanite) [$CaTiSiO_5$] consists of chains of corner-sharing titania octahedra cross-linked by independent silica tetrahedra to form a framework with irregular cavities of sevenfold coordination to house Ca^{2+} and rare-earth ions.

TABLE 2-3 Garnet Compositions

Structural formula $R_3^{VIII}R_2^{VI}T_3^{IV}O_{12}$

Site	Occupants
R^{VIII}	Ca, Mg, Fe^{2+}, Mn^{2+}, Y, trivalent lanthanides
R^{VI}	Al, Cr, Fe^{3+}, Ti
T^{IV}	Si, Al, Fe^{3+}, Ti

Major naturally occurring garnet end members

Pyrope	$Mg_3Al_2Si_3O_{12}$
Almandine	$Fe_3Al_2Si_3O_{12}$
Spessartine	$Mn_3Al_2Si_3O_{12}$
Grossular	$Ca_3Al_2Si_3O_{12}$
Hydrogrossular	$Ca_3Al_2Si_2(OH)_4O_{12}$
Andradite	$Ca_3Fe_2Si_3O_{12}$

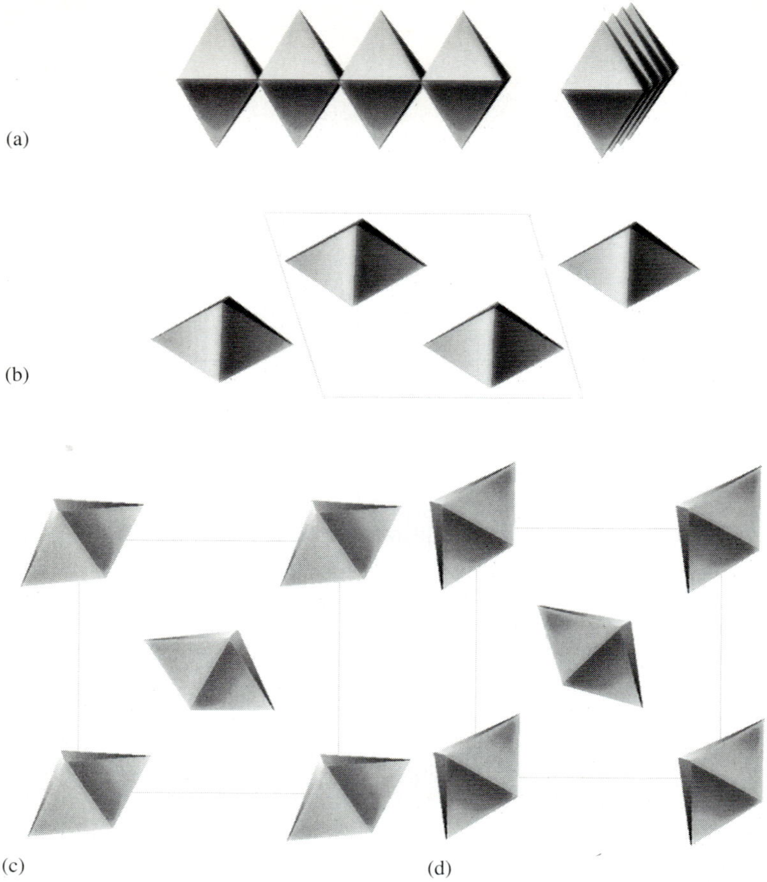

FIGURE 2-14 Aluminum silicate structures. (a) Chains of AlO_6 octahedra sharing edges are depicted in two views, one along the chain and one end on view. (b) Octahedral chains viewed end on as in kyanite structure. (c) Arrangement of octahedral chains as in sillimanite structure. (d) Arrangement of octahedral chains as in andalusite structure. Octahedral chains are cross-linked by SiO_4 tetrahedra and by aluminum ions in fourfold (sillimanite), fivefold (andalusite), and sixfold (kyanite) coordination with oxygen ions.

Epidotes A dimer of two silica tetrahedra sharing a common O^{2-} gives a structural unit of $(Si_2O_7)^{6-}$ (Fig. 2-14) (sorosilicates), an example of which is lawsonite $[CaAl_2(Si_2O_7)(OH)_2 \cdot H_2O]$. A mixture of double and single tetrahedra characterize the structures of minerals of the epidote group $[X_2^{VIII}Y_3^{VI}(Si_2O_7)(SiO_4)O(OH)]$. Note how different structural groups are formulated in this and other silicate structures. Epidote structures consist of edge-sharing octahedral chains cross-linked by silica monomers and

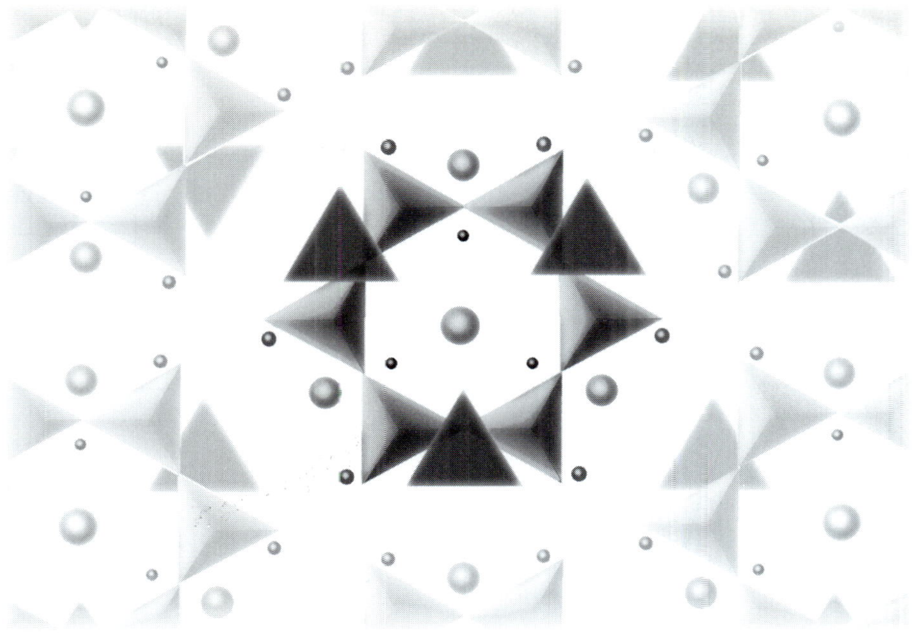

FIGURE 2-15 Tourmaline structure. Tourmaline minerals are built of stacks of six-membered Si_6O_{18} rings (Fig. 2-13e) alternating with BO_3 trigonal planar groups (triangles). Individual stacks are bonded by (Mg,Fe) ions (small dark spheres) in octahedral coordination between tetrahedra and triangles. Stacks are cross-linked by Al ions (large dark spheres) in octahedral coordination with tetrahedra, triangles, and hydroxyls. Hydroxyls alternate with Na ions down stack centers. Slight tilting of alternate tetrahedra in each six-membered ring is not shown.

dimers. Zoisite and clinozoisite have Ca^{2+} in eightfold coordination for X and Al^{3+} in octahedral coordination for Y. (The prefix *clino-* means that one internal angle of a unit cell is not 90°.) The species epidote has some octahedral Al^{3+} replaced by Fe^{3+}, giving it its distinctive green color. Allanite is a partial half-breed derivative of epidote with trivalent RE elements replacing some Ca^{2+} with an equal amount of Fe^{2+} octahedrally replacing trivalent ions.

Tourmalines Silica tetrahedra can share two of their four corners to form rings (cyclosilicates, Fig. 2-14). Mineral examples exist for independent rings of three, four, six, eight, and double-six tetrahedra, but only rings of six tetrahedra $(Si_6O_{18})^{12-}$ are common, namely tourmaline minerals $[XY_3Z_6(BO_3)_3(Si_6O_{18})(OH,F)_4]$. This structure consists of stacks of six-member silica tetrahedral rings (Fig. 2-14b) alternating with BO_3

trigonal planar groups (Fig. 2-15). These stacks are cross-linked with octahedral *Y* divalent and *Z* trivalent cations with monovalent or divalent *X* ions situated within each six-membered ring. Common dravite has ($NaMg_3Al_6$) and schorl ($NaFe_3Al_6$) in the variable part of the tourmaline formula. Commonly, gem elbaite contains (Li,Al) for *Y*. Six-membered rings are slightly puckered, but their apices all point in the same direction in each stack. This arrangement makes tourmaline crystals polar, so opposite electrostatic charges on opposite ends of a crystal may be induced by heating or rubbing.

2-5 CHAIN AND SHEET SILICATES

Sharing of O^{2-} between corners of silica tetrahedra can yield groups that are unbounded except at an end or an edge of a crystal. By sharing two of four corners with adjacent tetrahedra, a chain of effectively infinite (from an atom's point of view) length results (Fig. 2-16a; Prog. 2-8). Stacks of these chains may then be cross-linked with other cations to form electrostatically neutral structures (inosilicates, Table 2-4). Single chains with composition $(SiO_3)_n^{2-}$ characterize two mineral groups, the pyroxenes and the pyroxenoids. Lay two of these single tetrahedral chains side by side and cross-link them with a third shared O^{2-} ion at alternate tetrahedra along each chain to create a double chain of composition $(Si_4O_{11})_n^{6-}$ (Fig. 2-16b). Bound together by other cations, stacks of these double chains characterize the amphibole group of minerals. Fibrous minerals with triple and quadruple chains and with mixed-chain structures have been discovered in recent years. Complete gradation between single chains of tetrahedra and sheets of tetrahedra may actually exist in minerals (Fig. 2-16c).

Pyroxenes Minerals of the pyroxene group have structural formula $X^{\mathrm{VIII}}Y^{\mathrm{VI}}T_2^{\mathrm{IV}}O_6$. Coordination about *X* changes from VIII when this site is occupied by Ca^{2+} (120 pm, 1.20 Å) to VI when occupied by Mg^{2+} (80 pm, 0.80 Å). This change in coordination is possible because only six O^{2-} ions are active—that is, have an unsatisfied negative valence charge (Fig. 2-17; Prog. 2-8). The other two O^{2-} ions are bridges between two tetrahedra with valence charges satisfied by those tetrahedra; hence, they are inactive anions. Octahedra about Y^{VI} form zigzag chains by sharing edges. These octahedral chains run parallel between tetrahedral apices of adjacent chains, with these three units forming an **I** beam. When X^{VI} is small, these octahedra share edges with Y^{VI} in octahedral ribbons. When X^{VIII} is large, ribbons merge into layers.

Wollastonite [$CaSiO_3$] structures consist of single silicate chains that, unlike pyroxene chains, are kinked in their repeat direction.

FIGURE 2-16a Single chain of tetrahedra. A single chain of silica tetrahedra with composition $(SiO_3)_n$ is depicted with spheres representing oxygen ions at left grading into tetrahedra at right. Pyroxenes and pyroxenoids have similar chains.

FIGURE 2-16b Double chain of tetrahedra. A double chain of silica tetrahedra with composition $(Si_4O_{11})_n$ is depicted with spheres representing oxygens at left grading into tetrahedra at right. Amphiboles have similar chains.

FIGURE 2-16c Sheet of tetrahedra. An infinite sheet of corner-sharing silica tetrahedra with composition $(Si_2O_5)_n$ is depicted with spheres representing oxygens at left grading into tetrahedra at right. Micas and other layered silicates have these sheets.

Amphiboles Minerals of the amphibole group have structural formula $\square_{1-0}X^{\mathrm{VIII}}_{2-3}Y^{\mathrm{VI}}_{5}T^{\mathrm{IV}}_{8}O_{22}(OH)_2$. As in pyroxenes, six O^{2-} ions about X are active and two are inactive. A $\square$ site, which may or may not be occupied, depending on the charge requirements of the amphibole compositions, lies between bases of rings in these double chains (Fig. 2-18; Prog. 2-8). Thus, eight to twelve inactive O^{2-} ions surround a $\square$ site. Six apical O^{2-}

TABLE 2-4 Chain Silicate Minerals

Pyroxene structural formula $X^{VIII}Y^{VI}Z_2O_6$

Site	Occupants
X^{VIII}	Ca, Na
Y^{VI}	Mg, Fe^{2+}, Mn^{2+}, Ni, Li, Al, Ti, Fe^{3+}
T^{IV}	Si, Al, Fe^{3+}

Amphibole structural formula $\square_{1-0}X^{VIII}_{2-3}Y^{VI}_{5}Z^{IV}_{8}O_{22}(OH)_2$

Site	Occupants
$\square$	Na, K
X^{VIII}	Mg, Fe^{2+}, Na, Ca, K, Ba, Li, Mn^{2+}
Y^{VI}	Mg, Fe^{2+}, Fe^{3+}, Al, Mn^{2+}, Mn^{3+}, Ti, Cr, Ni, Zn
T^{IV}	Si, Al, Fe^{3+}

Comparison of selected pyroxene and amphibole minerals

Pyroxene group	Amphibole group
	Orthorhombic
Enstatite $MgSiO_3$	
Hypersthene $(Mg,Fe)SiO_3$	Anthophyllite $(Mg,Fe)_7Si_8O_{22}(OH)_2$
	Monoclinic
Clinoenstatite $MgSiO_3$	Cummingtonite $(Mg,Fe)_7Si_8O_{22}(OH)_2$
Ferrosilite $FeSiO_3$	
Diopside $CaMg(SiO_3)_2$	Tremolite $Ca_2Mg_5Si_8O_{22}(OH)_2$
Pigeonite $(Ca,Mg,Fe)(SiO_3)_2$	Actinolite $Ca_2(Mg,Fe)Si_8O_{22}(OH)_2$
Augite $(Ca,Mg,Fe^{2+},Fe^{3+},Al)_2(SiO_3)_2$	Hornblende $(Ca,Na,K)_{2-3}(Mg,Fe^{2+},Fe^{3+},Al)_5(Si,Al)_8O_{22}(OH)_2$
Acmite $NaFe^{3+}(SiO_3)_2$	Riebeckite $Na_2Fe^{2+}_3Fe^{3+}_2Si_8O_{22}(OH)_2$
Jadeite $NaAl(SiO_3)_2$	Glaucophane $Na_2Mg_3Al_2Si_8O_{22}(OH)_2$

ions in tetrahedral rings of double chains leave space for an OH^- polyanion that may be replaced by F^-, Cl^-, or even O^{2-} if an amphibole is highly oxidized. A strip of edge-sharing Y^{VI} octahedra parallels double chains of silica tetrahedra and lies sandwiched between inward-facing apical O^{2-} ions. These **I** beams are cross-linked by small X^{VI} octahedra or large X^{VIII} distorted cubes.

Pyroxenes and amphiboles have very similar physical properties, including well-developed prismatic cleavage. Since double chains are approximately twice as wide as single chains, prismatic cleavage between chains is 87° for single-chain structures, but 56° for double chains.

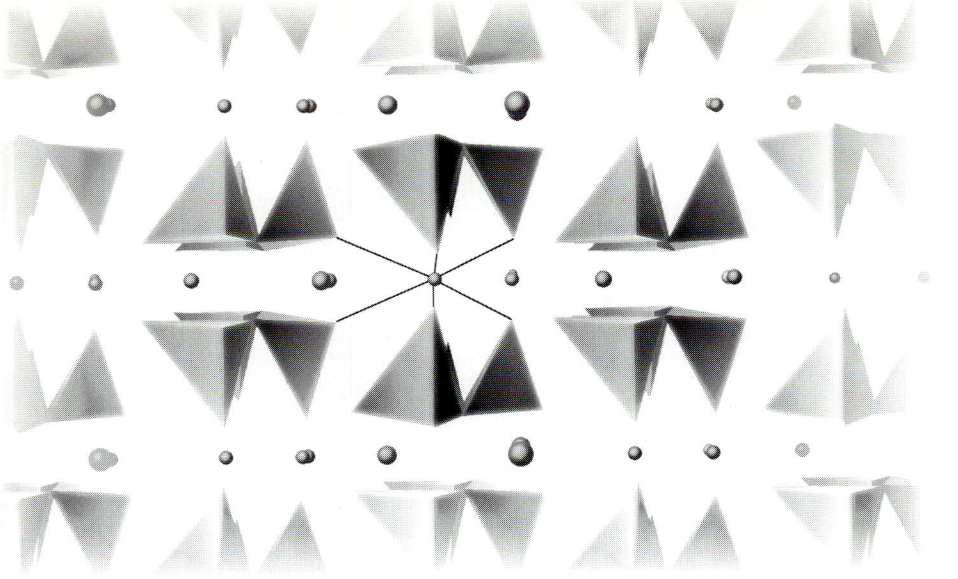

FIGURE 2-17 Diopside structure (pyroxene). Single chains of silica tetrahedra (Fig. 2-16a) are shown end on. These infinite chains are cross-linked by small divalent cations (small spheres) in octahedral coordination and by small or large cations in six- or eightfold coordination with inactive oxygen ions that are shared between adjacent tetrahedra in the chain taking part in coordination polyhedra of large cations.

Layered Silicates Sheets of silica tetrahedra occur, where each tetrahedron shares three corners with three other adjacent tetrahedra in a two-dimensional infinite array (phyllosilicates) (Prog. 2-9). Each tetrahedron in such a sheet has a net -1 charge located at the unshared apical O^{2-} ion, shared ones being all inactive. Each tetrahedral layer has formula $(Si_2O_5)_n^{2-}$. Layered silicate minerals differ from one another in the way in which their Si_2O_5 sheets are stacked and bonded together by octahedral sheets and in the amount of tetrahedral Al^{3+} substitution for Si^{4+}.

Kaolinite-Serpentine Group Kaolinite, a clay mineral, consists of one silica tetrahedral sheet (Fig. 2-16c) and one gibbsite sheet (Fig. 2-7b). Viewed from the top, each tetrahedral sheet appears to consist of hexagonal rings of active O^{2-} ions all pointing upward. Addition of an OH^- to all ring centers yields a closest-packed layer of mixed O^{2-} and OH^- ions, a bottom side for an octahedral sheet. Add a closest-packed sheet of OH^- to this sheet and put Al^{3+} in two thirds of the resultant dioctahedral layer

FIGURE 2-18 Tremolite structure (amphibole). Double chains of silica tetrahedra (Fig. 2-16b) are shown end on. Hydroxyl ions (large light spheres) occur at apex level of each six-membered ring of these chains. Double chains are cross-linked by small cations (small dark spheres) in octahedral coordination and by large cations (large dark spheres) in eightfold coordination. A □ site (cubes) surrounded irregularly by inactive oxygen ions of tetrahedral chains may be occupied by an alkali ion in some alkali-rich amphiboles.

to complete the kaolinite layered structure with composition $Al_4(OH)_8Si_4O_{10}$ (Fig. 2-19; Prog. 2-9).

All layered silicates with this fundamental structure of one tetrahedral sheet and one octahedral sheet are sometimes called 1:1 layered silicates. Since this 1:1 layer is 713 pm (7.13 Å) thick, they are also called 7-Å layered silicates. Minerals in the kaolinite group differ in the way in which successive kaolinite sheets are stacked. Kaolinite has a repeat distance of one sheet, dickite a repeat distance of two sheets, and nacrite a repeat distance of six sheets. Halloysite $[Al_4(OH)_4Si_4O_{10}\cdot 8H_2O]$ differs from kaolinite by having a monolayer of H_2O molecules between each kaolinite layer. Little ionic substitution occurs in these minerals; they are chemically very pure.

Serpentines are 1:1 7-Å layered silicates with divalent cations creating trioctahedral sheets (Fig. 2-7a). Serpentine $[Mg_6(OH)_8Si_4O_{10}]$ has Mg_6 instead of Al_4 in its trioctahedral sheet, and the mineral greenalite has Fe_6.

FIGURE 2-19 Kaolinite structure. Infinite sheets of corner-sharing tetrahedra (Fig. 2-16c) are depicted with an edge-on view. Hydroxyl ions (large spheres) occur at apex level in the center of each six-membered ring to form an approximate closest-packed sheet. A sheet of closest-packed hydroxyl ions rests on the apex-level layer of oxygen and hydroxyl ions with Al^{3+} ions occupying ⅔ of the resulting octahedral voids between these two closest-packed sheets of a gibbsite structural unit, making them dioctahedral (Fig. 2-7b). Minerals of the serpentine group have 3/3 of octahedral voids occupied by Mg^{2+} ion in a brucite structural unit, making them trioctahedral (Fig. 2-7a). Note that all tetrahedral apices point in the same direction.

Spacing is slightly different in the OH^- sheet than in the (O,OH) sheet shared with its tetrahedral sheet in these 1:1 layered silicates, and structural stresses build up in growing crystals over fairly short atomic distances. These stresses result in very small crystals, generally below the resolving power of an optical microscope but clearly revealed with electron microscopy, in minerals of the kaolin group. Serpentines, on the other hand, resolve these stresses by curling, with the result that crystals of chrysotile occur as rolls approximately 28 nm (280 Å) in diameter but up to decimeters in length—an asbestiform mineral. Antigorite, with the same chemical composition and structure, relieves its intraplanar stresses by corrugation rather than by curling into rolls. Lizardite is a platy serpentine mineral that, like kaolinite, is extremely fine-grained. Polygonal serpentine is fibrous, with polygonal fibers up to 1 μm in diameter wrapped around a chrysotile core.

Talc-Pyrophyllite Group The talc-pyrophyllite structure is a 2:1 layered structure of one octahedral sheet (Fig. 2-7) sandwiched between two tetrahedral sheets (Fig. 2-16) pointing inward toward it (Prog. 2-9). Thus, both sides of its octahedral layer are closest-packed (O,OH) sheets preventing buildup of intraplanar stress. Talc [$Mg_3(OH)_2Si_4O_{10}$] is trioctahedral, and pyrophyllite [$Al_2(OH)_2Si_4O_{10}$] is dioctahedral. Minnesotaite is an Fe^{2+} analog of talc found in the iron ranges of that state. Van der Waals bonding between layers gives talc its distinctive smooth feel in coarse crystals and in finely crushed talcum powder.

Micas Mica-group structures may be derived from talc-pyrophyllite by replacing every fourth Si^{4+} with Al^{3+} in tetrahedral sheets, producing a -1 charge on the 2:1 layer and introducing Na^+, K^+, Ca^{2+}, or H_3O^+ between layers to maintain electrostatic neutrality (Fig. 2-20, Prog. 2-9). This interlayer cation has a six-membered ring of inactive O^{2-} ions on each side of it similar to $\square$ in amphiboles. Muscovite [$K_2Al_4(AlSi_3O_{10})_2(OH)_4$] and paragonite [$Na_2Al_4(AlSi_3O_{10})_2(OH)_4$] are thereby derived from pyrophyllite. Phlogopite [$K_2Mg_6(AlSi_3O_{10})_2(OH)_4$] is derived from talc, and annite from minnesotaite. Biotite is a trioctahedral mica with composition between phlogopite and annite. Lepidolite [$K_2Li_4Al_2(Si_4O_{10})_2(OH)_4$], with no tetrahedral Al^{3+}, gets its layer-charge imbalance from two Li^+ replacing one Al^{3+} in its trioctahedral layer.

Glauconite [$\square_{1.2-2.0}Y_4(T_4O_{10})_2(OH)_4 \cdot nH_2O$] may be chemically derived from muscovite with less than one fourth of tetrahedral Si^{4+} replaced by Al^{3+}, with octahedral Al^{3+} partially replaced by Fe^{3+}, Fe^{2+}, and Mg^{2+}, and with interlayer K^+ replaced by Na^+, Ca^{2+}, and variable amounts of H_2O. Although structurally resembling biotite, its small grain size and occurrence in marine sediments associates it with clays.

Sericite is predominantly very fine grained muscovite or paragonite. Illite is a general term for clay-sized particles having a mica structure. These are useful mineralogic terms when precise structures and compositions have not been determined.

Smectites Smectite-group structures, including montmorillonite and vermiculite, may be derived from talc-pyrophyllite by introducing variable amounts of Al^{3+} into its tetrahedral sheet, generally less than one in four tetrahedra as in micas. Much of the negative charge on each 2:1 sheet, however, comes from charge deficiency in the octahedral layer. Small amounts of interlayer hydrated Na^+, Ca^{2+}, and Mg^{2+} maintain electrostatic neutrality. Montmorillonite is a dioctahedral smectite with low layer charge. Vermiculite is a trioctahedral smectite with a high (but less than biotite) layer charge. Smectites have the capacity to take on water

FIGURE 2-20 Muscovite structure (micas). Infinite sheets of corner-sharing tetrahedra (Fig. 2-17c) are depicted in an edge-on view. Apical directions of these sheets alternate. Hydroxyl ions (middle-sized spheres) occur at apex level central to each six-membered ring, resulting in an approximate closest-packed sheet of oxygen and hydroxyl ions. Al^{3+} ions (smallest spheres) occupy ⅔ of octahedral voids between two closest-packed sheets to form a gibbsite structural unit (Fig. 2-7b) between tetrahedral layers in muscovite. Biotite has a brucite structural unit (Fig. 2-7a) of (Mg,Fe^{2+}) occupying ³⁄₃ of these octahedral voids. Every fourth tetrahedron has an Al^{3+} ion replacing Si^{4+} with electrostatic neutrality preserved by K^+ ions (largest spheres) between the bases of tetrahedral layers (compare the □ site of Fig. 2-18).

reversibly, like zeolites, causing them to shrink or swell drastically, unlike zeolites, with changes in humidity. Called expansive clays, smectites are an expensive construction hazard.

Chlorites Chlorite structures may be derived from that of talc by adding a complete brucite layer between talc layers, thereby making it a 14-Å 2:2 structure. Chlorite minerals are mostly trioctahedral with variable proportions of Fe^{2+} and Mg^{2+}. Since some Al^{3+} and Fe^{3+} enter octahedral sheets and some Al^{3+} enters tetrahedral sheets, talc and brucite layers are electrostatically bonded. Chlorites differ from serpentines in the apical directions of the tetrahedral sheets; these directions alternate in 14-Å chlorites but point one way in 7-Å serpentines. Septechlorites are the stable polymorphs at surface temperatures.

Polytypy is common in layered silicates. In addition to regular stacking patterns (Fig. 2-21), stacking may be disordered. Mineral grains may also contain layers from more than one mineral species. This mixed layering and stacking disorder, coupled with submicroscopic grain size in sedimentary materials and hydrothermal alteration products, presents a formidable challenge in analysis and identification of these minerals.

2-6 FRAMEWORK SILICATES

A three-dimensional framework of linked tetrahedra (tektosilicates) results from corner sharing of all four corners with each O^{2-} bonded to two Si^{4+} ions. Different polymorphs of SiO_2—quartz, tridymite, cristobalite, and coesite—have tetrahedra linked in different patterns. Octahedral SiO_2 is known only in stishovite, a mineral with rutile structure (Fig. 2-5) formed by meteorite impact in sandstone and other quartz-rich rocks, and postulated in mantle minerals.

Silica Minerals Quartz, tridymite, and cristobalite have high- and low-temperature polymorphs that result from slight changes in bond angles and notable changes in crystal symmetry. High-low polymorphic inversions are rapid and nonquenchable since they involve no rupture of Si—O bonds. These high-low transitions are also named α and β inversions and forms, but, since these designations reverse at national and disciplinary boundaries, we may ignore them here.

Low quartz is the stable polymorph of silica at the earth's surface, but high-temperature tridymite, cristobalite, and high-pressure coesite and stishovite are found in rocks and preserved in collections. In addition, crystals of quartz that, by crystal faces they exhibit, could only have grown above its high-low inversion at 573°C are found as paramorphs in some volcanic rocks.

A three-dimensional framework of silica tetrahedra in cross-linked double helices represents the structure of high quartz (Fig. 2-22; Prog. 2-10). Low quartz has the same fundamental structure, but Si—O—Si bond directions are kinked between tetrahedra. Since a helix can have either a right or a left sense of rotation around a channel, both right and left enantiomorphs (mirror images) of quartz are found in equal amounts. Channels in quartz left by these helices are large enough to house Li^{+}.

High tridymite has a more open framework than quartz (Fig. 2-23). Although not a "layered" structure, a tridymite framework may be visualized as tetrahedral "sheets" with alternate apical O^{-} pointed in

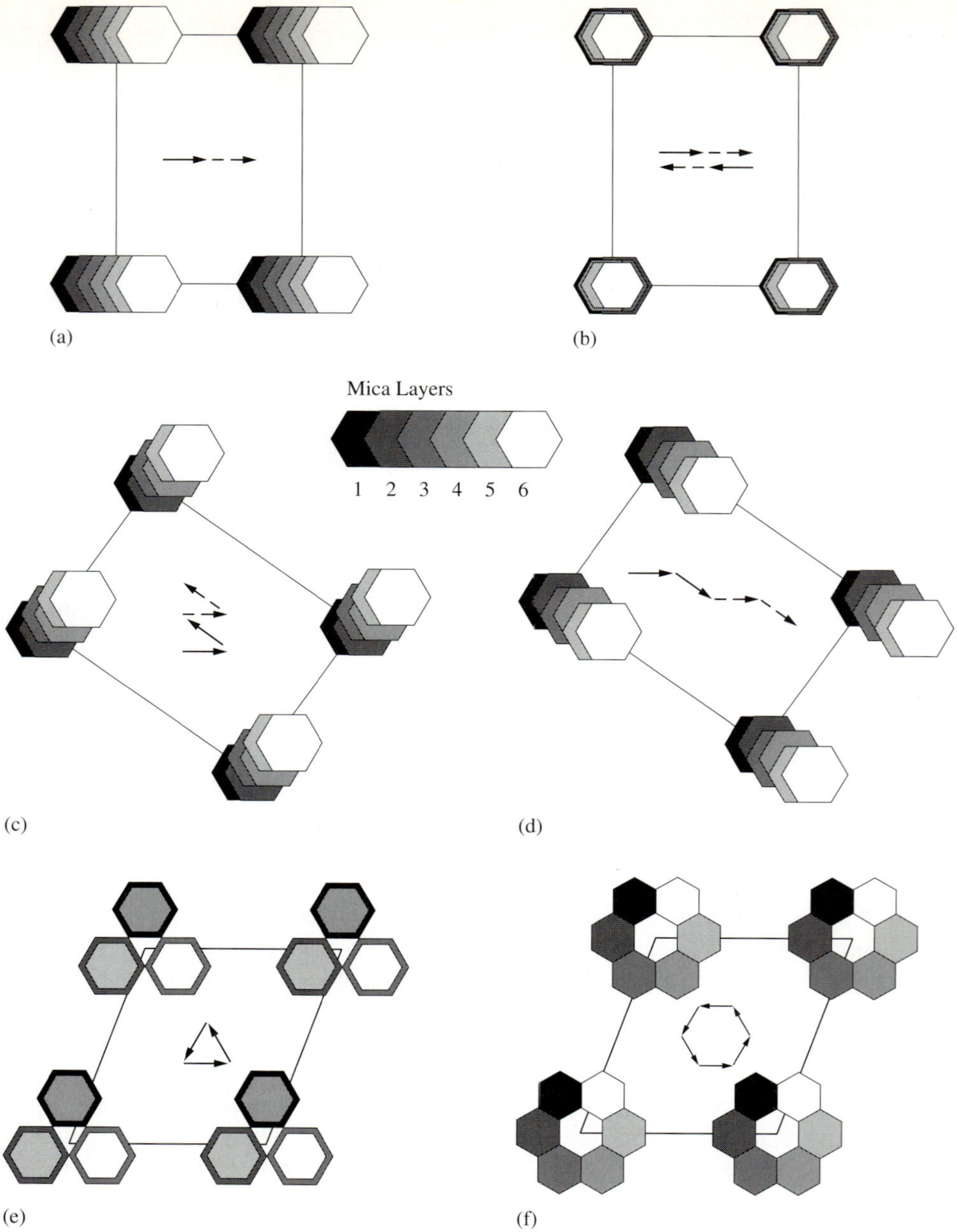

FIGURE 2-21 Mica polytypism. Mica layers may be stacked in six simple theoretical ways. Arrows connect identical points in adjacent layers. (a) One-layer unit cell with monoclinic symmetry (symmetries are defined in Chap. 3). (b) Two-layer unit cell with orthorhombic symmetry. (c, d) Two-layer unit cells with monoclinic symmetry. (e) Three-layer unit cell with trigonal symmetry. (f) Six-layer unit cell with hexagonal symmetry. Stacking may also be disordered. [After J. V. Smith and H. S. Yoder, *Min. Mag.* 31 (1956): p. 209.]

FIGURE 2-22 High-quartz structure. Apparent six-membered "rings" are double helices in projection. Beginning with a silica tetrahedron at zero level in a unit cell, one of its upper corners shares an oxygen ion with a lower corner of an adjacent tetrahedron at the ⅓ level. An upper corner of each ⅓-level tetrahedron shares an oxygen with a lower corner of an adjacent tetrahedron at the ⅔ level in this structure. Halfway around this apparent "ring" a second helix begins and continues like the first, while the first helix proceeds into the next unit cell above the plane of the page. Adjacent helices share tetrahedral corners (apparent three-membered rings composed of tetrahedra at 0, ⅓, and ⅔ elevation in this unit cell) to form a three-dimensional network of all corner-sharing silica tetrahedra. Low quartz differs in that adjacent tetrahedra are kinked slightly with respect to one another. (Left-handed spirals give right-handed quartz.)

opposite directions. These apical O^- are then shared between adjacent identical "sheets" with their "rings" aligned. Individual tetrahedra are slightly rotated in low tridymite. Beginning with the same "sheets," but stacking them offset or rotated above and below, yields the high cristobalite structure (Fig. 2-24). Channels in these high-temperature polymorphs of silica are large enough to house Na^+ and K^+.

A rare high-pressure polymorph of silica was synthesized and described by L. Coes, Jr., in 1953, and was subsequently discovered in sandstones shocked by meteorite impact and as an inclusion in diamond. The structure of this rare mineral, coesite, is important because feldspar

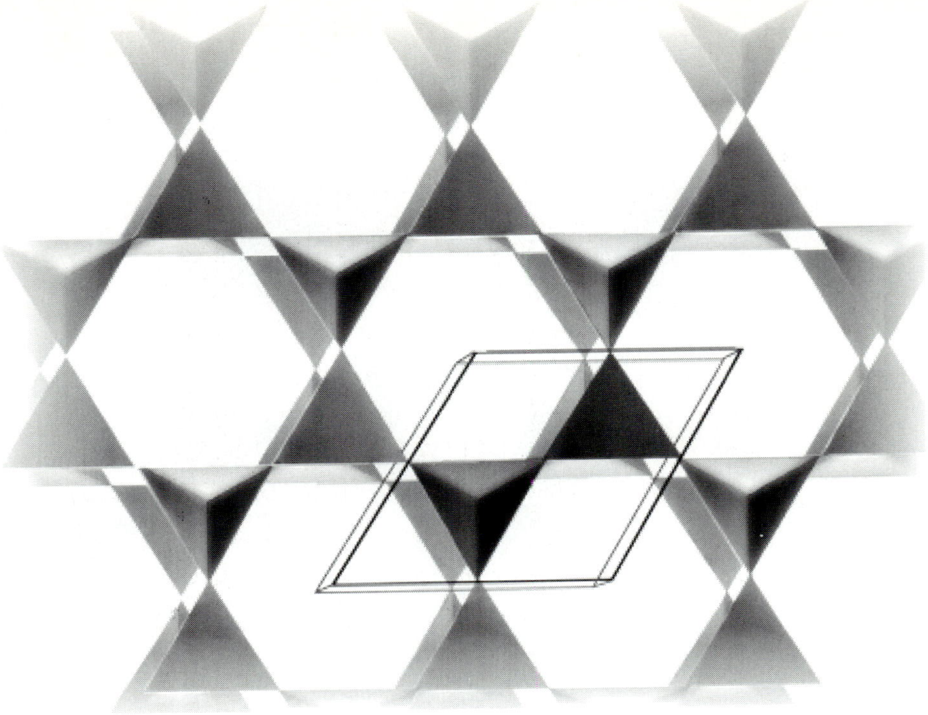

FIGURE 2-23 High-tridymite structure. Silica tetrahedra share three corners to form apparent "sheets" with alternate tetrahedral apices pointing in opposite directions. Corner sharing between superimposed sheets creates a three-dimensional framework of all corner-shared silica tetrahedra. Low-tridymite structure differs in that adjacent tetrahedra are kinked slightly with respect to one another.

structures are stuffed derivatives of it. In the coesite structure, silica tetrahedra link into two kinds of four-membered "rings" (Fig. 2-25). Each such ring has eight corners not shared within a ring, half being shared with adjacent rings to form puckered "chains," and half being shared between adjacent chains to form a framework. Note that while rings and chains may be used to describe components of coesite structure, the result is a framework.

Feldspars Feldspar minerals have structures based on the coesite structure, but Al^{3+} replaces one fourth to one half of tetrahedral Si^{4+}, thereby giving this framework a net negative electrostatic charge. Stuff Na^+, K^+, Ca^{2+}, or Ba^{2+} into cavities in this framework to neutralize this charge imbalance (Fig. 2-26). Since these cations can partially substitute one for another, leading to crystal solution series, order-disorder possibili-

FIGURE 2-24 High-cristobalite structure. Silica tetrahedra form apparent "sheets" as in high tridymite (Fig. 2-23). In high-cristobalite structure, however, adjacent sheets are rotated with respect to one another so that alternate tetrahedra on one sheet appear below "rings" of adjacent sheets. Low cristobalite differs in that adjacent tetrahedra are kinked slightly with respect to one another.

ties exist within cavities as well as in its tetrahedral framework (Fig. 2-27, Prog. 2-11).

In alkali feldspars, Na^+ and K^+ are interchangeable above about 800°C; they are disordered in the feldspar structure. Annealing below 800°C permits the smaller Na^+ to collect into collapsed six to seven oxygen-coordinated cavities in the framework, whereas the larger K^+ collects into nine expanded oxygen-coordinated cavities. Depending on duration of recrystallization and availability of water, these domains range in size from submicroscopic lamellae to distinctly visible grains in a rock. They are called perthite when microcline predominates and antiperthites when albite predominates.

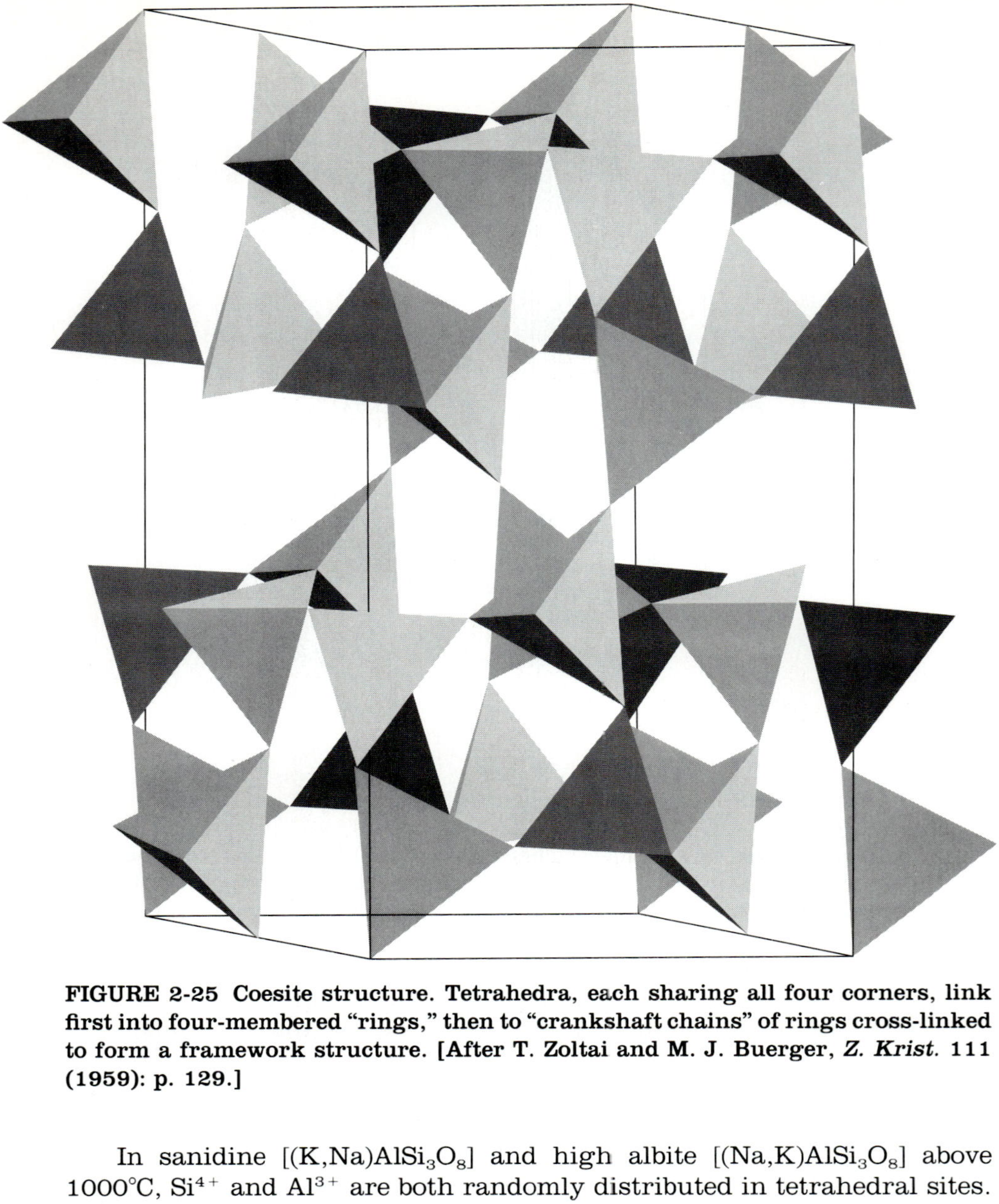

FIGURE 2-25 Coesite structure. Tetrahedra, each sharing all four corners, link first into four-membered "rings," then to "crankshaft chains" of rings cross-linked to form a framework structure. [After T. Zoltai and M. J. Buerger, *Z. Krist.* 111 (1959): p. 129.]

In sanidine [(K,Na)$AlSi_3O_8$] and high albite [(Na,K)$AlSi_3O_8$] above 1000°C, Si^{4+} and Al^{3+} are both randomly distributed in tetrahedral sites. These tetrahedral sites are not identical, however, with one site (T_1) closer to interframework alkali ions than the other (T_2). On annealing below 1000°C, Si^{4+} preferentially selects T_2 sites, while Al^{3+} and Si^{4+} remain disordered in T_1 sites. This degree of ordering is characteristic of orthoclase and intermediate albite. At still lower temperatures, Al^{3+} collects preferen-

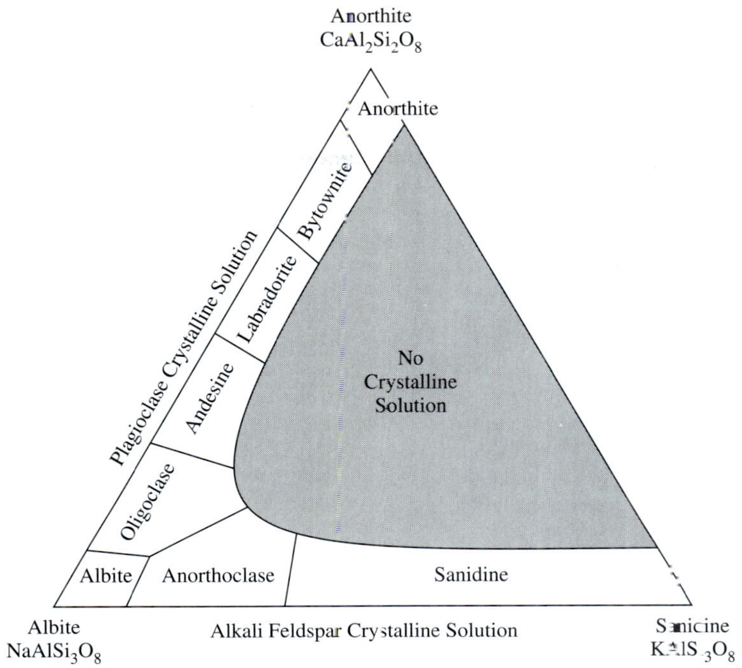

FIGURE 2-26 Feldspar minerals. Complete crystal solution exists between sanidine and albite and between albite and anorthite at high temperature. At low temperatures microcline and albite are immiscible, and plagioclase crystal solution is immiscible in a complex fashion.

tially on just one of two T_1 sites, while Si^{4+} collects on the other. Complete T-site order characterizes low albite [$NaAlSi_3O_8$] and maximum microcline [$KAlSi_3O_8$] with various states of intermediate order found in individual crystals of these minerals.

In anorthite [$CaAl_2Si_2O_8$] and celsian [$BaAl_2Si_2O_8$], with their Al:Si ratio of 1:1, cation-cation repulsion between Si^{4+} ions tends to cause silica tetrahedra and alumina tetrahedra to alternate periodically except close to their melt points. This disorder permits crystal solution between anorthite and albite (plagioclase series) and between celsian and sanidine close to melting, but not at lower temperatures. Indeed, at low temperatures, unit cells of end members of these crystal solution series are totally incompatible. In plagioclase crystals of intermediate composition, lamellae of different incompatible compositions and structures may exsolve. Clay blebs along these lamellae then cause visible wavelengths of light to diffract optically and cause characteristic plagioclase iridescence, as seen in many labradorite cleavage fragments. Inversion from high- to low-

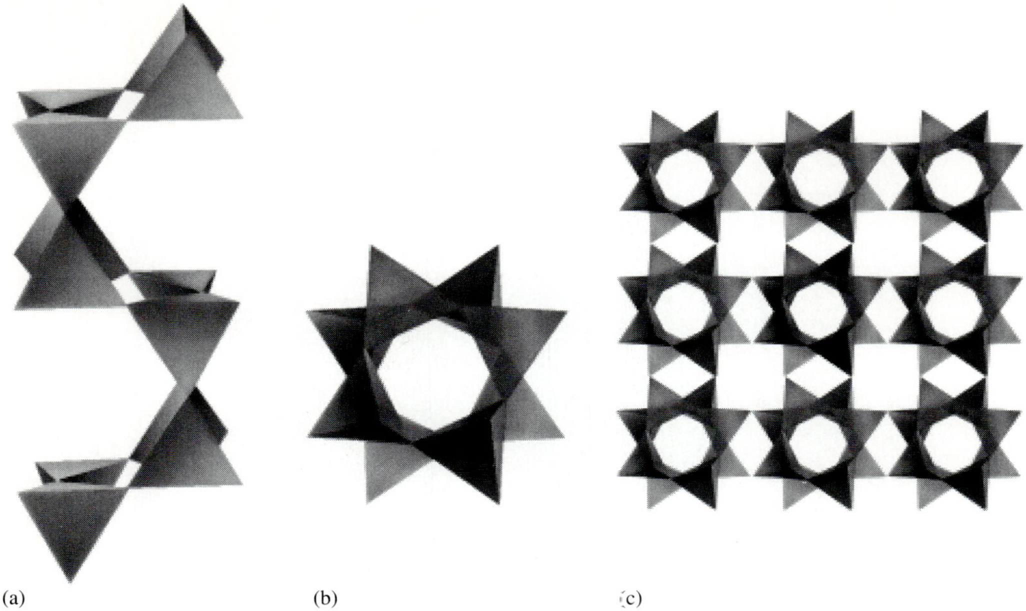

FIGURE 2-27 Feldspar structure. (a) Four-membered "rings" of tetrahedra share half their corners to form a "crankshaft chain" of tetrahedra. (b) Idealized "crankshaft chain" of four-membered "rings" is depicted in an end-on view. (c) Unshared tetrahedral corners of each "crankshaft chain" are shared between adjacent "chains" to form an idealized three-dimensional framework of tetrahedra. Between ¼ and ½ of these tetrahedra have Si^{4+} replaced by Al^{3+}, with electrostatic neutrality maintained by alkali and alkali-earth ions in cavities within this framework structure.

temperature structures is sluggish to the extent that minerals with a wide variety of structural states (degrees of disorder) are preserved in nature and in mineral collections.

Feldspathoids Closely related to feldspar structures are a group of important rock-forming minerals called feldspathoids. These minerals are characterized by a lower Si:Al ratio and, hence, are incompatible with quartz in rocks. Leucite [$KAlSi_2O_6$] has four- and six-membered "rings" of tetrahedra linked into a three-dimensional framework with K^+ in 12-fold coordination in framework cavities. Analcime [$NaAlSi_2O_6 \cdot H_2O$] is similar, with H_2O occupying large cavities housing K^+ in leucite and Na^+ in smaller cavities. Nepheline [$KNa_3Al_4Si_4O_{16}$] has a structure (Fig. 2-28) based on a distortion of the high-tridymite structure (Fig. 2-23). Half the Si^{4+} tetrahedra have been replaced by Al^{3+} tetrahedra, giving this framework a net negative charge. A 1:3 ratio of K^+ to Na^+ results from

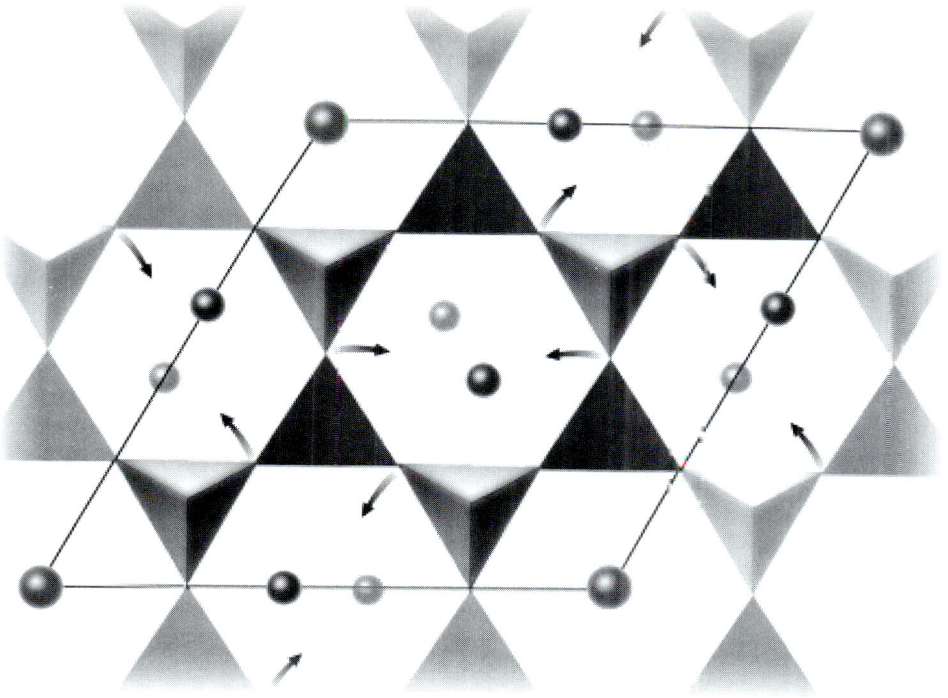

FIGURE 2-28 **Nepheline structure. Nepheline is a stuffed derivative of tridymite (Fig. 2-23). In ideal nepheline, ¼ of these tetrahedra have Al^{3+} replacing Si^{4+} with electrostatic neutrality maintained by stuffing K^+ (large spheres) and Na^+ (small spheres) into spaces in this tetrahedral framework. This framework is distorted as indicated by arrows to produce large cavities for K^+ and small cavities for Na^+ in a 1:3 ratio. Lightly shaded small spheres represent Na^+ ions below the plane of the page.**

a distortion of the tridymite structure, wherein three fourths of the framework cavities collapse into a CN of VIII with Na^+ and one fourth have a CN of IX with K^+.

Beryl and Cordierite The replacement of Si^{4+} by Al^{3+} in feldspar and feldspathoid structures and the resulting framework charge imbalance neutralization by nonframework ions characterize these mineral groups. Other ions that can proxy for Si^{4+} in tetrahedral coordination in framework silicates include Be^{2+}, P^{5+}, Ge^{3+}, Ga^{4+}, and Fe^{3+}. Beryl [$Al_2Be_3Si_6O_{18}$] is a framework silicate composed of six-membered "rings" of silica tetrahedra cross-linked by berylia tetrahedra. Each tetrahedron in a beryl ring is rotated outward as compared with tourmaline rings; consequently beryl lacks the polar properties of tourmaline. Cordierite [$(Mg,Fe)Al_4Si_5O_{18}$]

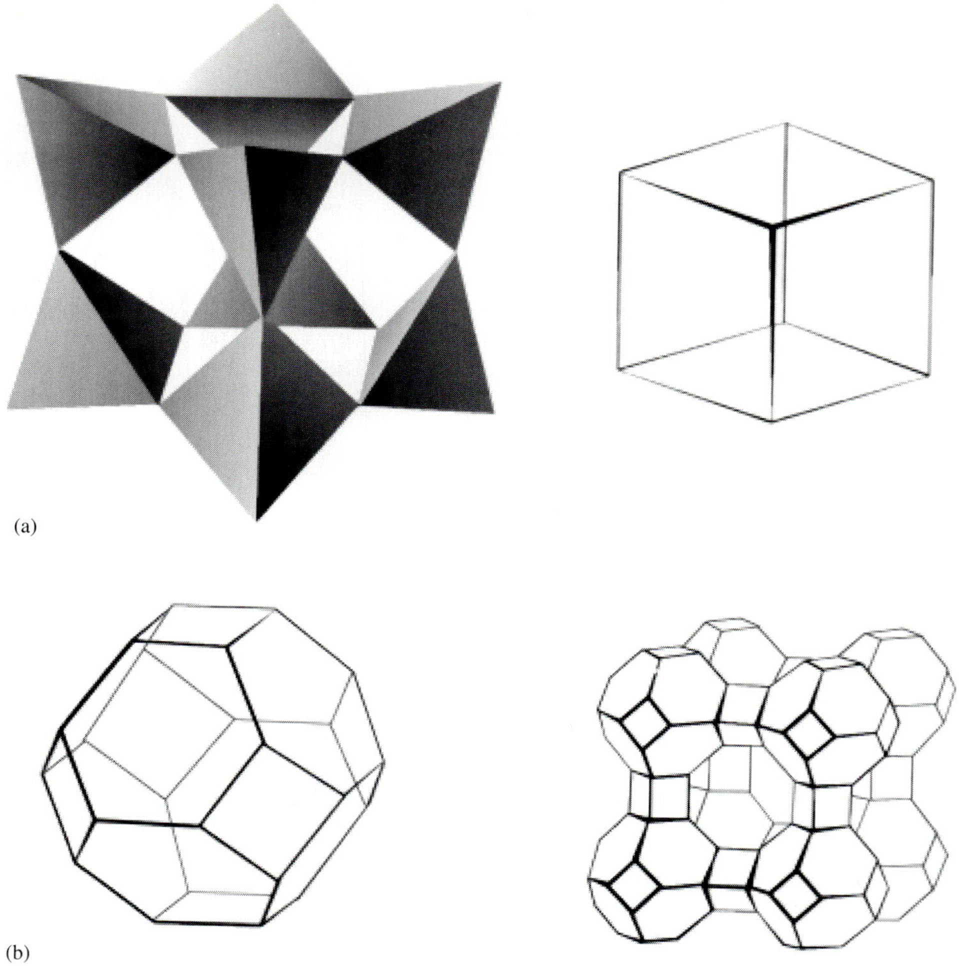

FIGURE 2-29 Zeolite-A structure. (a) Two four-membered “rings” share adjacent corners to form a small cage. *Left:* Cage depicted by tetrahedra. *Right:* Same cage depicted by lines with each node representing a location of a tetrahedral ion with oxygen ions located at midpoints between nodes. (b) *Left:* Six cages of eight tetrahedra each (squares) share adjacent corners to form an intermediate cage of 24 tetrahedra in four- and six-membered “rings.” *Right:* Eight intermediate cages are linked by eight small cages to form a large cage bounded by four-, six-, and eight-membered rings. Ion exchange, dehydration, and rehydration occur in zeolites because these rings permit passage through this three-dimensional lace framework of tetrahedra.

contains "rings" of five silica tetrahedra and one alumina tetrahedra cross-linked by the remaining alumina tetrahedra into a framework with (Mg,Fe) in octahedral framework cavities.

Zeolites Zeolites are a large group of aluminosilicates with interesting structural complexities. Formed by diagenesis or at the very lowest temperatures of metamorphism, they have wide industrial application as molecular sieves, ion exchangers, and catalysts. As with garnets and spinels, industrial interest has led to synthesis of numerous molecular sieves with no natural counterparts. Zeolite structures may be characterized as lacy tetrahedral frameworks of 4-, 5-, 6-, 8-, and 12-membered "rings." Large and small cavities in these frameworks contain water, which may be boiled off and reintroduced reversibly without destroying the original structures.

Zeolite structures and properties may be illustrated by a synthetic molecular sieve Type A [$Na_{12}(Al_{12}Si_{12}O_{48})\cdot 27H_2O$]. Its primary building unit is its silica and alumina tetrahedra, and its secondary building unit (SBU) is a double four-membered "ring" (Fig. 2-29). Six SBUs surround a cage, a truncated octahedron. This cage has an internal diameter of 112 pm (11.2 Å), with 42-pm (4.2-Å) channels connecting the cages. Dehydration is stepwise, with a large first surge followed by smaller ones as temperature rises with no structural changes. Natural zeolites are more complex in structure, but in principle they are built the same way.

FURTHER READINGS

Bailey, S. W. (ed.), *Micas.* Washington, DC: Mineralogical Society of America, 1984.

Bragg, W. L., G. F. Claringbull, and W. H. Taylor, *Crystal Structures of Minerals.* Ithaca, NY: Cornell University Press, 1965.

Deer, W. A., R. A. Howie, and J. Zussman, *Rock-Forming Minerals,* vols. 1–5. London: Longman, 1962–1963; vol. 1A, 1982; vol. 1B, 1986; vol. 2A, 1978.

Deer, W. A., R. A. Howie, and J. Zussman, *An Introduction to the Rock-Forming Minerals.* London: Longman, 1966.

Frye, K. (ed.), *Encyclopedia of Mineralogy.* New York: Van Nostrand Reinhold, 1981.

Mumpton, F. A. (ed.), *Mineralogy and Geology of Natural Zeolites,* 2nd printing. Washington, DC: Mineralogical Society of America, 1981.

Prewitt, C. T. (ed.), *Pyroxenes.* Washington, DC: Mineralogical Society of America, 1980.

Reeder, R. J. (ed.), *Carbonates: Mineralogy and Chemistry.* Washington, DC: Mineralogical Society of America, 1983.

Ribbe, P. H. (ed.), *Orthosilicates,* 2nd ed. Washington, DC: Mineralogical Society of America, 1982.

Ribbe, P. H. (ed.), *Sulfide Mineralogy,* 4th printing. Washington, DC: Mineralogical Society of America, 1982.

Ribbe, P. H. (ed.), *Feldspar Mineralogy,* 2nd ed. Washington, DC: Mineralogical Society of America, 1983.

Rumble, D., III (ed.), *Oxide Minerals,* 2nd printing. Washington, DC: Mineralogical Society of America, 1981.

Veblen, D. R. (ed.), *Amphiboles and Other Hydrous Pyriboles—Mineralogy,* 2nd printing. Washington, DC: Mineralogical Society of America, 1985.

Wells, A. F., *Structural Inorganic Chemistry,* 4th ed. London: Oxford University Press, 1984.

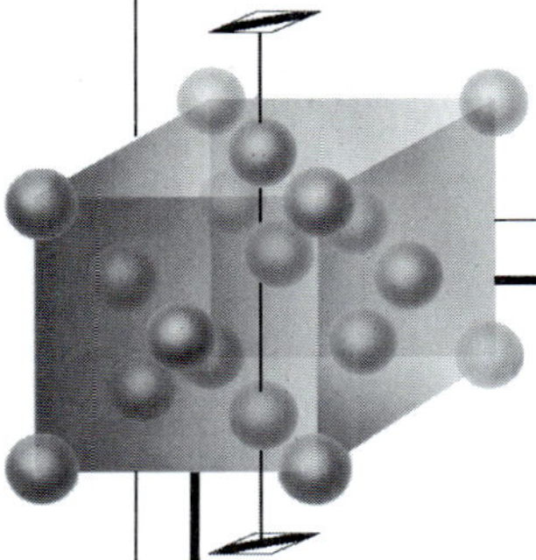

3

CRYSTAL SYMMETRY

Crystallography began as a branch of natural science in the 17th century. As late as 1600, popular opinion held that mineral crystals grew in the same manner as living things and that transparent gem crystals were ice that somehow had been congealed by extreme cold under influence of some ill-defined force. Indeed, the word *crystal* (*krystallos*) derives from a Greek word for ice and was usually applied to rock crystal—quartz.

As a modern science, crystallography began with a demonstration in 1669 by Niels Stensen (Nicolaus Steno) that angles between the same two faces of quartz crystals are identical for all quartz crystals, regardless of the size of each crystal or the relative sizes of these two faces. This constancy of interfacial angles is known as Steno's law, the first law of crystallography. This observation opened a period of crystallographic investigation that lasted through most of the 17th and 18th centuries. Activities of crystallographers of this period consisted primarily of systematic observation, of classification, and of speculation about the meaning of these observations.

Atomic Hypotheses Without any direct evidence (see Sec. 1-4), a concept evolved that crystals were built of atoms. Johannes Kepler, in 1611, used an idea of packing of spheres to account for shapes of snowflakes, and Robert Hooke extended this idea to other crystals in 1665. In 1690, Christiaan Huygens postulated ellipsoidal atoms to account for rhombic cleavage and double refraction of calcite. Robert Boyle and Isaac Newton independently proposed, on the other hand, that atoms that make up crystals must be small polyhedra so as to avoid a necessity of void spaces between atoms. In the late 18th century, Romé de l'Isle sought to classify crystals on a basis of external geometric shape. One of his students invented, in 1783, a contact goniometer for measurement of angles between crystal faces. This development led to enumeration of over 100 different kinds of crystal shapes.

A leading school of crystallography at the end of the 18th and the beginning of the 19th centuries was headed by René Haüy. He sought to analyze cleavage fragments to determine shapes of the ultimate building blocks of matter. He concluded that only three shapes of atoms existed: parallelopipeds, triangular prisms, and tetrahedra. Haüy concluded that angles made by crystal faces were restricted to those made by boundaries of these ultimate building blocks. This idea restricted angles to those with tangents in integer proportions—an early form of the second law of crystallography, the law of rational intercepts.

Crystal Shapes Christian Weiss, who critically translated Haüy's mineralogy textbook, found a more convenient way of visualizing crystal shapes with reference to a set of three coordinate axes. This line of study began a second period of crystallographic investigation, which lasted from 1815, when Weiss succeeded in identifying four crystal systems, until 1912, when Laue effected the first X-ray diffraction by a crystal structure. This period is characterized by development of the theoretical foundations of crystallography on a mathematical basis. Weiss also proposed that crystal faces could be easily represented in terms of their intercepts on crystallographic axes at integer multiples of their lengths along those axes and that certain crystal faces could be symmetrically related.

Within a decade of Weiss' discovery, Friedrich Mohs, who devised a hardness scale used to this day in mineralogy, discovered two more crystal systems. The 32 point groups, which are all of the crystallographically possible combinations of symmetry elements intersecting at a point, were derived in 1830. Auguste Bravais, in 1848, derived the 14 space lattices, which are arrays of translationally equivalent points in a geometrical pattern. Independently, at the end of the 19th century, E. S. Federov in Russia, Artur Schönflies in Germany, and William Barlow in Britain derived the 230 space groups. This phase of geometrical crystallography was mathematically complete in the last decade of the century.

Atomic Theory A third period of crystallographic investigation began in Munich in 1912 with the discovery that crystalline substances diffract X rays. Development of this tool, which permitted crystallographers to see internal structures in crystals, made it possible to verify or disprove speculations of previous periods. The year after Laue supervised the first diffraction experiment, William L. Bragg began systematic determination of crystal structures while still an undergraduate at Cambridge University.

At the University of Leeds Professor W. H. Bragg, William's father, constructed an X-ray spectrometer with which he was able to measure characteristic radiation of many metals. His studies led to design of X-ray tubes that could produce monochromatic radiation.

Since that time, crystallographers have used X-ray diffraction to determine internal crystal structures of crystalline compounds, both inorganic and organic, both natural and synthetic.

3-1 SYMMETRY OPERATIONS

In Chap. 2, structures of crystals were represented in terms of atomic positions referred to a unit cell. This unit cell of a crystal structure is a small volume that contains the simplest asymmetric unit and symmetry elements of the space group that, when repeated infinitely in three dimensions, contains all ions of a structure and all three-dimensional interrelationships among those ions. Thus, a unit cell, while an arbitrary choice, is usually taken as the simplest building block of a crystal structure. A crystal may be envisioned as a periodic array of all constituents and all properties of these unit cells. Periodicity—patterned repetition in space—inherently generates symmetry, the kind of symmetry determined by the kind of periodicity.

Symmetric Identity An operation of symmetry is an imaginary transformation such that, when a transformation is completed, a resulting configuration is indistinguishable from its original configuration. That is, object and image are identical. Stated formally, a system of ions and their properties is invariant under transformation by a symmetry operation. Ions within a unit cell that are interchangeable by symmetry operations are symmetrically identical, and ions of different unit cells within a structure are also symmetrically identical. An entire crystal structure, therefore, can be built from a unit cell by these conceptual transformations. Such discrete equivalence operations are contained within that elegant branch of mathematics called group theory.

Infinite parallel repetition of a unit cell in three-dimensional space was used informally in Chap. 2. Formally, this parallel repetition is an operation of translation. Three translations necessary to build a crystal structure from a unit cell are parallel to the three unit-cell edges (Fig. 3-1; Prog. 3-1). These translations need not be of equal length. In halite (Fig. 2-2) they are, but in rutile (Fig. 2-5) one is clearly different from the other two. All three may be different. Neither do these three translations need to be orthogonal. In halite and rutile, they are; in calcite (Fig. 2-8), they are not. Linear translations and their allowed combinations properly fall into the mathematical discipline of vector and tensor analysis.

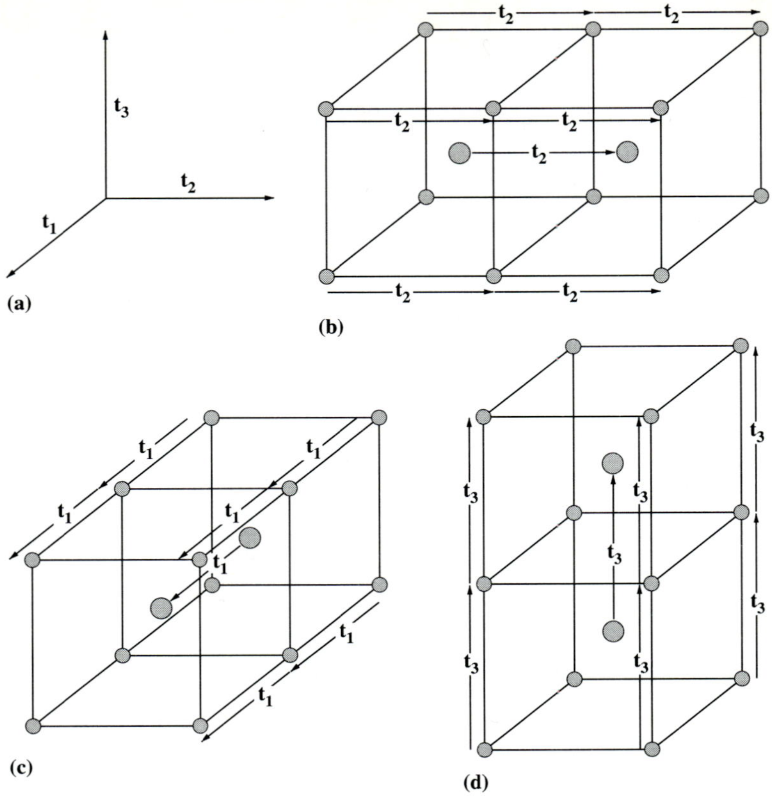

FIGURE 3-1 Translations of a unit cell. (a) Three translation vectors parallel to each unit-cell edge and of length equal to each edge. (b) Unit cell translated parallel to $\mathbf{t}_2$. (c) Unit cell translated parallel to $\mathbf{t}_1$. (d) Unit cell translated parallel to $\mathbf{t}_3$.

Symmetric Rotation Rotational symmetry occurs when a unit cell or an entire structure rotates about an imaginary axis for some fraction of a complete revolution to reveal a structure that is indistinguishable from (symmetrically identical to) its original structure for each and every ion and chemical bond. The simplest rotation is a monad, a rotation of one full revolution of 360°.

A diad is a rotation of 180°. In rutile, diads connect vertical edge centers (Fig. 3-2; Prog. 3-1). Ions located on a symmetry axis are clearly not moved by operation of that axis. A second operation of each diad completes a revolution of 360°. A set of operations required to complete a full rotation constitutes a closed group, its order indicating the number of repetitions necessary to close a group.

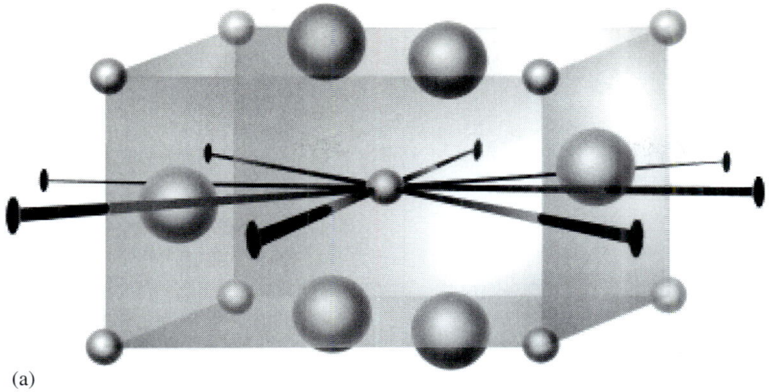

(a)

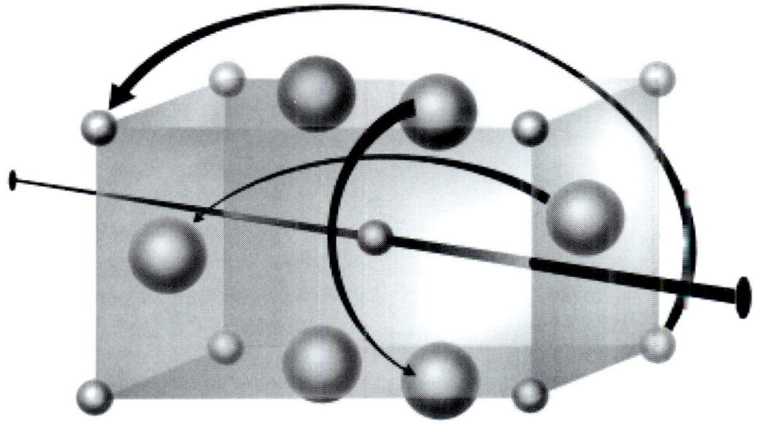

(b)

FIGURE 3-2 Diad. The unit cell of rutile (Fig. 2-5) has four horizontal diads of rotational symmetry. (a) Four diads in rutile. (b) Operation of a diad with three pairs of symmetrically equivalent ions indicated by arrows.

A triad is a rotation of 120°. Axes passing through a trigonal planar void in a closest-packed layer are triads (Fig. 3-3). Two additional triad operations complete a revolution of 360°. In any unit cell in which the three translations are both equal and at right angles, four triads pass through opposite corners of a cube (Fig. 3-4).

A tetrad is rotation of 90° (Fig. 3-5). A vertical axis through rutile (Fig. 3-2) and three axes through the face centers of the halite structure are tetrads. Four repetitions complete a revolution. (A pentad operation is conceivable, but pentagonal unit cells cannot fit together without gaps.)

A hexad is a rotation of 60° (Fig. 3-6). Six repetitions of 60° rotations complete a revolution of 360°.

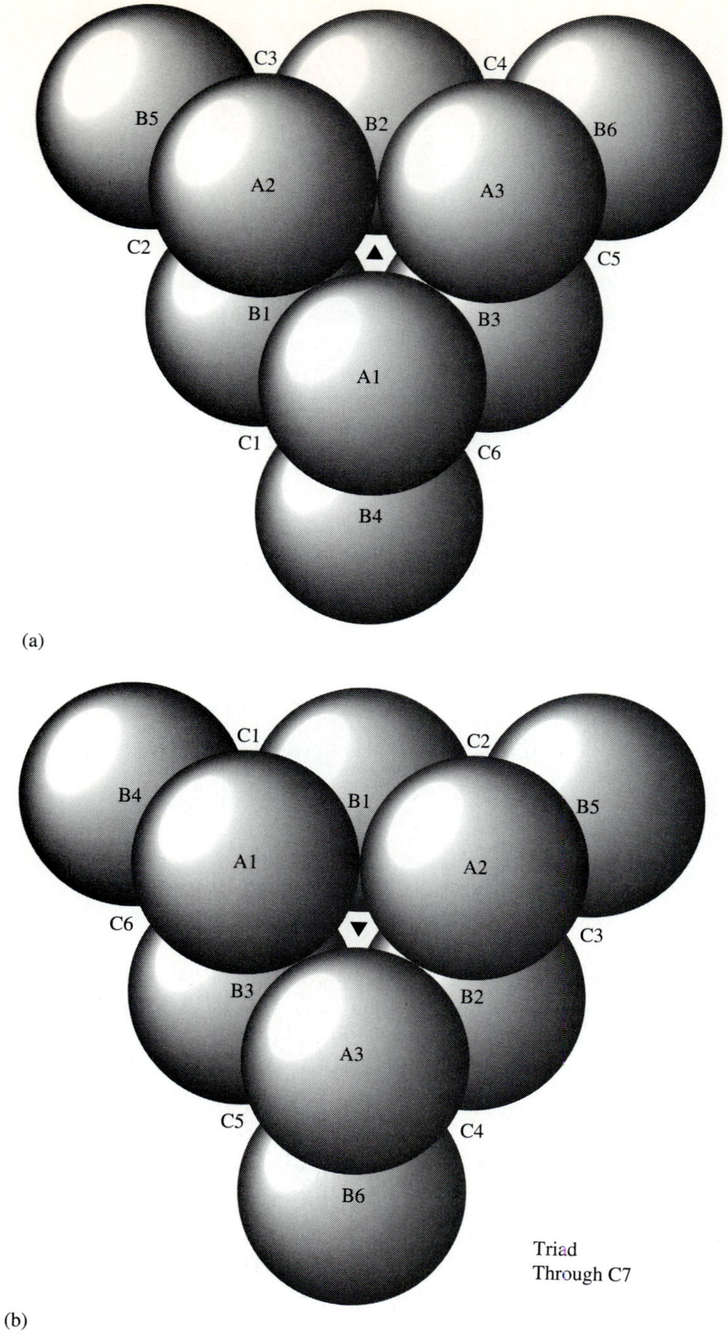

FIGURE 3-3 Triads. (a) Three layers in CCP (FCC) array (compare Fig. 1-7), C layer shown by position only. (b) Rotation about a triad passing through ion C 7. A second rotation would produce an identical configuration, but with numbers moved. A third rotation returns numbers to original positions.

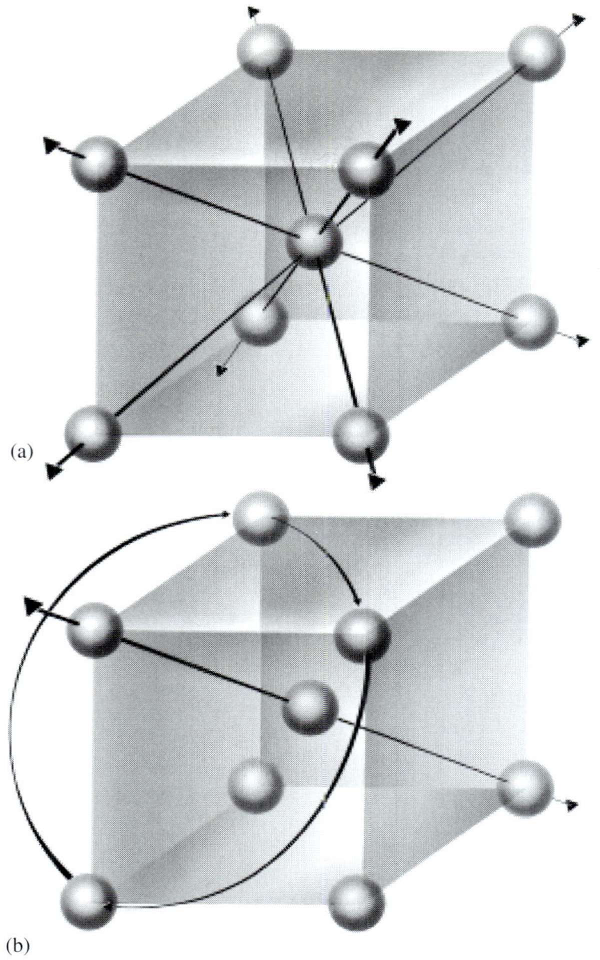

FIGURE 3-4 Triads in a cube. (a) Four triads are located along each body diagonal of a cubic unit cell of native iron. (b) Three symmetrically related iron atoms are indicated by arrows for one of the triads.

Asymmetric Units Objects rotated in these examples are individual ions represented by perfect spheres. No inherent limitation exists on shapes of symmetrically related things in a crystal structure. Symmetrically related objects can be radical or any cluster of ions constituting a portion of a crystal structure. Since an object operated on symmetrically need not itself have symmetry, the name asymmetric unit is adopted for such objects (Fig. 3-7). Additionally, properties such as hardness or magnetic moment are symmetrically oriented in crystal structures.

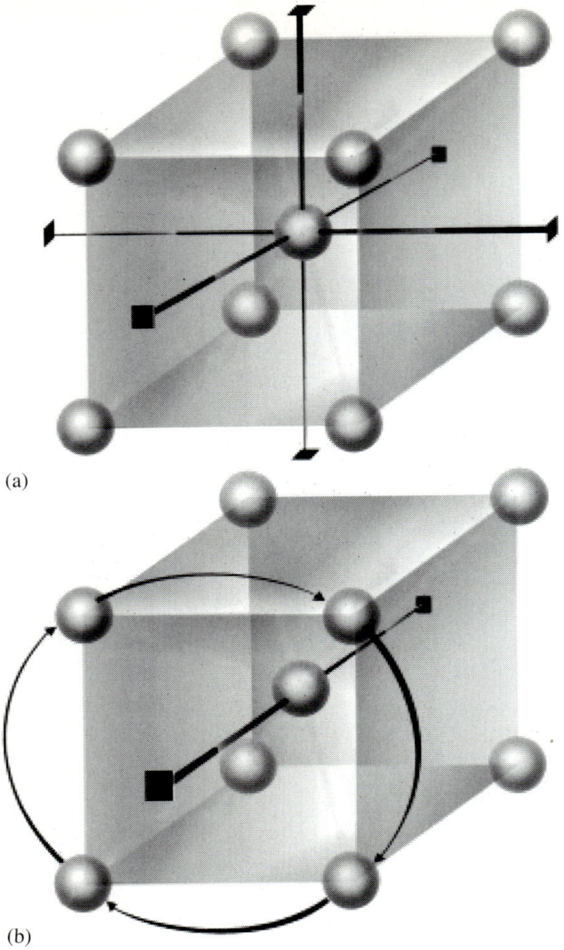

FIGURE 3-5 Tetrads. (a) Three tetrads pass through unit-cell faces of a cube. (b) Four symmetrically related atoms in native iron are indicated by arrows for one of these axes.

Had an object transformed by any rotation been an asymmetric unit such as might be represented by a human hand, its sense of handedness would not have changed. A pair of hands held forth in a prayerful position represent symmetry across a mirror plane (m). A mirror plane of symmetry bisects a structure such that each half is a mirror image of the other half (Fig. 3-8). Right-handedness changes to left-handedness, and vice versa, across a mirror plane of symmetry.

A pair of hands turned such that the palms are parallel but the fingers point in opposite directions is also symmetrically related. At opposite ends

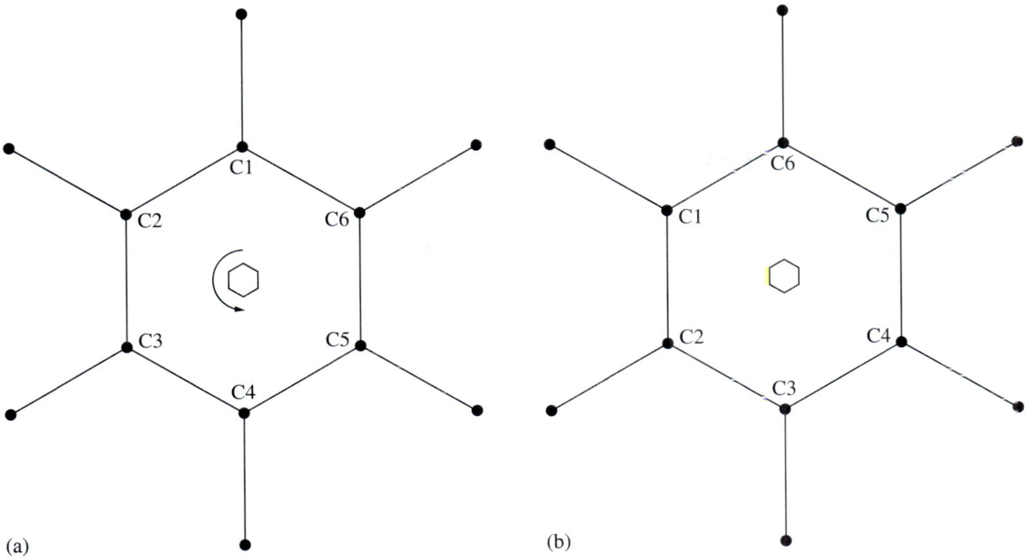

FIGURE 3-6 Hexads. (a) Part of the native graphite structure with carbon ions numbered. (b) One operation of a hexad passing through the center of a hexagonal ring.

of lines that pass through a midpoint located between two palms are identically paired fingers, thumb diametrically opposite thumb, and so on. An operation relating such centrosymmetric points is an inversion (i) through a center of symmetry (Fig. 3-9). An asymmetric unit clearly reverses its sense of handedness upon inversion.

A combination of two operations into one may describe some symmetrical relationships in crystal structures (Fig. 3-10). A combination of any order of rotational symmetry with a mirror plane generates a rotoreflection operation (Fig. 3-10a), which is indicated by a tilde (~) over its order number. A combination of a rotation with an inversion generates a rotoinversion operation (Fig. 3-10b, c). A bar over an order number indicates rotoinversion. (Monads and triads double their order when inverted.) Rotoreflection and rotoinversion are designated improper rotations to set them apart from proper rotations. Improper rotations reverse handedness; proper rotations do not. Since each improper operation has an equivalent, preferred designations follow convention (Table 3-1).

Periodicity Symmetry in a crystal structure results directly from its unit-cell periodicity and point symmetry. An abstraction of periodicity *per se* thus requires representation. A row of equally spaced points represents periodicity in one dimension, each point being removed from the next by a translation vector $\mathbf{t}_1$. Identical parallel rows with each point removed

FIGURE 3-7 Asymmetric unit. A schematic two-dimensional crystal is depicted by four-membered rings of $AlSi_3O_{12}$ tetrahedra. Three possible asymmetric units that can be operated by elements of symmetry to complete this pattern are outlined.

from a point in an adjacent row by a translation vector $\mathbf{t}_2$ constitute a net (Fig. 3-11). Parallel nets with each net point removed from an adjacent net by a translation vector $\mathbf{t}_3$ constitute a lattice (a Bravais or space lattice).

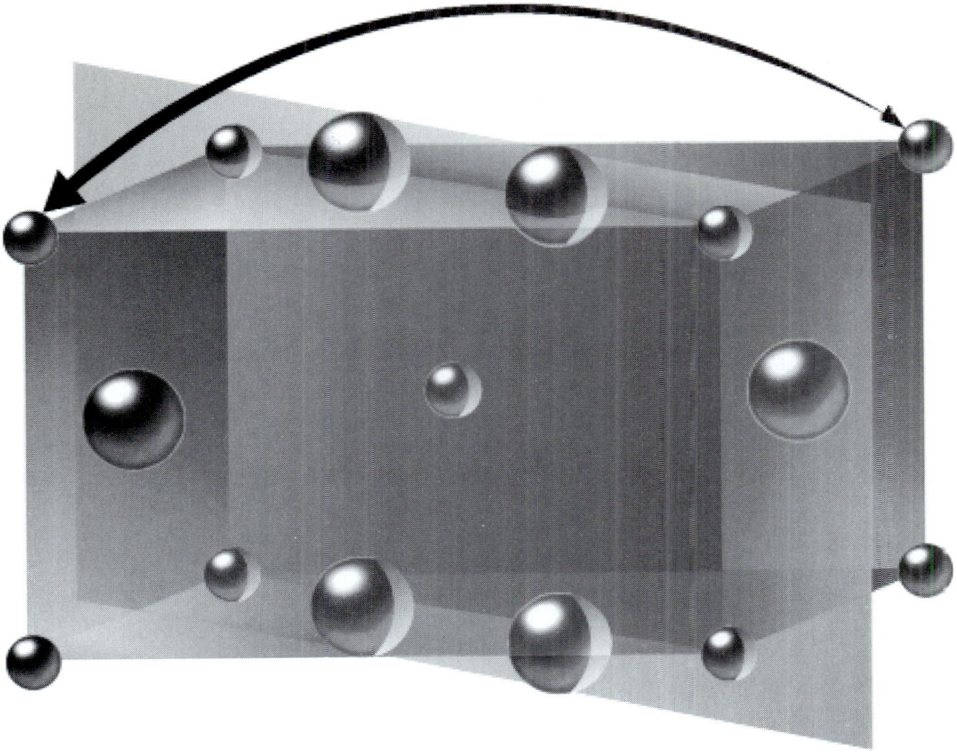

FIGURE 3-8 Mirror plane of symmetry. One of four vertical mirror planes in the rutile structure (Fig. 2-5) is shaded. Two symmetrically related titanium ions are connected by an arrow.

(Note that a lattice is a mathematical construction and refers to a perfect array of dimensionless points. Lattices do not inherently permit dislocations, defects, or vibrations.) Any lattice is a three-dimensional, periodic array of points wherein each point has an identical surrounding pattern of neighboring points. Thus defined, each lattice has inherent elements of symmetry, an element of symmetry being any location where symmetry operations can occur, and all lattices are centrosymmetric.

All crystal structures, therefore, may be referred to an appropriate lattice with an identical asymmetric unit assigned to each and every lattice point. Lattice symmetry is at least as great as that of an associated crystal structure (which need not be centrosymmetric). Many crystallographic relationships, therefore, may be considered solely with references to lattices (see Sec. 3-5).

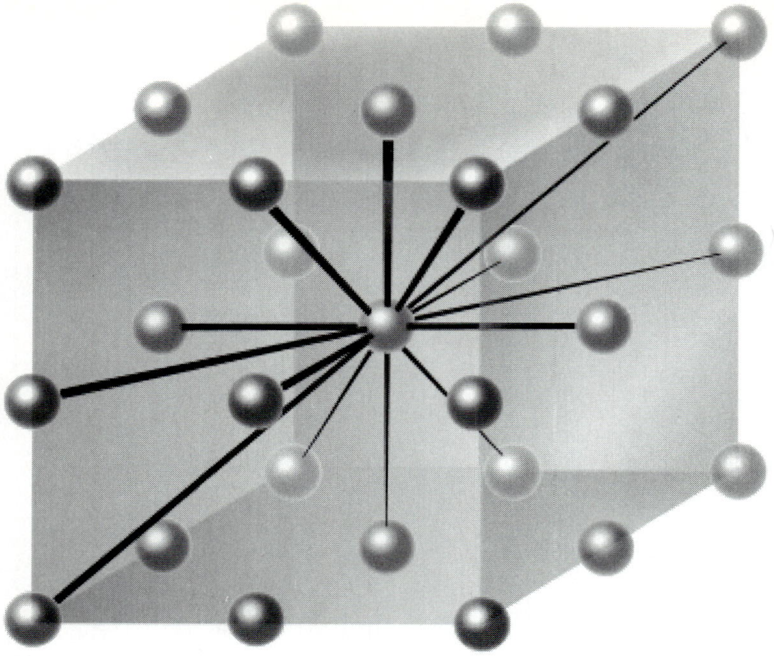

FIGURE 3-9 Inversion. A center of symmetry for the halite unit cell (Fig. 2-2) designates the operation of inversion. Several centrosymmetric ions are indicated by lines connecting each pair.

TABLE 3-1 Equivalence of Symmetry Axes

Improper axis	Decomposition into elements	Equivalent improper axis	Preferred designation
$\bar{1}$	$1 \cdot i$	$\tilde{2}$	$\bar{1}$
$\bar{2}$	$1 \cdot m$	$\tilde{1}$	m
$\bar{3}$	$3 \cdot i$	$\tilde{6}$	$\bar{3}$
$\bar{4}$	—	$\tilde{4}$	$\bar{4}$
$\bar{6}$	$3 \cdot m$	$\tilde{3}$	$\bar{6}$
$\tilde{1}$	$1 \cdot m$	$\bar{2}$	m
$\tilde{2}$	$1 \cdot i$	$\bar{1}$	$\bar{1}$
$\tilde{3}$	$3 \cdot m$	$\bar{6}$	$\bar{6}$
$\tilde{4}$	—	$\bar{4}$	$\bar{4}$
$\tilde{6}$	$3 \cdot i$	$\bar{3}$	$\bar{3}$

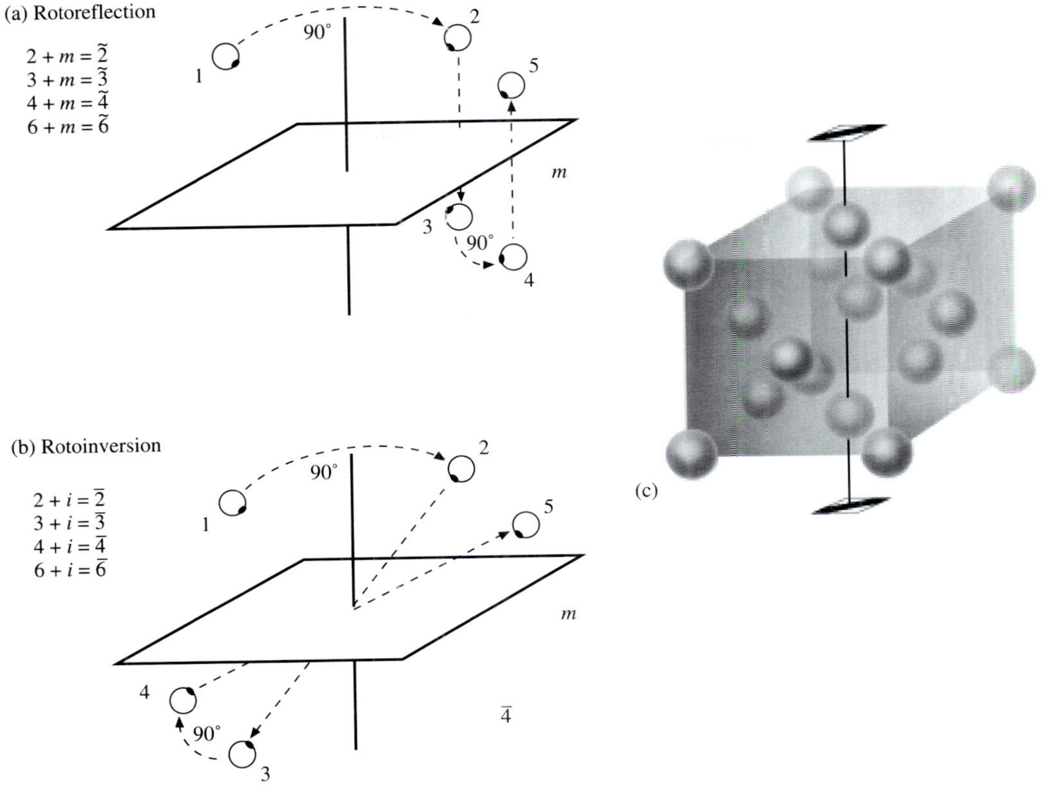

FIGURE 3-10 **Combined symmetry operations. (a) Rotoreflection. A tetrad rotation followed by reflection across a mirror plane is shown in steps 1–3 and repeated in steps 3–5. (b) Rotoinversion. A tetrad rotation is followed by inversion through a center of symmetry in steps 1–3 and repeated in steps 3–5. (c) Rotoinversion in the diamond unit cell (Fig. 2-1). Rotation by 90° about the axis indicated followed by inversion through the center relates the two darkest interior carbon ions.**

3-2 DIRECTIONS AND PLANES

Directions of lines and orientations of planes in lattices and in crystal structures may be indicated rigorously by various means. In crystallography, spatial orientation refers to three translation vectors $\mathbf{t}_1$, $\mathbf{t}_2$, $\mathbf{t}_3$ defined by the three unit-cell edges. Since unit-cell repetition is a fundamental characteristic of crystal structures, this repetition may be represented by a lattice with identical translation vectors (Fig. 3-1). By crystallographic convention, $\mathbf{t}_1$ designates the **a** axis (plotted toward an observer), $\mathbf{t}_2$ the **b** axis (positive to the right), and $\mathbf{t}_3$ the **c** axis (positive upward).

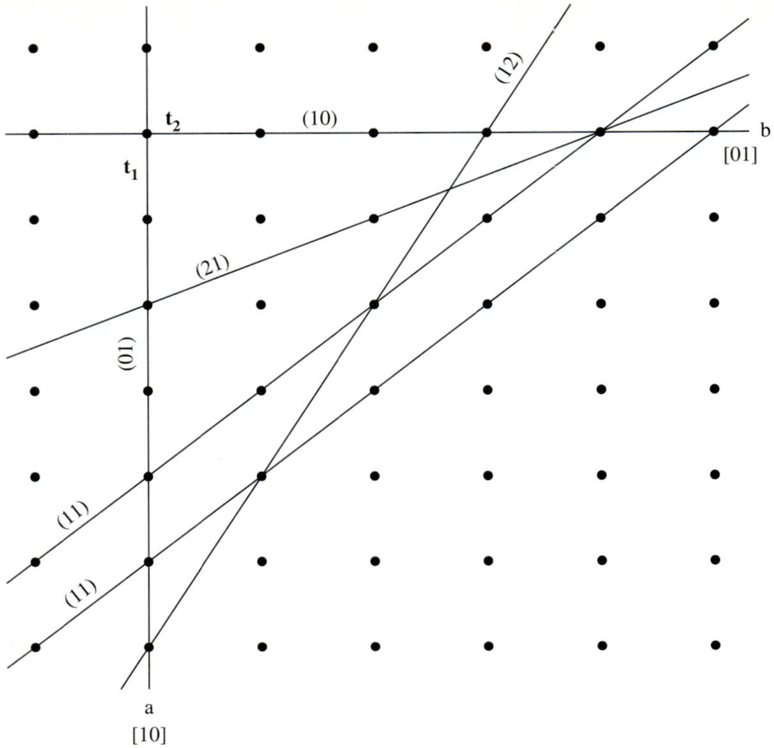

FIGURE 3-11 Retangular net with indices. The translations of this net are indicated by $\mathbf{t}_1$ and $\mathbf{t}_2$. The resulting coordinate axes are a and b. Indices (*hk*) are reciprocals of axial intercepts cleared of fractions and common factors.

Crystal Directions Crystallographic directions are stated in terms of multiples of translation distances in each coordinate direction. A [111] direction results from unit translations parallel first to **a**, then to **b**, and last to **c** (Fig. 3-12). How far the end point of these three translations lies from the origin is of no importance; this direction is defined as the [111] direction (read as one, one, one). Where translation $\mathbf{t}_3$ is zero along the **c** axis and unity along the **a** and **b** axes, the resultant direction is [110] (read as one, one, zero) (Fig. 3-12). The direction [010] (read as zero, one, zero) is parallel to **b**. Since direction, not magnitude, is of crystallographic interest, a [222] direction resulting from two units of translation along each axis is identified with [111]. Negative directions are indicated with a bar over each negative index number; thus, [$\bar{2}\bar{1}\bar{3}$] direction (read as bar two, bar one, bar three) points into the all-negative octant (Fig. 3-12).

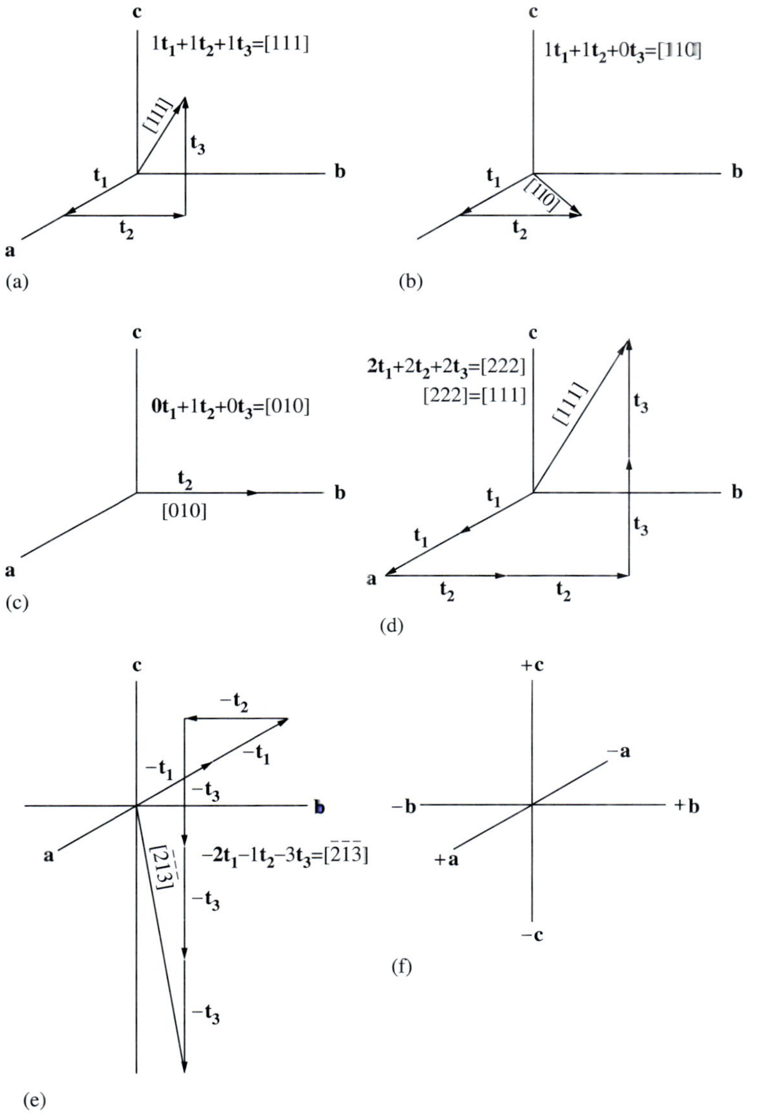

FIGURE 3-12 Directions in crystal space. (a) The [111] direction is the sum of successive unit translations parallel to $\mathbf{t}_1$, $\mathbf{t}_2$, and $\mathbf{t}_3$. (b) The [110] direction is the sum of successive unit translations parallel to $\mathbf{t}_1$ and $\mathbf{t}_2$ with no translation parallel to $\mathbf{t}_3$. (c) The [010] direction is parallel to $\mathbf{t}_2$. (d) Translation of two units in each direction produce the [111] direction. (e) The $[\bar{2}\bar{1}\bar{3}]$ direction results from two unit translations in the negative $\mathbf{t}_1$ direction, one unit translation in the negative $\mathbf{t}_2$ direction, and three unit translations in the negative $\mathbf{t}_3$ direction. (f) Coordinate axes labeled according to crystallographic convention.

Since lattices are not necessarily orthogonal nor are translation vectors necessarily equal in magnitude, orientations of lattice planes may be designated with reference to intercepts of any plane with these coordinate axes. Reciprocals of these intercepts of a plane with crystallographic axes constitute the now universally used Miller indices of a plane (singular—index).

Let translation vectors $\mathbf{t}_1$, $\mathbf{t}_2$, $\mathbf{t}_3$ define axial directions **a**, **b**, **c**, not necessarily orthogonal to one another. Let the magnitudes of these vectors, not necessarily equal, define unit distances in each axial direction. Then planes of lattice points have intercepts with each axis at an integral multiple of these unit distances. Reciprocals of intercepts so defined, when cleared of fractions and common factors, constitute Miller indices of a lattice plane (Fig. 3-13).

Rational Indices A two-dimensional net of points illustrates these relationships (Fig. 3-11). Any nonrational line across a net meets a point only coincidently. Rows of points intercept each axis only at integral multiples of point translation. All parallel rows of net points have a common factor both in their intercept values and in reciprocals of these intercepts. Since angles between net rows and, in three dimensions, between lattice planes are of paramount importance according to Steno's first law of crystallography, common factors are removed.

Now form a three-dimensional lattice by setting $\mathbf{t}_3$ at an angle to any net plane. Rows in nets then become traces of planes in a lattice. All planes parallel to $\mathbf{t}_3$ lack a third axial intercept; they intercept $\mathbf{t}_3$ only at infinity. The reciprocal of infinity, however, is zero. Hence, a third index in these Miller indices is zero, and all planes parallel to $\mathbf{t}_3$ have Miller indices ($hk0$). The letters h, k, and ℓ designate general intercept reciprocals when no specific integer is specified. Thus, ($hk\ell$) designates *any* plane in a lattice that has rational intercepts with all three crystallographic axes (Prog. 3-2). A specific lattice plane with axial intercepts of 2, 4, and 8 gives reciprocals of 1/2, 1/4, and 1/8, which, after clearing of fractions through multiplying by 8, give Miller indices of (421). (Note: Do not use any closures other than parentheses to indicate Miller indices of a plane. See Table 3-2.)

In crystal structures and lattices that display a unique three- or sixfold axis of rotation, Bravais' modification of Miller indices describes planes and directions. A closest-packed layer possesses a sixfold axis of rotational symmetry at right angles to it (Fig. 3-14a). Two alternative unit cells completely describe this structure. First, the entire layer may be described by repeating hexagons connecting centers of the six circles that surround a circle. Second, the same area may be "tiled" by a pattern of rhombs (shaded). This second alternative is simpler, contains fewer circles, and requires but two coplanar axes to describe it. The first alternative, however, obviously relates to gross patterns of this two-dimensional arrangement,

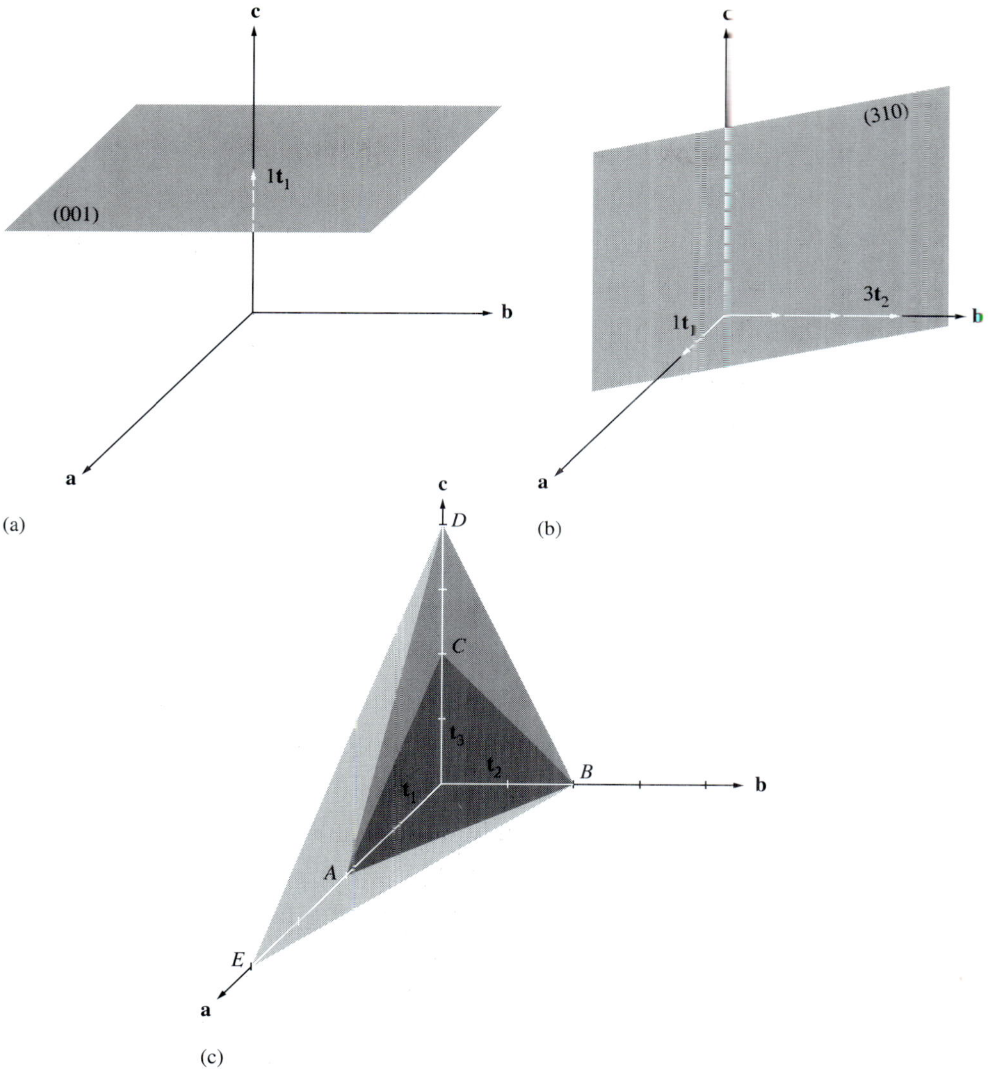

FIGURE 3-13 Miller indices. (a) Plane intercepts **c** axis at unity and **a** and **b** axes at infinity. Intercept reciprocals are $1/\infty$, $1/\infty$, and $1/1$, which invert to Miller indices (001). (b) Plane intercepts **a** axis at $1\mathbf{t}_1$, **b** axis at $3\mathbf{t}_2$, and **c** axis at infinity. Intercept reciprocals are $1/1$, $1/3$, and $1/\infty$, yielding Miller indices (310). (c) Indices of planes: *ABC*, $1/2$, $1/2$, $1/2$ = (111); *ABD*, $1/2$, $1/2$, $1/4$ = (221); and *EBD*, $1/4$, $1/2$, $1/4$ = (121).

TABLE 3-2 Closures for Crystallographic Indices

Individual plane	$(hk\ell)$
Symmetrically related planes (form)	$\{hk\ell\}$
Crystallographic direction	$[uvw]$
Symmetrically related directions	$\langle uvw \rangle$
Location of a point	h,k,ℓ
Bragg X-ray diffraction plane	$hk\ell$

the hexad axis lying at its center (and each corner), and three coplanar coordinate axes, $\mathbf{a}_1$, $\mathbf{a}_2$, and $\mathbf{a}_3$, lying at 120° to one another. (When two or three coordinate axes in the hexagonal and trigonal systems are symmetrically equal in length and differ only in direction, they are labeled **a**.) This book follows the latter convention with its redundant third coplanar axis for better visualization of structures and lattices.

In a three-dimensional lattice with a unique triad or hexad symmetry axis, the **c** axis is orthogonal to the **a** crystallographic plane. A plane with axial intercepts of 1 on $\mathbf{a}_1$ and $\mathbf{a}_2$ must of geometrical necessity intercept $\mathbf{a}_3$ at $-\frac{1}{2}$. This plane, if parallel to **c**, has intercept reciprocals of $\frac{1}{1}$, $\frac{1}{1}$, $-\frac{2}{1}$, and $\frac{1}{\infty}$, which reduce to the Bravais-Miller indices $(11\bar{2}0)$ (Fig. 3-14b). (The sum of the first three integers in Bravais-Miller indices must, of geometrical necessity, equal zero in all cases.)

Intersection of two planar surfaces is a straight line. Therefore, intersection of two lattice planes is a row of points. Such rows of points have directions indicated by $[hk\ell]$ in Miller indices and $[hki\ell]$ in Bravais-Miller indices. For all symmetrically related rows, $\langle hk\ell \rangle$ or $\langle hki\ell \rangle$ designates the resulting zone axes.

Crystal Projections Accurate and meaningful portrayals of three-dimensional objects on two-dimensional paper created no little difficulty in presentation of crystal structures in Chap. 2. Now yet another type of presentation must be introduced to show symmetry relationships and crystal faces in succeeding sections. One presentation that faithfully preserves angular relationships is stereographic projection.

First, surround lattice planes or faces of a crystal to be projected with a spherical shell. Consider, for example, a cube modified by an octahedron and a dodecahedron (Fig. 3-15a, faces *a*, *o*, and *d*, respectively). Project each face normal from the center to this spherical surface where it becomes that face's pole (Prog. 3-3). Polar angles represent interfacial angles, and interfacial angles measured on a crystal are angles of dips between planes (Figs. 3-16, 3-17).

To derive a stereographic projection from a spherical projection, project each pole in the northern hemisphere to the south pole of this

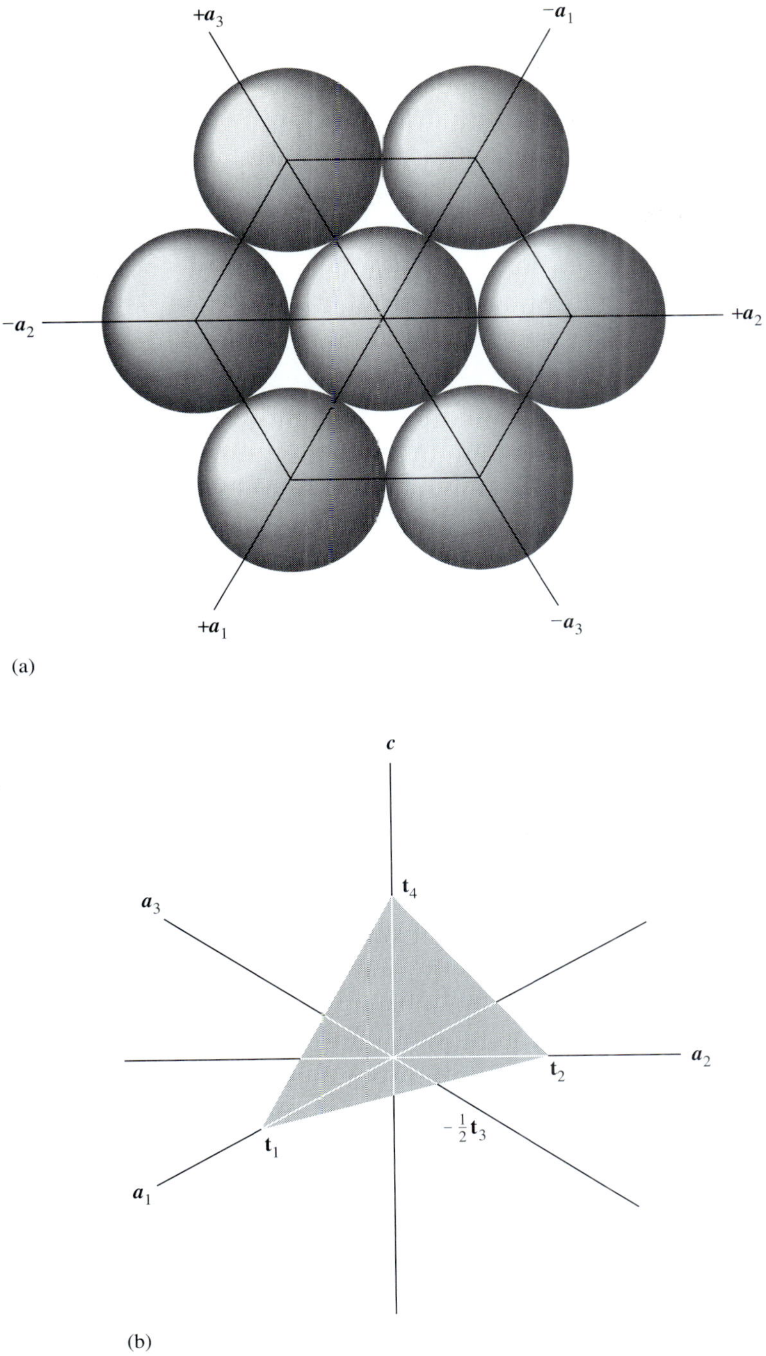

FIGURE 3-14 Directions in trigonal and hexagonal systems. (a) Closest-packed layer with **a** axes labeled. A hexad **c** is normal to the intersection of the **a** axes. (b) Plane $(11\bar{2}1)$ in trigonal and hexagonal coordinates.

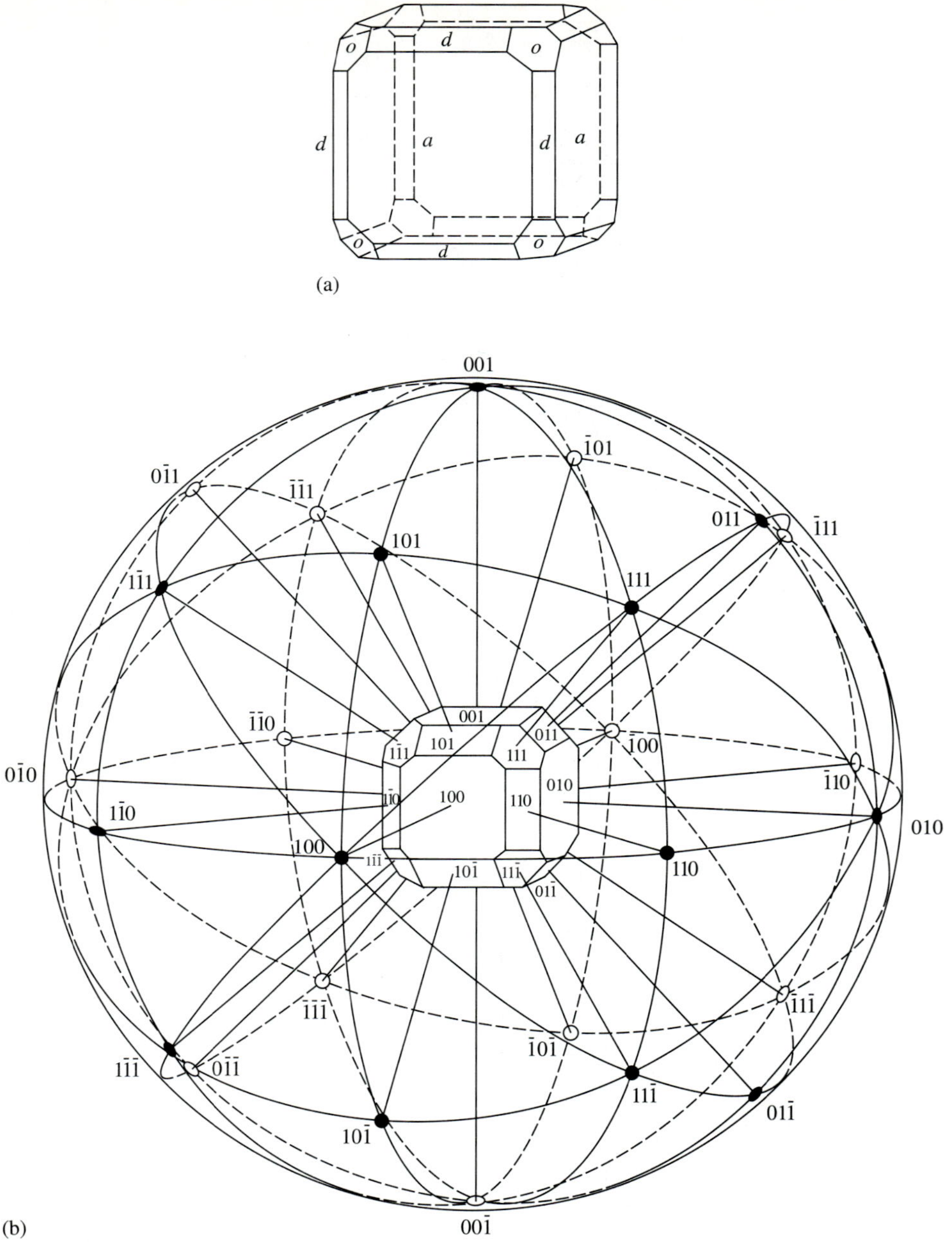

FIGURE 3-15 Spherical projection. (a) Cube *a*, octahedron *o*, and dodecahedron *d*. (b) Poles of crystal faces project as points on the surface of a sphere. (After W. E. Ford, *Dana's Textbook of Mineralogy*. New York: Wiley, 1932.)

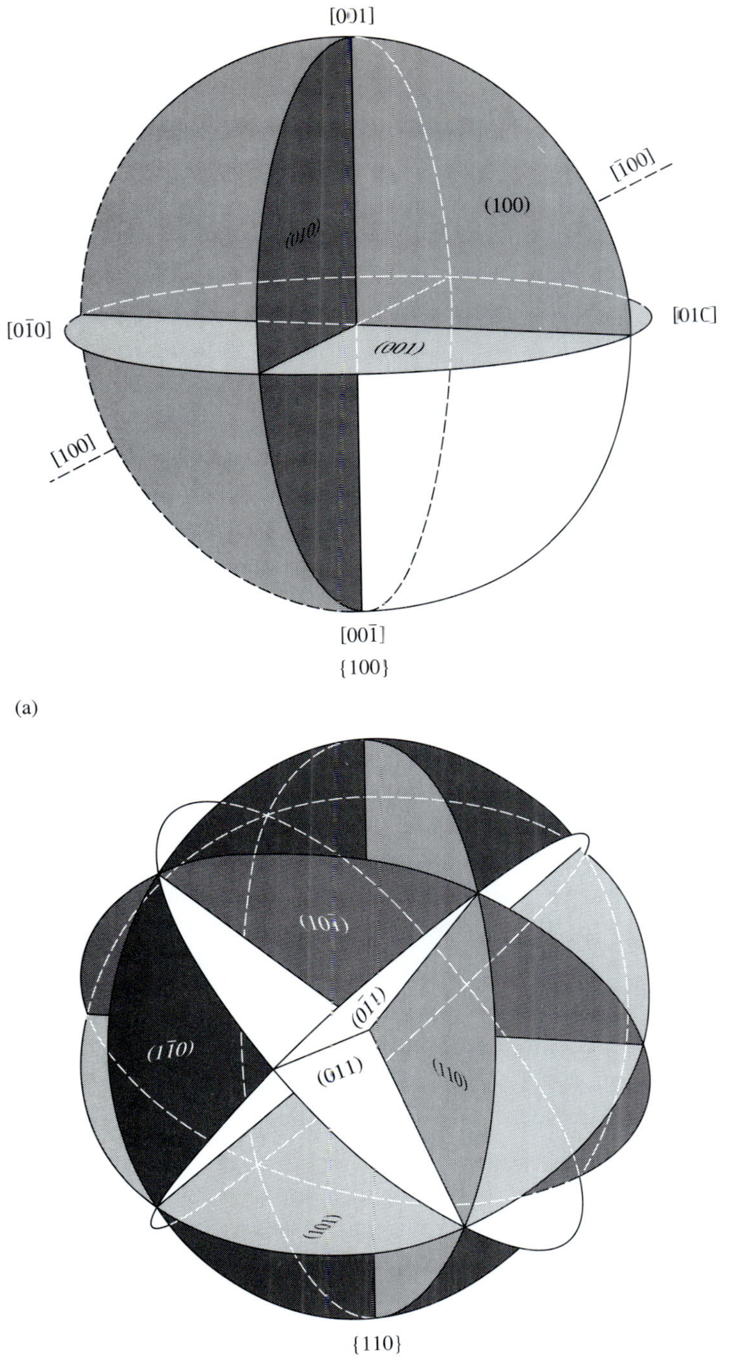

FIGURE 3-16 Spherical projections of crystallographic planes. These planes are so transposed as to place all of them passing through the center of a sphere. Projection of such a plane is a great circle on the sphere's surface. (a) Cube. (b) Dodecahedron.

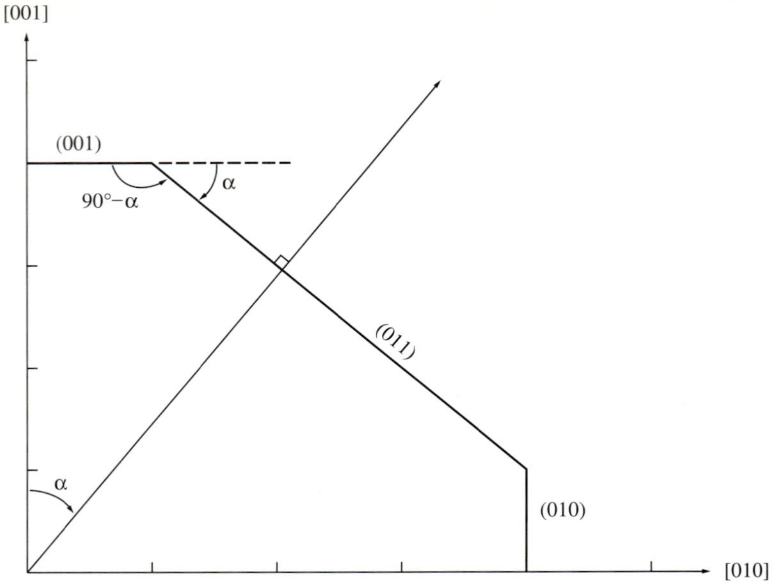

FIGURE 3-17 Relationship between polar angles and planar angles. The angle between two face poles is the same as the external angle of dip and the complement of the internal angle between these faces.

reference sphere, and each pole in the southern hemisphere to the north pole (Fig. 3-18; Prog. 3-4). (Equatorial poles remain fixed.) Intersection between lines of this last projection and the equatorial plane constitute a stereographic projection. All meridians of longitude and parallels of latitude on a reference sphere plot as arcs of circles (or straight lines that are arcs of circles of infinite radius) in stereographic projection. For this reason, crystallographic relationships measured on a crystal may be plotted accurately with a compass and ruler. In practice, however, a Wulff net with lines of longitude and latitude printed at 2° intervals suffices for most crystal-data plotting (Figs. 3-19, 3-20).

3-3 POINT GROUPS

Ten symmetry operations (1, 2, 3, 4, 6, $\bar{1} = i$, $\bar{2} = m$, $\bar{3}$, $\bar{4}$, and $\bar{6}$) have been identified and illustrated within unit cells of various crystal structures (Sec. 3-1). Some unit cells were used to illustrate more than one kind of symmetry operation; hence, more than one kind of symmetry is possible in most unit cells. To show all symmetrical relationships in these unit cells by means of arrows or numbers would be confusingly complex. Hence, we develop new notations.

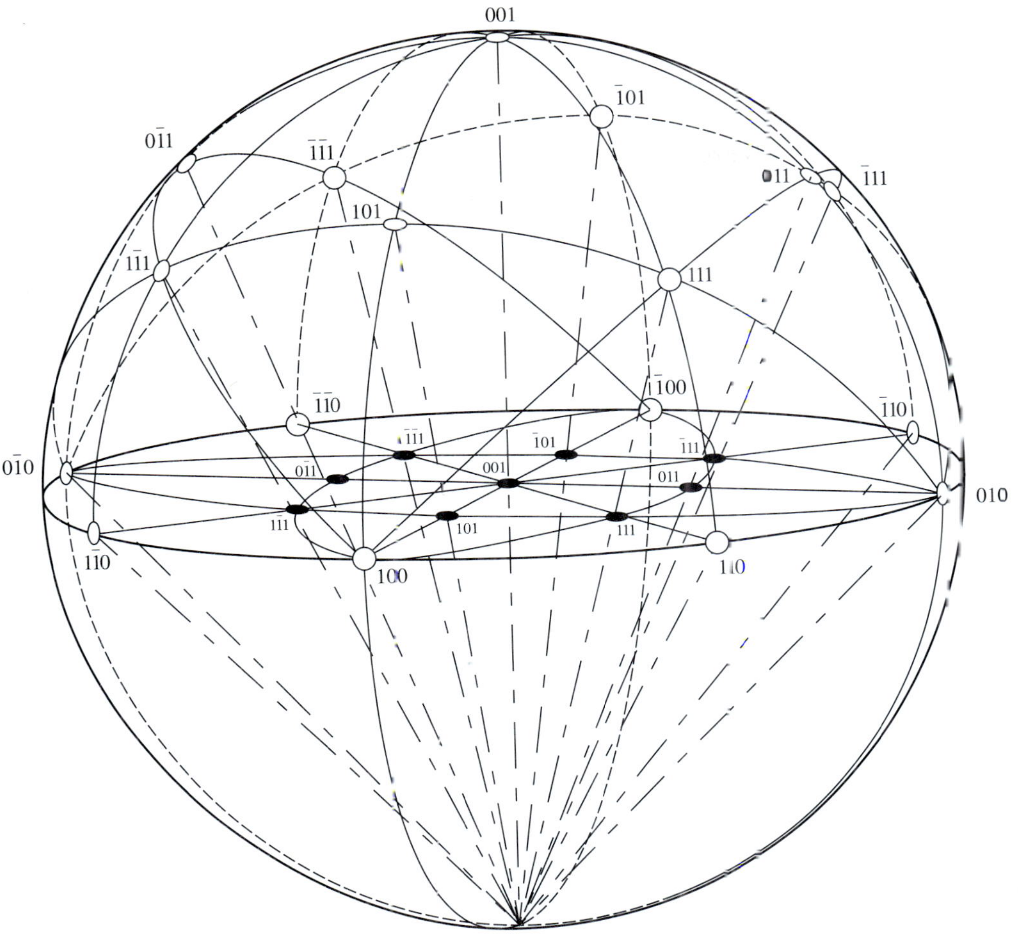

FIGURE 3-18 Relationships between spherical and stereographic projections. Poles in spherical projection project onto the equatorial plane along a line connecting face poles with the south spherical pole. (Poles in the southern hemisphere project onto the equatorial plane by the north spherical pole.)

Elements of Symmetry Symmetry elements, a static concept, can replace a dynamic concept of symmetry operations. A symmetry element is the location of a point, line, or plane around which an operation may be repeated; each symmetry element passes through the center of a unit cell of a lattice or crystal structure. These symmetry elements, singly or in combination, can then plot stereographically on stereograms.

Each symmetry element and combination of symmetry elements simultaneously intersecting in a unit-cell center constitutes a point group.

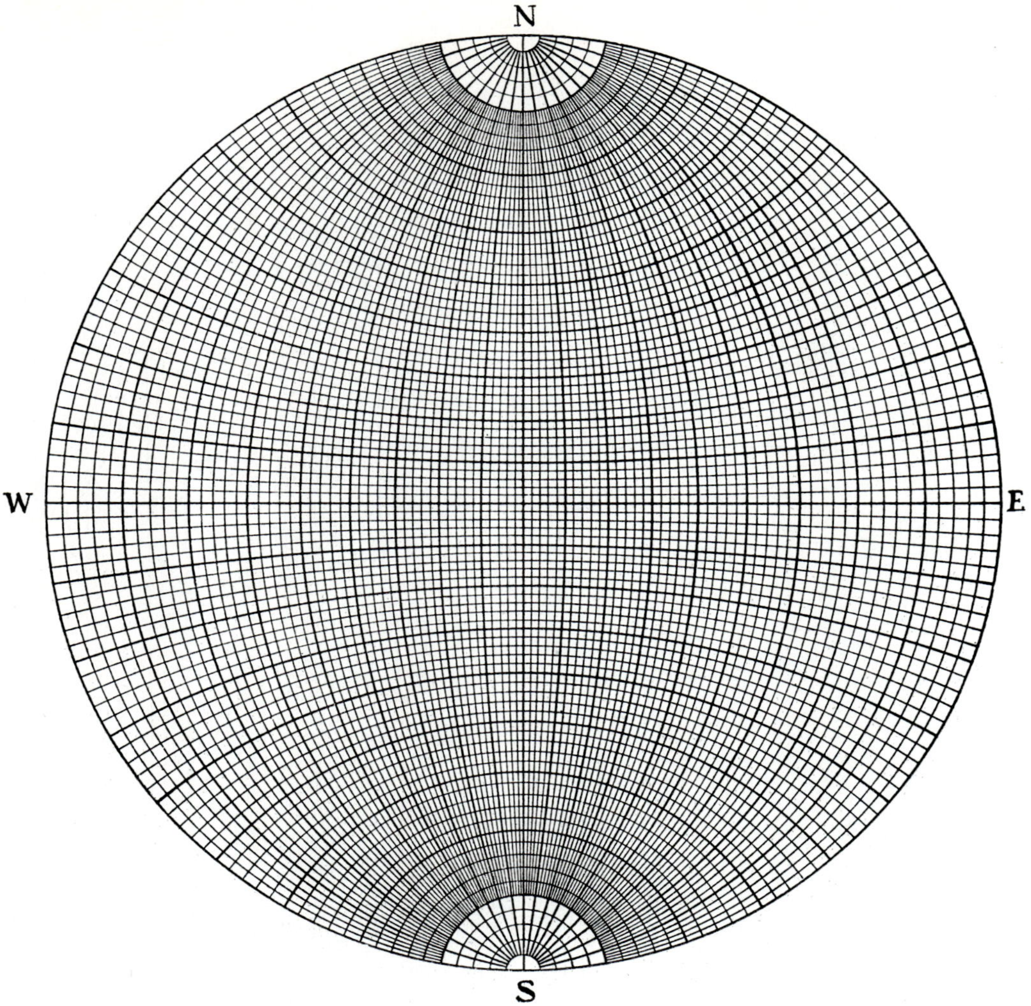

FIGURE 3-19 Wulff net. A Wulff net is a stereographic projection of meridians and parallels at 2° intervals. Note that Wulff net north and south poles are 90° to spherical north and south poles, which plot at center of a Wulff net.

Combinations of symmetry elements, of course, must also be symmetrically arrayed. This geometrical requirement limits the number of point groups to 32. All crystal structures that have the same point group are members of the same crystal class. (Note: A point group is a collection of symmetries; a crystal class connotes those morphological forms admissible by a point group. They are different kinds of things with a one-to-one correspondence. In this book, however, crystal classes are named for their point-group symmetries.)

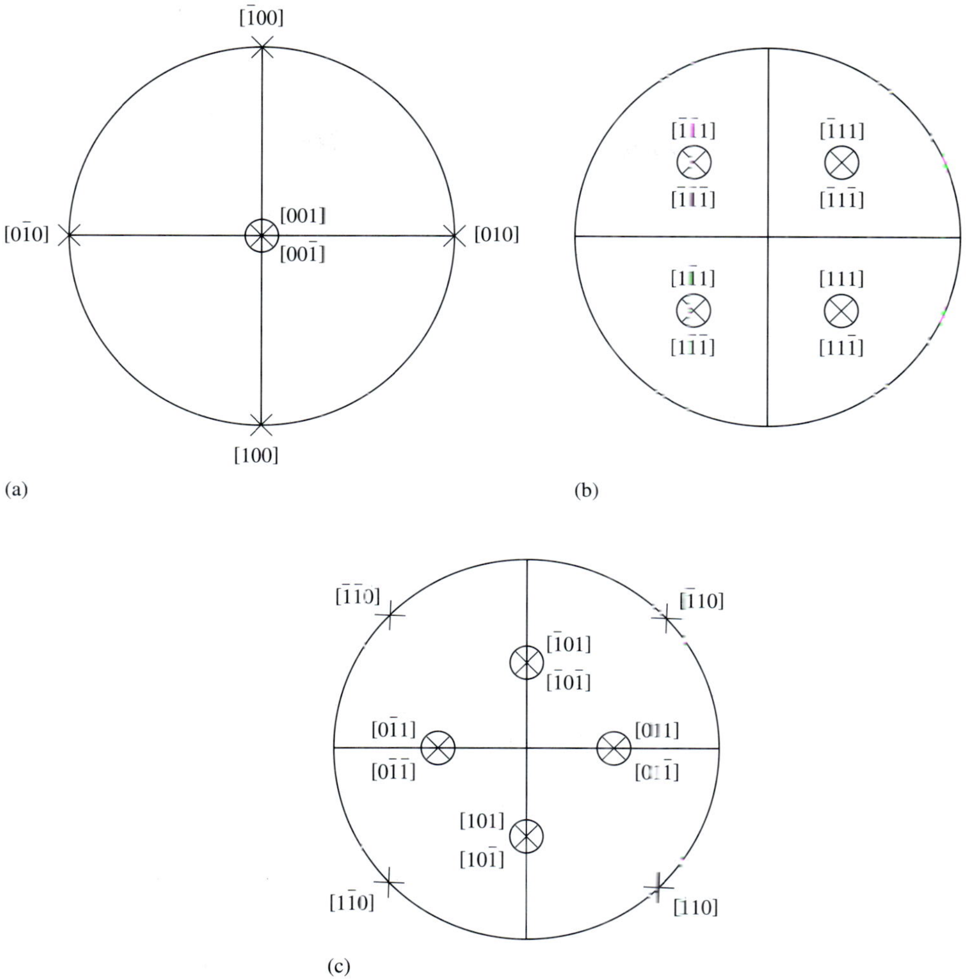

FIGURE 3-20 Stereographic projections. Poles projected from the northern hemisphere plot as × and poles from the southern hemisphere as ○. (a) Cube. (b) Octahedron. (c) Dodecahedron.

Symmetry Elements Combined The 32 crystallographic point groups are set forth systematically in Fig. 3-21. Each row in this figure characterizes specific combinations of symmetry elements, where X and $\bar{X}$ indicate the order of proper and improper rotation axes. (Note again that odd rotoinversion axes have order twice their numerical value.) The symbol $X2$ means a symmetrical set of diads lies at right angles to an X-order axis; Xm indicates a symmetrical set of mirror planes parallel to an X-order axis; X/m indicates a mirror plane normal to an X-order axis; and

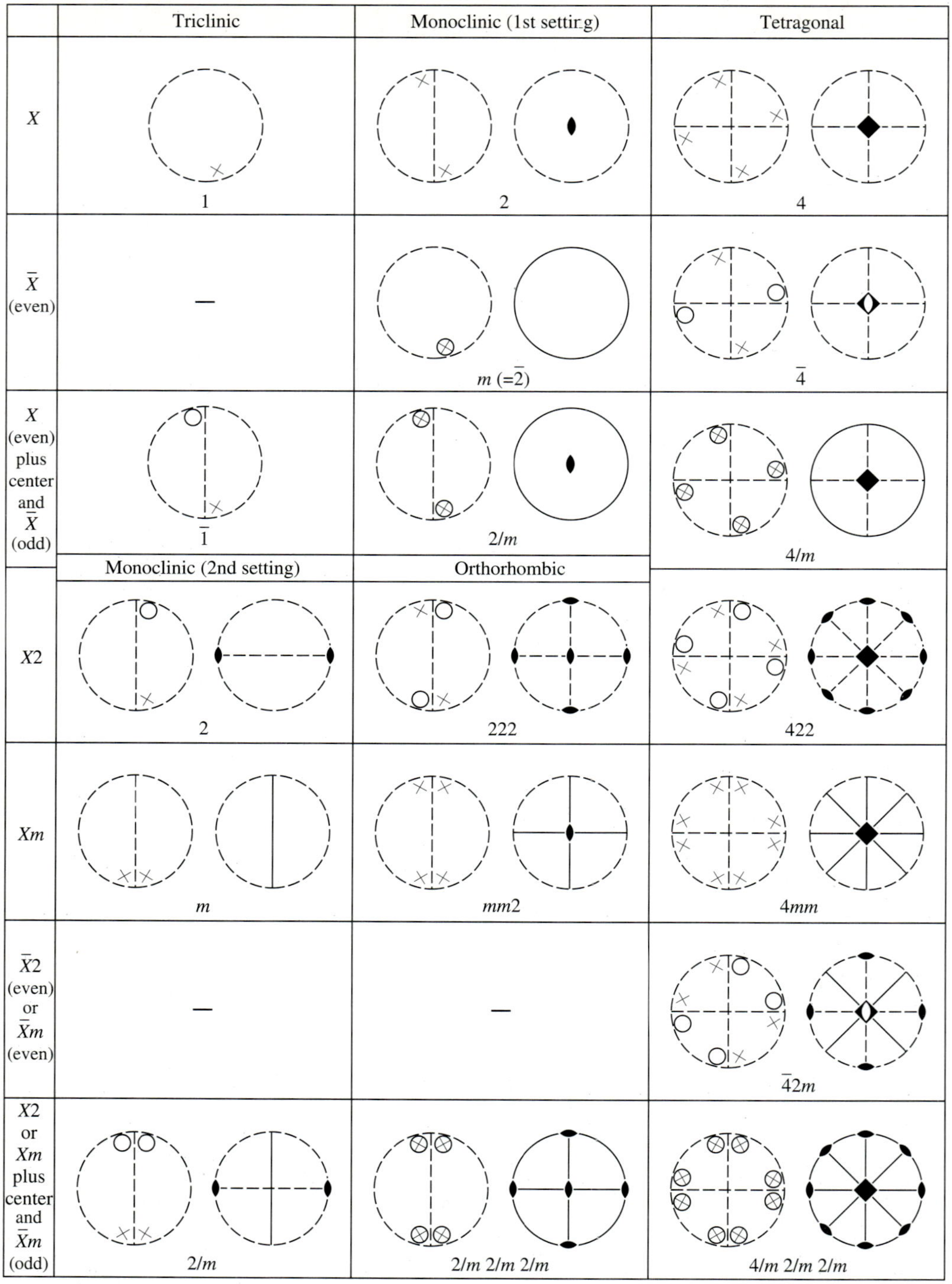

FIGURE 3-21 Point groups. (International Tables for X-ray Crystallography).

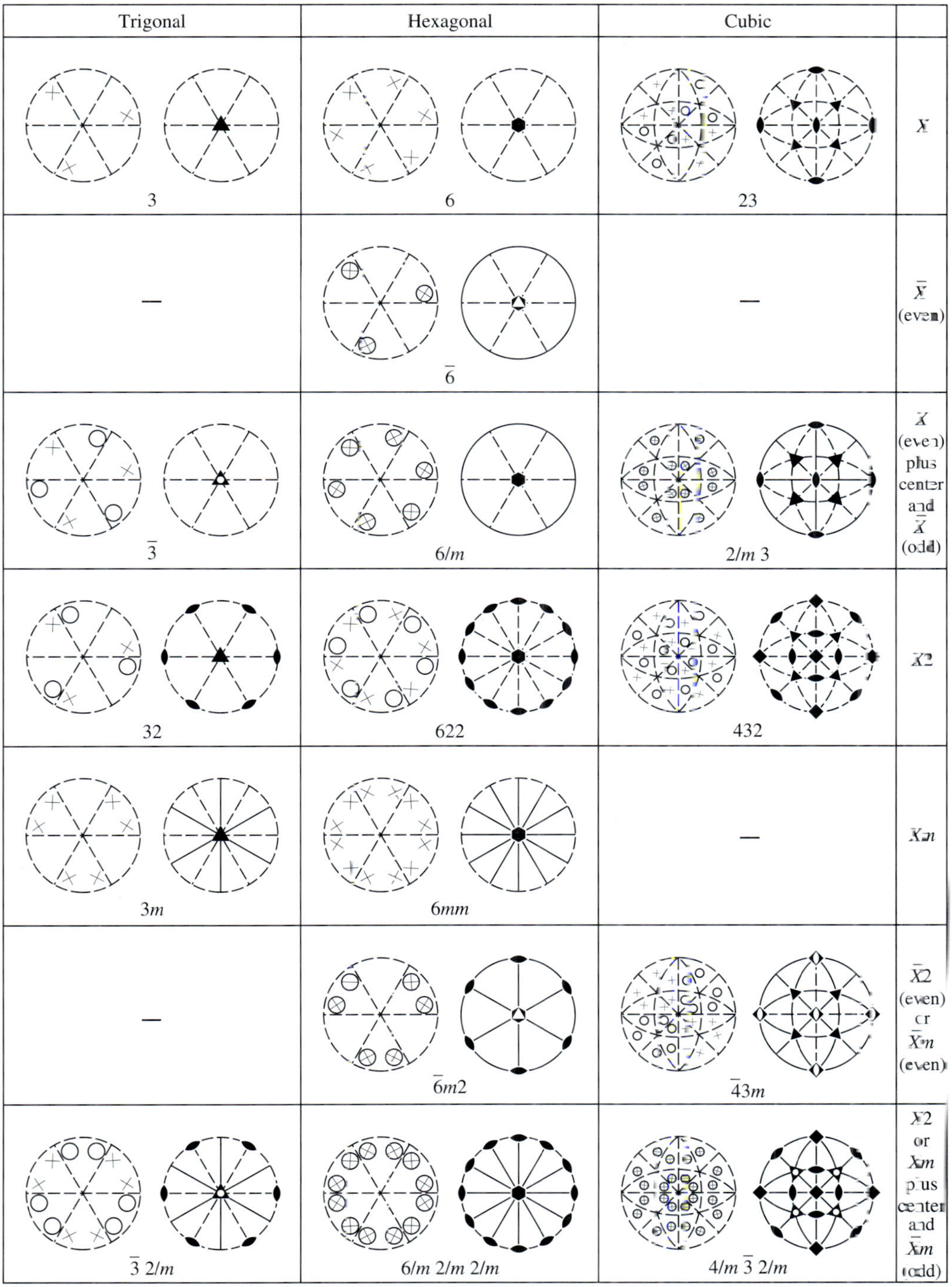

FIGURE 3-21 continued

X/m m signifies both a mirror plane normal to and a symmetrical set parallel to an *X*-order axis.

Each column in Fig. 3-21 refers to the order of the *X*-fold axis—1, 2, 4, 3, 6, and *X*3 (the last meaning four diagonal triads). Thus, each column portrays a crystal system (Sec. 3-6). Each intersection represents a single point group. (Note: Two settings are given for monoclinic symmetry; most mineralogists set the unique diad (remember $m = \bar{2}$) parallel to the **b** axis, which is called the second setting.)

Each point-group intersection contains two stereograms. (By convention, the **a** axis is positive toward the bottom of the page, the **b** axis positive to the right, and the **c** axis positive out of the page.) Each right-hand stereogram shows graphically the symmetry elements of each point group (see Fig. 3-22). No graphic symbol represents a center of symmetry, and its presence or absence must be detected from distributions of other symmetry elements. Each left-hand stereogram shows poles of symmetrically identical general directions (a general pole does not fall on any element of symmetry). Upper-hemisphere poles are indicated by × and lower-hemisphere poles by ○. These poles are generated from any general pole $[hk\ell]$ operated on by all symmetry elements in each point group.

Although generation of symmetrically related poles should be obvious by inspection (Fig. 3-21), step-by-step operation about some elements of symmetry may be instructive. Consider point groups $\bar{3}$, $2/m$, $2/m\ 2/m\ 2/m$, $\bar{3}\ 2/m$, and $4/m\ \bar{3}\ 2/m$ (Figs. 3-23 to 3-27). (Read as bar three; two over em; two over em, two over em, two over em; bar three, two over em; and four over em, bar three, two over em, respectively.)

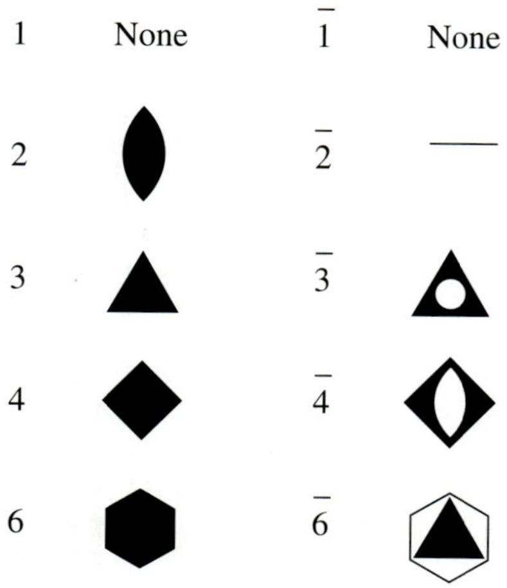

FIGURE 3-22 Graphic representation of symmetry elements.

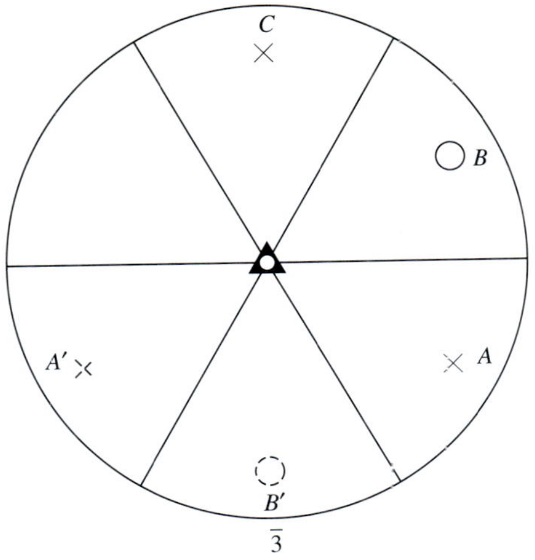

FIGURE 3-23 Operation of $\bar{3}$ is important in its own right as point group for the symmetry of dolomite and ilmenite and as a key element in point group of trigonal and isometric (cubic) minerals. Beginning with a general pole *A* (indicated by a cross), the first operation rotates 120° to a position *A′* and then inverts it through the center to pole *B* (indicated by a circle) in the lower hemisphere. A second rotation of 120° arrives at position *B′*, also in the lower hemisphere, and inversion generates pole *C*. Four remaining $\bar{3}$ operations of this rotoinversion axis to close the group (that is, to arrive back at pole *A*) are left as exercises.

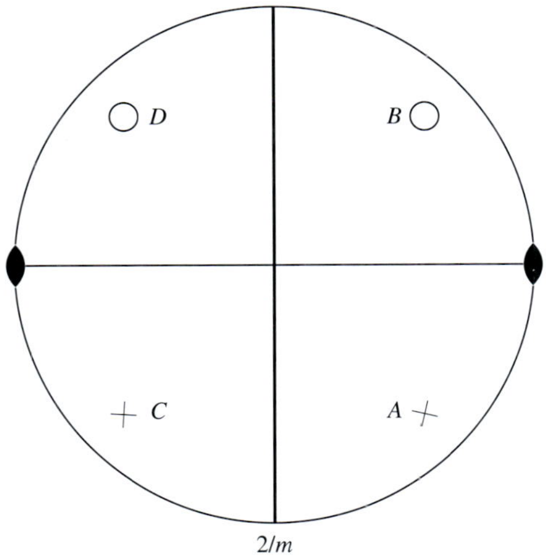

FIGURE 3-24 Since many minerals crystallize with symmetry 2/*m*, this operation is illustrated step by step. Beginning with a pole at *A* in the upper hemisphere, operation of a diad generates pole *B* in the lower hemisphere. Operation of a mirror plane of symmetry on pole *A* generates pole *C* in the upper hemisphere, while pole *B* generates pole *D* in the lower hemisphere. A second operation of the diad exchanges *B* for *A* and *D* for *C*; no new symmetrically related poles are obtained.

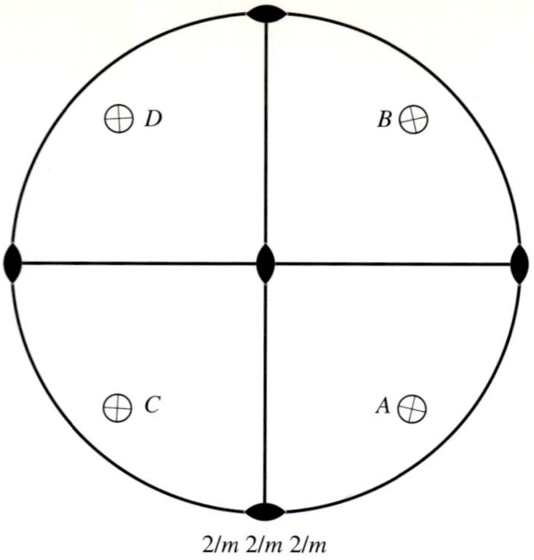

FIGURE 3-25 The identity, $mmm = 2/m\,2/m\,2/m$, may be demonstrated by finding all poles symmetrically related to a general pole A by means of three orthogonal mirror planes and testing a diad to determine if additional poles are generated. East-west m reflects A to B. North-south m reflects A to C and B to D. Horizontal m reflects those four poles to identical graphic poles in the lower hemisphere. Now operation of east-west diad merely relates A above and B below, B above and A below, C above and D below, and D above and C below. Operation of the remaining diads is left as an exercise.

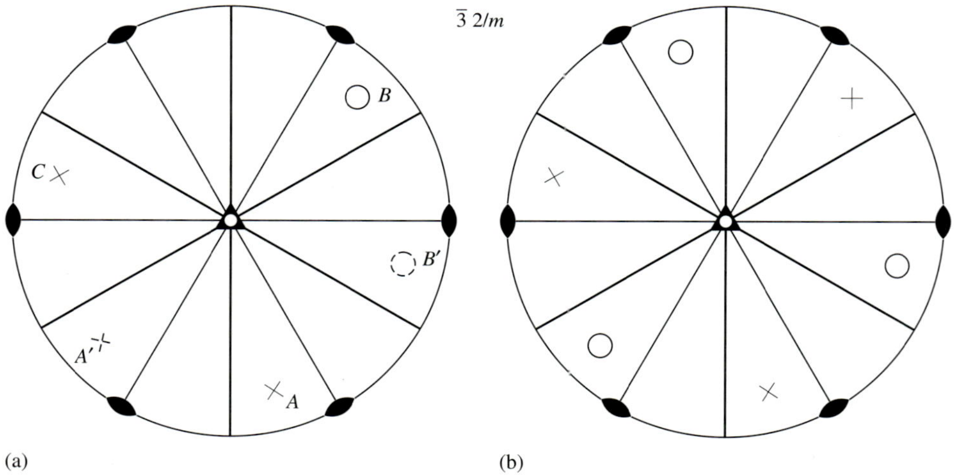

(a) (b)

FIGURE 3-26 Point group $\bar{3}\ 2/m$ contains the symmetry of the all-important calcite group. (a) Beginning with pole A in the upper hemisphere, operate $\bar{3}$ to A', and invert to B in the lower hemisphere. A second operation of $\bar{3}$ rotates to B' which inverts to C in the upper hemisphere. (b) Completion of $\bar{3}$ leads to a distribution of six poles that are not symmetrical either with regard to the twofold axes or to the vertical mirrors. Operation of any of the three symmetrically related mirror planes generates 12 poles as shown in Fig. 3-21.

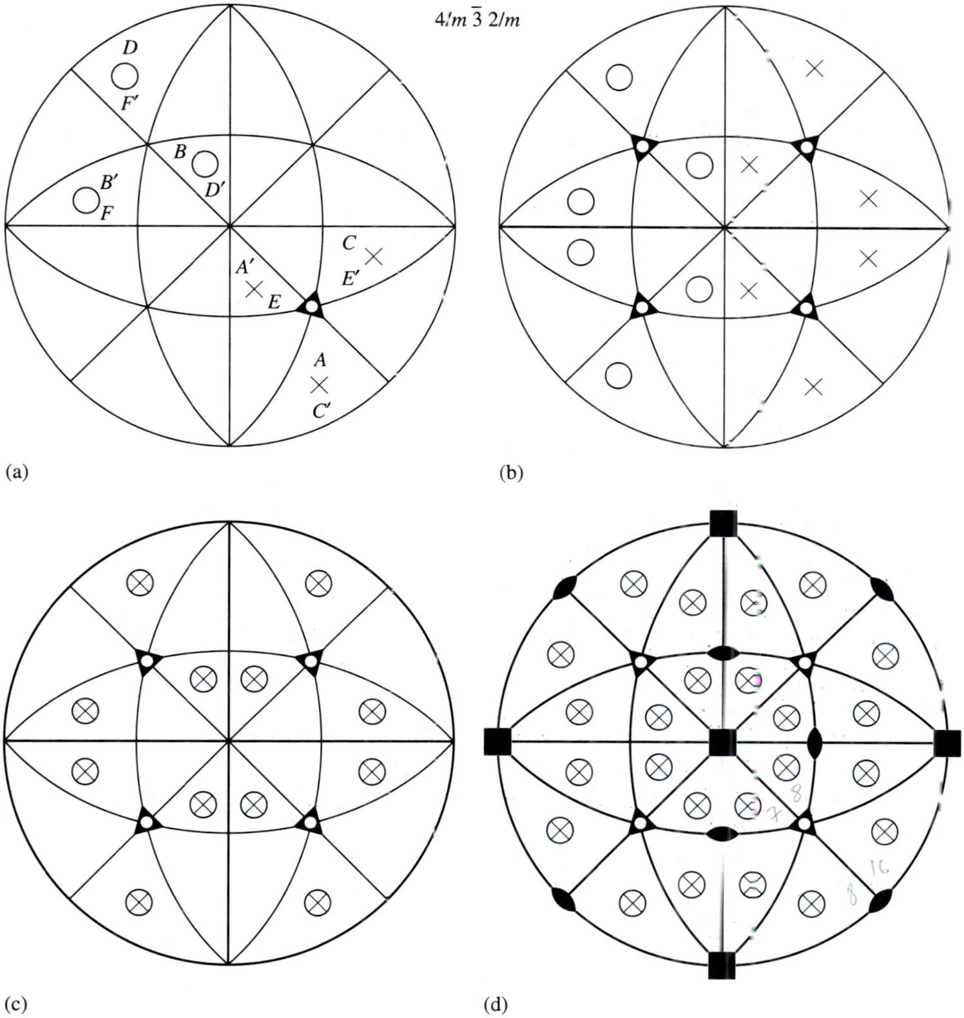

FIGURE 3-27 The most highly symmetric crystallographic point group is $4/m\ \bar{3}\ 2/m$ (= $m3m$). (a) Consider general pole A operated on successively by the rotoinversion triad at [111]. Pole A rotates 120° to A' and inverts through the center to B in the lower hemisphere. Pole B rotates to B' and inverts to C. Continue to pole F, which rotates and inverts back to pole A, generating 6 poles. (b) The east-west vertical mirror doubles the number of poles to 12. (c) The horizontal mirror again doubles the number of poles to 24. (d) Any diagonal mirror then generates the full set of 48 symmetrically related poles and the diads and tetrads.

Symmetrical Structures Crystal structures have symmetry defined by one of these 32 point groups. Thus, X-ray diffraction patterns from minerals will be determined by crystal class, although this pattern itself does not always permit unique assignment of every structure to its class (see Sec. 5-7). A crystal form is a collection of crystal faces made identical by symmetry elements of the point group for a crystal class (see Sec. 3-6). Hence, if appropriate forms are present on a crystal, it may be assigned its correct crystal class. Additional crystal faces may be observed on inner walls of etch pits when a crystal face is corroded by a suitable reagent.

Point-group symmetry also controls optical properties of transparent crystals. Isometric crystal structures are optically isotropic; tetragonal, trigonal, and hexagonal are anisotropic uniaxial; and orthorhombic, monoclinic, and triclinic are anisotropic biaxial (Sec. 5-6). In addition, some crystal structures and their associated point groups permit optical activity. The quartz structure (point group 32) may be described as cross-linked helices of silica tetrahedra (Fig. 2-22). A structure in which tetrahedra climb this helix in the opposite sense is equally probable. Such mirror-image structures are enantiomorphous and can occur only in point groups lacking a center of symmetry. Figure 2-22 represents the crystal structure of right-handed quartz; view this structure with a mirror for left-handed quartz. Plane polarized light traveling up the **c** axis rotates in the opposite sense in right- and left-handed quartz. This rotation of light vectors is optical activity.

Other properties that can exist only in minerals lacking centers of symmetry are pyroelectricity (electric moment produced by heat), piezoelectricity (electric moment produced by pressure), and magnetic moment (Sec. 4-4). Magnetic symmetry need not be the same as structural symmetry, however; magnetite belongs structurally to the centric point group $4/m\ \bar{3}\ 2/m$ but magnetically to the acentric point group 32.

3-4 SPACE LATTICES

Crystal structures are built by infinite repetition (translation) of identical unit cells or asymmetric units in three dimensions. Each atomic particle thus repeats itself periodically throughout a crystal structure. Such periodicity inherently possesses symmetry. If a symmetry element exists in a unit cell, it must also extend through every unit cell along its axis throughout a crystal structure. Hence, point-group symmetries extend throughout crystal structures. In addition symmetry elements other than translation may relate adjacent unit cells. For example, each halite (Fig. 2-2) unit cell is an exact mirror of each neighboring unit cell that is adjacent to each of its six faces.

Point Arrays Every crystal structure has associated with it a Bravais space lattice. A lattice is a three-dimensional array of identically spaced points—an array that is inherently symmetrical. What then are possible symmetries of lattices? Since each lattice point has identical point surroundings, wherever a point is found at u, v, w, a corresponding point must be found at $\bar{u}$, $\bar{v}$, $\bar{w}$. In terms of vectors, if there is a point at $+\mathbf{t}$, there must be an identical point at $-\mathbf{t}$. All lattices are thus centrosymmetric. The 11 centrosymmetric point groups are $\bar{1}$, $2/m$, $2/m\ 2/m\ 2/m$, $4/m$, $4/m\ 2/m\ 2/m$, $\bar{3}$, $\bar{3}\ 2/m$, $6/m$, $6/m\ 2/m\ 2/m$, $2/m\ \bar{3}$, and $4/m\ \bar{3}\ 2/m$.

Because lattice points have no identifiable symmetry (a dimensionless point "looks" the same from any view), each of four pairs of centrosymmetric point groups is dimensionally indistinguishable: $4/m$ and $4/m\ 2/m\ 2/m$, $\bar{3}$ and $\bar{3}\ 2/m$, $6/m$ and $6/m\ 2/m\ 2/m$, and $2/m\ \bar{3}$ and $4/m\ \bar{3}\ 2/m$. Hence, lattice symmetries are possible corresponding to point groups $\bar{1}$, $2/m$, $2/m\ 2/m\ 2/m$, $4/m\ 2/m\ 2/m$, $\bar{3}\ 2/m$, $6/m\ 2/m\ 2/m$, and $4/m\ \bar{3}\ 2/m$. Unit cells of these lattices are primitive in that they have only one lattice point per unit cell. (Each of eight corner lattice points is shared among eight adjacent unit cells.)

In some primitive unit cells, however, major elements of lattice symmetry do not coincide with unit-cell edges. In these cases primitive cells have less symmetry than does a lattice as a whole. In addition, some lattices have orthogonal rows that are not parallel to primitive unit-cell edges. Nonprimitive unit cells, larger than the primitive cell of a lattice and including, therefore, more than one lattice point, conveniently eliminate these problems.

Consider five nets (Fig. 3-28). Four are primitive with one net point per unit cell, but one includes an additional net point at the unit-cell center, giving it a total of two net points. This rectangular nonprimitive net can be referred to as a primitive unit-cell parallelogram (diamond), but edge orthogonality and coincidence of unit-cell edge with net symmetry are both lost. Hence, a rectangular net may be primitive or nonprimitive; nonprimitive unit cells are used in lattices for the same reasons.

Stacking Nets Parallelograms stacked such that $\mathbf{t}_3$ is not at right angles to the plane of this net generates a primitive lattice of symmetry $\bar{1}$ (Fig. 3-29; Prog. 3-5). Stack these parallelograms such that $\mathbf{t}_3$ is at right angles to the net plane to generate a primitive lattice with symmetry $2/m$ (Fig. 3-30a). Now stack these parallelograms such that one point in the second layer is directly over the center of parallelograms of the first layer. A second such $\mathbf{t}_3$ translation brings the third layer directly over the first layer, and a third parallel translation puts the fourth layer directly over the second layer. In this case, an alternative $\mathbf{t}_3^*$ selected at right angles to these nets connects points in the first and third layers and gives this body-centered unit cell the $2/m$ symmetry of the full lattice (Fig. 3-30b).

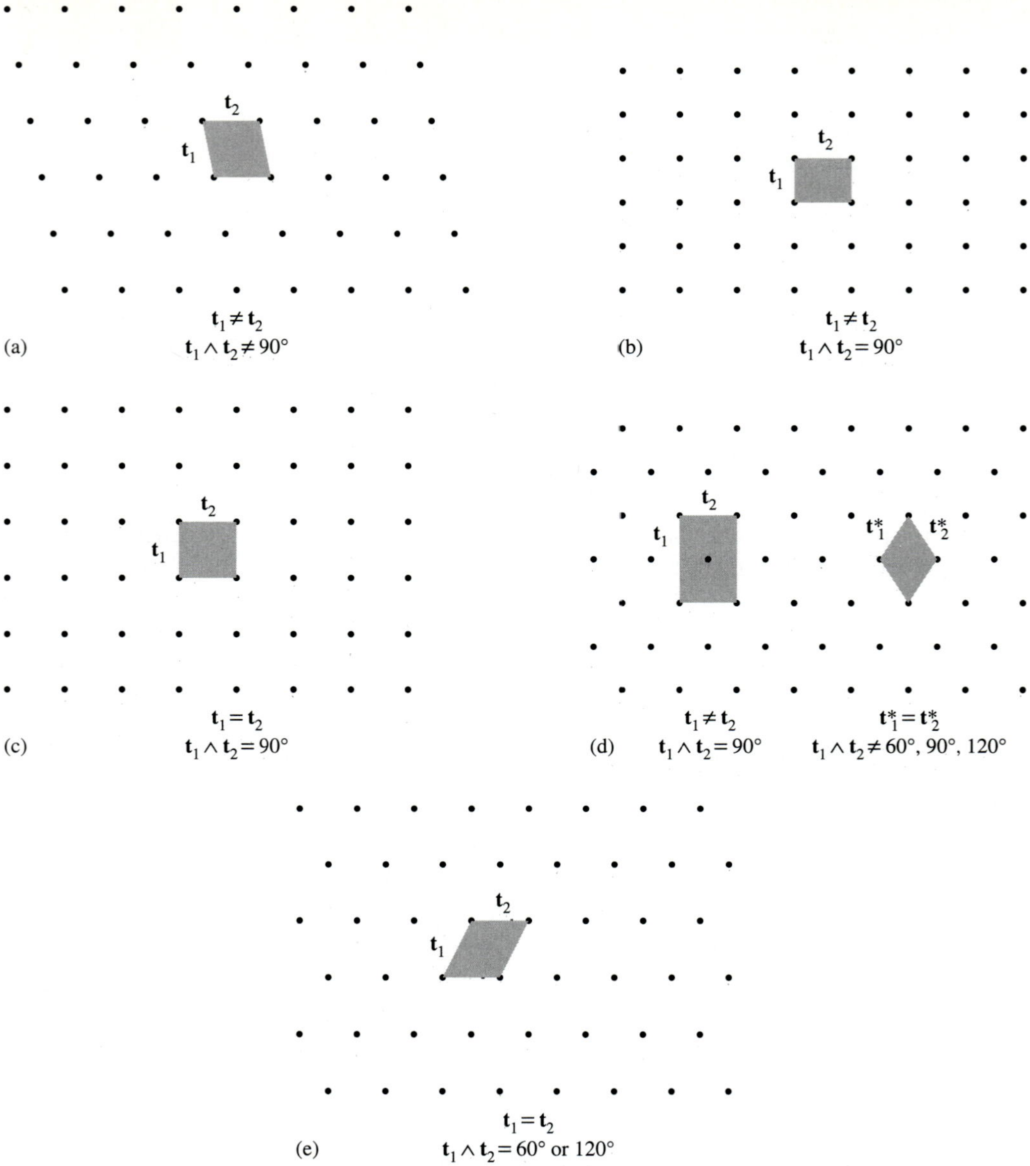

FIGURE 3-28 Five planar nets. (a) Oblique net. (b) Rectangular net. (c) Square net. (d) Centered rectangular (diamond) net. (e) Rhombic net.

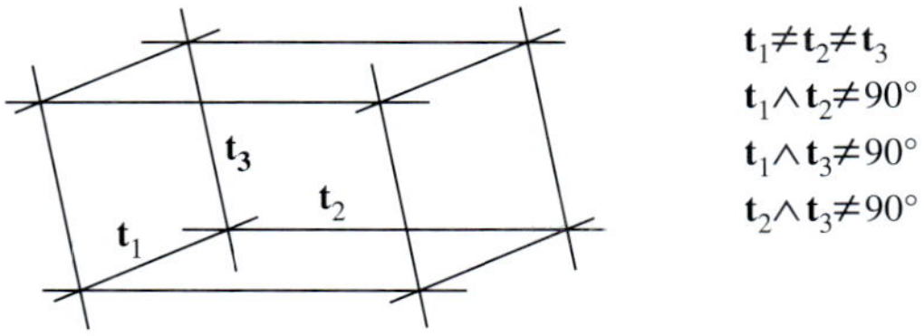

FIGURE 3-29 Triclinic lattice.

Alternatively, a lattice so derived may be assigned an end-centered unit cell. A lattice with symmetry $2/m$ may thus be primitive or nonprimitive.

Next consider possibilities of stacking rectangular nets (Prog 3-5). Set $\mathbf{t}_3$ orthogonal to the net plane with a magnitude different from both $\mathbf{t}_1$ and $\mathbf{t}_2$ to obtain a primitive lattice with symmetry $2/m\ 2/m\ 2/m$ (Fig. 3-31a). Now select $\mathbf{t}_3$ such that lattice points of the second layer are centered over the rectangular net, with the third layer directly over the first, and so on. An alternative $\mathbf{t}_3^*$ connecting first and third layers is at right angles to the net planes, giving a body-centered lattice with symmetry $2/m\ 2/m\ 2/m$ (Fig. 3-31b). Next stack centered rectangular (diamond) nets with an orthogonal $\mathbf{t}_3$ to obtain an end-centered lattice

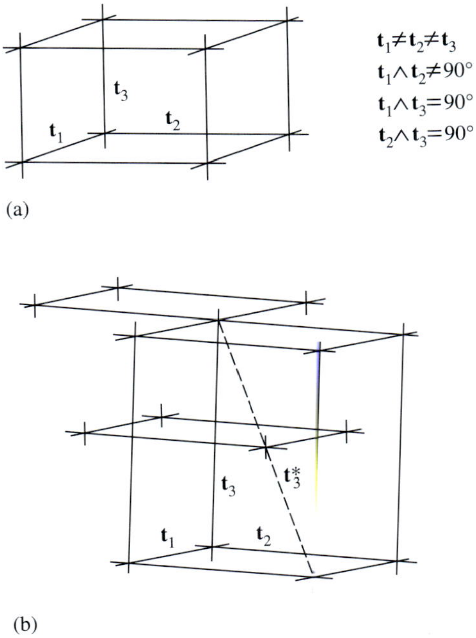

FIGURE 3-30 Monoclinic lattices. (a) Primitive monoclinic lattice. (b) Centered monoclinic lattice.

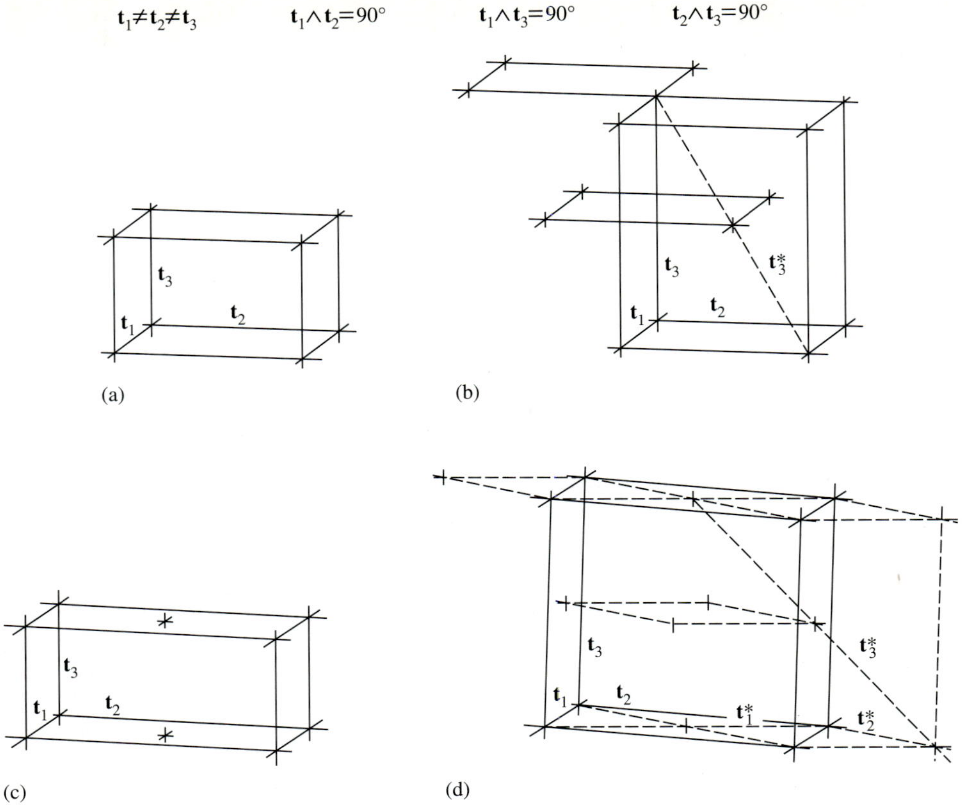

FIGURE 3-31 Orthorhombic lattices. (a) Primitive orthorhombic lattice. (b) Body-centered orthorhombic lattice. (c) End-centered orthorhombic lattice. (d) All-face-centered orthorhombic lattice.

with symmetry $2/m\ 2/m\ 2/m$ (Fig. 3-31c). These end-centered lattices are designated A, B, or C, depending on whether its centered end is in the $\mathbf{t}_1$, $\mathbf{t}_2$, or $\mathbf{t}_3$ direction. Finally, select a $\mathbf{t}_3$ such that points of the second layer of an end-centered rectangular net are over the centers of the primitive diamond net cell of the first layer. A second parallel translation brings the third layer over the first to generate an all-face-centered lattice with an orthogonal $\mathbf{t}_3^*$ and with symmetry $2/m\ 2/m\ 2/m$ (Fig. 3-31d).

Now consider stacking square nets with $\mathbf{t}_3$ not equal to $\mathbf{t}_1$ (Prog. 3-5). Select a $\mathbf{t}_3$ that is orthogonal to points in a square net to generate a primitive lattice with symmetry $4/m\ 2/m\ 2/m$ (Fig. 3-32a). Finally, select a $\mathbf{t}_3$ that puts points of a second layer directly over centers of the first layer. Now an alternative $\mathbf{t}_3^*$ connects the first and third layers orthogonally, giving a body-centered unit cell with symmetry $4/m\ 2/m\ 2/m$

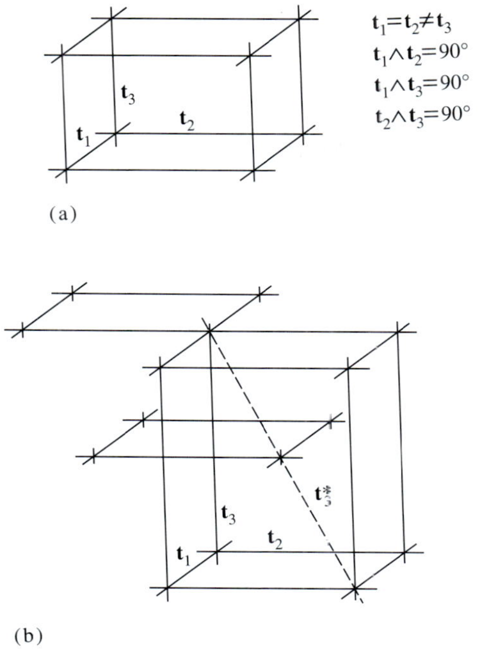

FIGURE 3-32 Tetragonal lattices. (a) Primitive tetragonal lattice. (b) Body-centered tetragonal lattice.

(Fig. 3-32b). Alternatively, use a face-centered square net to derive a face-centered unit cell that represents an identical symmetry.

Select $\mathbf{t}_3$ orthogonal to a rhombic net to obtain a primitive lattice with a unit cell that is a rhombic prism consistent either with symmetry $\bar{3}$ $2/m$ or with $6/m\ 2/m\ 2/m$ (Fig. 3-33a, Prog. 3-5). Another lattice consistent with symmetry $\bar{3}\ 2/m$ (but not with $6/m\ 2/m\ 2/m$) is primitive rhombohedral with three edges **a** of equal length and equal internal angles not equal to 90° between each pair of edges. Alternatively, to obtain a rhombohedral lattice, select $\mathbf{t}_3$ for a rhombic net such that its projection bisects the acute angle of the net and ends ⅓ along that long diagonal. A second $\mathbf{t}_3$ then places a point of a third layer at ⅔ along that long diagonal, and a third $\mathbf{t}_3$ puts a fourth layer over the first. Now select $\mathbf{t}_3$ to connect orthogonally the first and fourth layers to obtain the same rhombohedral lattice, but now described by a nonprimitive rhombic-prism unit cell (Fig. 3-33b).

Stack primitive square nets such that $\mathbf{t}_3$ is equal in length to edges of each square and is at right angles to them to obtain a primitive unit cell with symmetry $4/m\ \bar{3}\ 2/m$ (Fig. 3-34a; Prog. 3-5). Now select $\mathbf{t}_3$ to put lattice points of a second layer over square centers of the first layer at a level exactly half the length of a square edge above the first layer. This $\mathbf{t}_3$

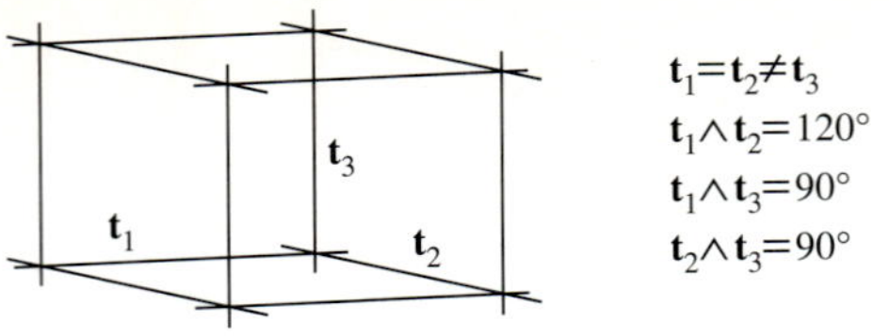

(a)

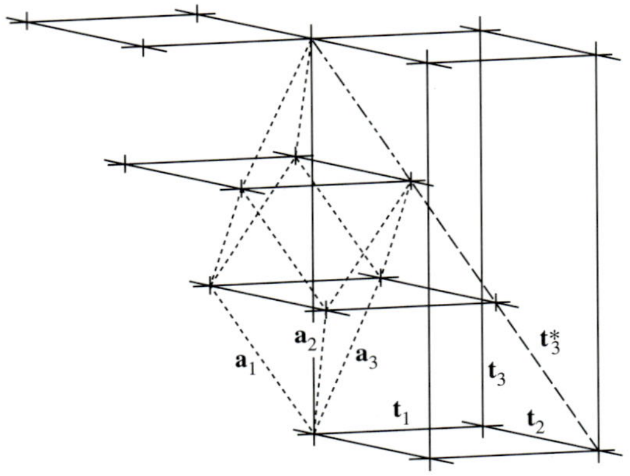

(b)

FIGURE 3-33 Hexagonal and trigonal lattices. (a) Primitive hexagonal or trigonal lattice. (b) Trigonal rhombohedral lattice.

puts points of a third layer directly over those of the first layer. Alternative $\mathbf{t}_3^*$ is now equal in length to square net edge lengths to give a body-centered lattice with symmetry $4/m\ \bar{3}\ 2/m$ (Fig. 3-34b). Finally, stack a centered square lattice with a $\mathbf{t}_3$ that puts points of the second layer above a net edge midway between lattice points of the first layer at a distance of one half a square net edge. A third layer falls directly over the first layer at a distance of one square edge above it to get a lattice and unit cell that is face-centered and has symmetry $4/m\ \bar{3}\ 2/m$ (Fig. 3-34c).

Six primitive lattices are dimensionally distinguishable. In addition, eight nonprimitive lattices may be derived so that unit-cell edges correspond to elements of lattice symmetry and to maximize orthogonality in lattice descriptions. Auguste Bravais, in 1848, demonstrated that these 14, and only these 14, space lattices exist in three-dimensional space. For example, an all-face-centered lattice with symmetry $4/m\ 2/m\ 2/m$ is easily conceived and drawn. But a new unit cell in this lattice that is body-centered may be selected without loss of unit-cell symmetry or orthogonality.

Lattice Parameters For a complete description of a lattice and its associated structure, lengths of translation vectors and angles between

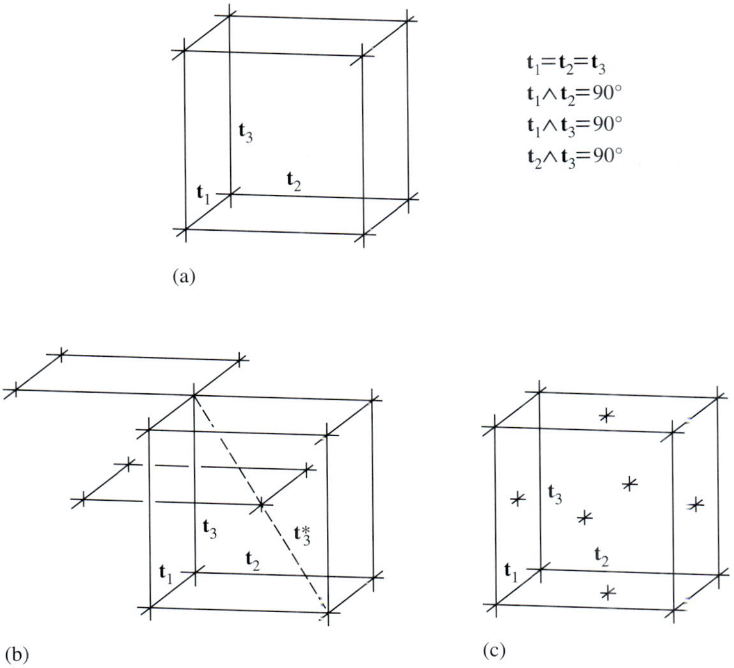

FIGURE 3-34 Isometric lattices. (a) Primitive isometric (cubic) lattice. (b) Body-centered isometric (cubic) lattice. (c) Face-centered isometric (cubic) lattice.

them, where not restricted by symmetry, must have numerical values—their lattice parameters. The three translation vectors are designated **a**, **b**, and **c** (symmetrical equivalency may reduce these to **a** and **c** or to **a**). Angles between translations are α (**b**∧**c**), β (**a**∧**c**), and γ (**a**∧**b**). A lattice with symmetry $\bar{1}$ requires all six parameters for a complete description. At the other extreme, a lattice with symmetry $4/m\ \bar{3}\ 2/m$ requires only the lattice parameter **a**, since all other relationships are restricted by symmetry (see Table 3-3 for other parameters).

A convenient method of designating specific lattice points (or atomic particles) in a unit cell uses translations parallel to unit-cell edges with the lower back left-hand corner commonly designated the origin. In a primitive unit cell, lattice points occur at 0,0,0; 0,0,1; 0,1,0; 1,0,0; 1,1,0; 1,0,1; 0,1,1; and 1,1,1. These numbers represent unit translations along **a**, **b**, and **c**, respectively. An additional point at ½, ½, ½ occurs in body centered lattices. Face-centered points are present at ½,0,½; 1,½,½; ½,½,0; ½,1,½; 0,½,½; and ½,½,1. Any pair of opposite face points represent end centering.

TABLE 3-3 Bravais Lattices

Lattice type	Minimum lattice parameters	Symmetry
Triclinic		
1. Primitive, *P*	*abc* α β γ	$\bar{1}$
Monoclinic		
2. Primitive, *P*	*abc* β	2/*m*
3. End-centered, *C* or *A*		
Orthorhombic		
4. Primitive, *P*	*abc*	2/*m* 2/*m* 2/*m*
5. End-centered, *C*, *B*, or *A*		
6. Body-centered, *I*		
7. Face-centered, *F*		
Hexagonal and rhombohedral		
8. Hexagonal and trigonal, *P*	*ac*	6/*m* 6/*m* 6/*m*, $\bar{3}$ 2/*m*
9. Rhombohedral, *R*	*ac* (a_r, α)	$\bar{3}$ 2/*m*
Tetragonal		
10. Primitive, *P*	*ac*	4/*m* 2/*m* 2/*m*
11. Body-centered, *I*		
Isometric (cubic)		
12. Primitive, *P*	*a*	4/*m* $\bar{3}$ 2/*m*
13. Body-centered, *I*		
14. Face-centered, *F*		

3-5 SPACE GROUPS AND CRYSTAL SYSTEMS

The concept of symmetry, by which the graphic and numerologic descriptions of crystals can be simplified, is central to the descriptions of minerals and their properties. Recognition of symmetry can greatly facilitate mineral recognition. The 14 Bravais space lattices and the 32 point groups were addressed in preceding sections. To recapitulate, a space lattice is a periodic array of points, and a point group contains all elements of symmetry that intersect at a point in space. Space groups result from application of point-group and translating-group symmetry to space lattices.

When symmetry is applied to space, two axial operations combine with translation to relate objects in adjacent unit cells. Since these operations are not restricted to symmetrical identity with a single unit cell, they do not form closed groups. That is, each translation can be repeated infinitely in space.

The first such translation operation is a screw axis of symmetry, which involves rotation about an axis of any allowed order followed by translation parallel to this axis of rotation, the resulting motion being

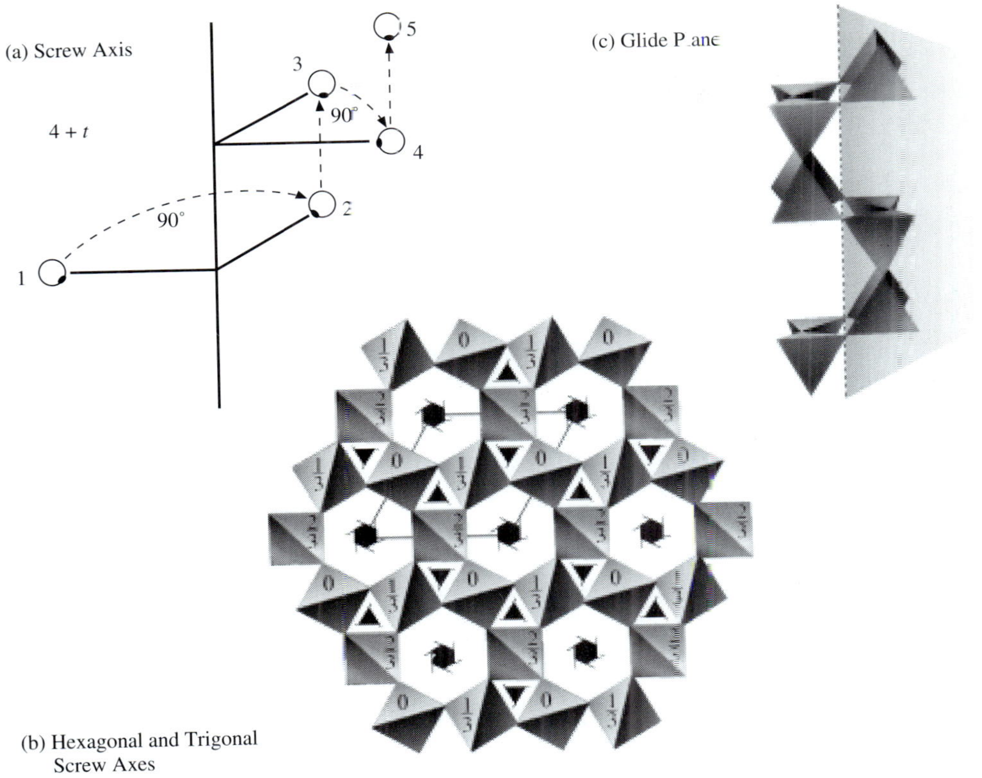

FIGURE 3-35 Combined symmetry operations. (a) Screw axis. A tetrad operation is followed by translation parallel to the rotation axis in steps 1–3. A second operation is shown in steps 3–5. Reflection, inversion, and translation may be combined with monads, diads, triads, and hexads as well. (b) Hexagonal (6_2) and trigonal (3_2) screw axes in quartz structure (compare Fig. 2-22). (c) Glide plane in a feldspar "crankshaft chain" (compare Fig. 2-27a). Translation of one side of shaded glide plane by half a unit-cell dimension permits mirror identity across that plane.

that of a screw (Fig. 3-35a, c). A second is a glide plane, which involves translation followed by reflection across a mirror plane parallel to that translation (Fig. 3-35b, d).

Plane Groups Two plane groups illustrate some properties of space groups (Fig. 3-36). (A plane group is to a space group as a net is to a lattice.) Thick lines represent unit-cell edges, and lattice points occur at the intersections of unit-cell edges. A rectangular plane group has net

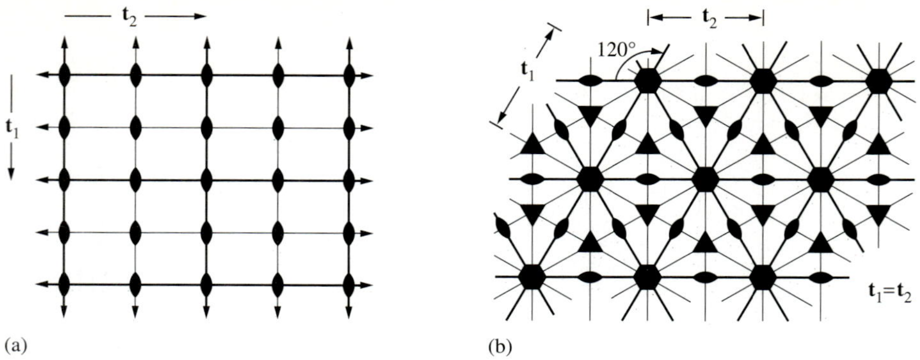

FIGURE 3-36 Two-dimensional plane groups. (a) Rectangular plane group. Heavy lines indicate unit cells that are also mirrors. Light lines are additional mirrors. Almonds indicate twofold rotation axes. Unit translations are orthogonal and unequal. (b) Hexagonal plane group. Lines indicate mirrors; heavy lines outline potential unit cells. Hexagons represent hexads, triangles triads, and almonds diads. Unit translations are equal and at 120°.

translations $\mathbf{t}_1$ and $\mathbf{t}_2$ at right angles and of unequal lengths. Lines connecting net points are mirror lines of symmetry, as are a parallel set of mirrors midway between net points. Each net point is the location of a diad, as are midpoints of unit-cell edges and of each unit cell. Operation of each one of these diads produces an identical net.

A hexagonal plane group has translations $\mathbf{t}_1$ and $\mathbf{t}_2$ of equal magnitude lying at 120°, making each unit cell a rhombus. Heavy lines indicate unit-cell and alternate unit-cell edges; light lines are mirrors. Hexads coincide with each lattice point. Diads coincide with midpoints of unit-cell edges and of the short diagonal of each unit cell (an alternative unit-cell edge $\mathbf{t}_3$). Triads lie midway among any three adjacent diad axes. Two mirror lines of symmetry intersect at each diad, three at each triad, and six at the hexad.

Space groups are similar arrays of symmetry elements, but in three dimensions. A description of the 230 space groups lies beyond the scope of this book, but crystallographic analysis of a mineral is not complete until its space group is determined.

Reading a Space Group Each space group is referred to one point group. In the Hermann-Mauguin notation used by crystallographers, point-group symmetry is inherent in space-group notation. The first letter in a space-group symbol designates lattice type: P = primitive; A, B, and C = end-centered; I = body- (interior) centered; F = all-face-centered; and R = rhombohedral. (Note: Except for R, lattice symmetry is *not* designated by the first letter of a symbol.) Axes of rotation and of rotoinversion are the same in space-group notation as in point-group notation. Subscripts after an axis indicate that it is a screw axis. Glide planes are designated *a*, *b*, *c*, *n*, and *d*.

Assignment of point-group symmetry to a space group may be accomplished by dropping lattice symbols, replacing glide-plane notation by *m*, and dropping subscripts from screw axes. Thus, space groups $C\,2/c$, $Pban$, $I\bar{4}2d$, $P6_3mc$, and $I4_132$ are contained in point groups $2/m$, mmm (= $2/m\;2/m\;2/m$), $\bar{4}2m$, $6mm$, and 432, respectively.

Crystal Systems Each of the 32 point groups and their associated crystal classes, each of the 14 Bravais space lattices, and each of the 230 space groups may be assigned to one of seven crystal systems (Fig. 3-37). This assignment is based on number and order of rotation axes. In each crystal system, one point group has the highest symmetry allowed by the system; it is holohedral (Greek *holos* = complete). All other point groups are merohedral (Greek *meros* = less than) in that they possess less symmetry than the holohedral (sometimes called normal) point group.

If monad (1 or $\bar{1}$) is the highest-order axis of a point group, its associated lattice is referred to a unit cell that is a general parallelopiped. Lattice parameters require lengths of all three unit-cell edges and all three angles between edges. Hence, these two point groups constitute the triclinic crystal system. The triclinic holohedral class has symmetry $\bar{1}$. Its unit cell is generally taken as the smallest primitive parallelopiped with internal angles as close to 90° as possible, but rules for assigning axial labels and angles are beyond the scope of this section (see Buerger, Chap. 9).

Three point groups have a unique diad as a major element of symmetry, $2/m$, 2, m (= $\bar{2}$). Since lattices associated with this symmetry are derived by orthogonal stacking of parallelograms, only three unit-cell dimensions and one internal angle constitute their lattice parameters. Hence, these point groups and lattices constitute the monoclinic crystal system. The unique diad symmetry axis is set as a crystallographic axis. In the first setting, this unique axis is designated **c** in concordance with the rule that **c** defines a unique axis. In the second setting, that used by most mineralogists, the diad is set as **b** with its single nonorthogonal angle designated β. Convention determines **a** and **c** directions (see Buerger, Chap. 9). Symmetry $2/m$ is holohedral.

Point groups consisting of three mutually orthogonal diads ($2/m\;2/m\;2/m$, 222, $mm2$ = $\bar{2}\bar{2}2$) constitute the orthorhombic crystal system. Since angles between unit-cell edges are orthogonal by symmetry, lengths of three unit-cell edges constitute the only needed lattice parameters. In point-group and space-group notation, the first axis is **a** crystallographically, the second **b**, and the third **c**. Conventionally, unit cells are oriented such that **b** > **a** > **c**, permitting most prismatic orthorhombic crystals to be elongated in their **c** direction (see Sec. 7-2). (This convention may be waived to permit

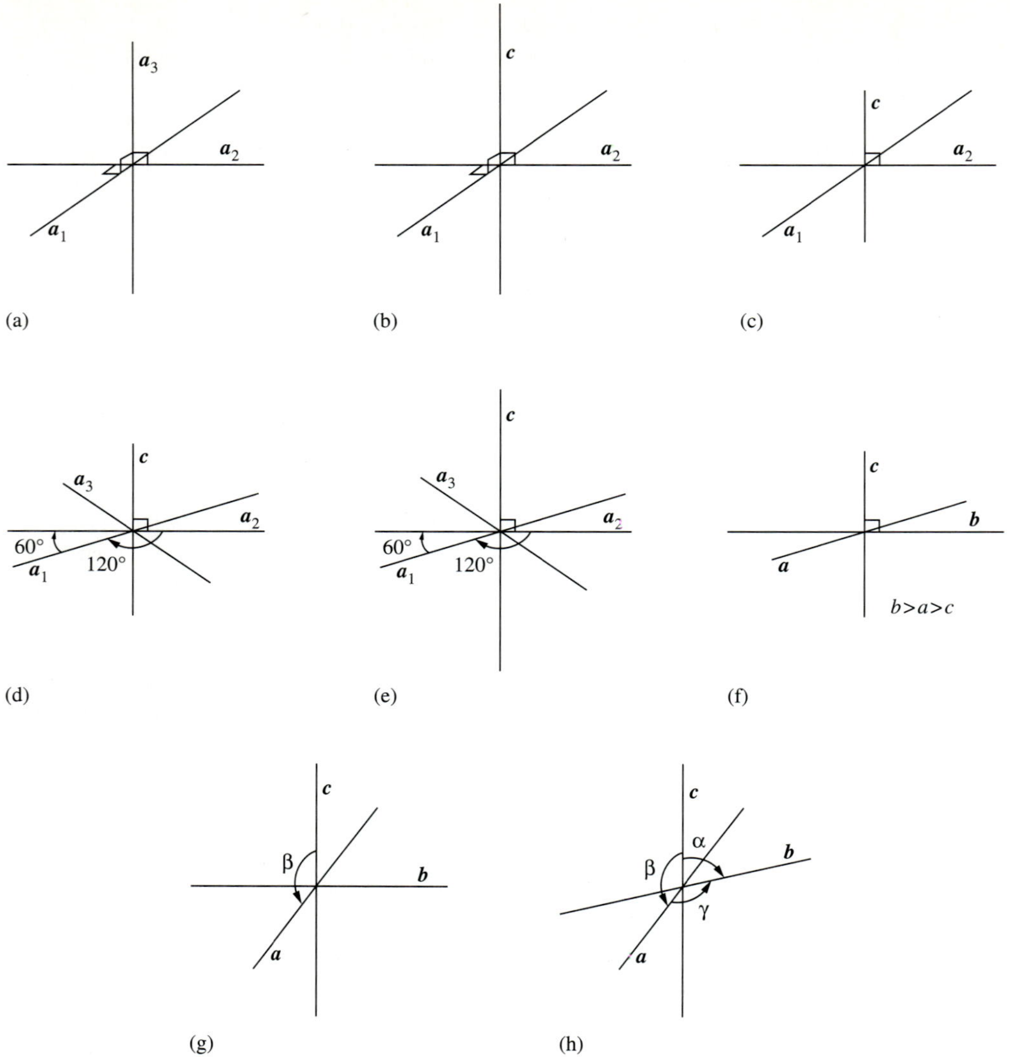

FIGURE 3-37 Reference coordinates for crystal systems. (a) Isometric (cubic) coordinates. All orthogonal axes have the same unit length. (b, c) Tetragonal coordinates. Two orthogonal axes have the same unit length with a third orthogonal axis longer (b) or shorter (c). (d, e) Hexagonal and trigonal axes. Three coplanar axes have the same unit length at 120° and one axis normal to that plane with shorter (d) or longer (e) unit length. (f) Orthorhombic coordinates. Three mutually orthogonal axes of different unit lengths. Axial lengths are conventionally $\mathbf{b} > \mathbf{a} > \mathbf{c}$. (g) Monoclinic coordinates. Three axes of different unit length, two at mutual right angles and one inclined to that plane. (h) Triclinic coordinates. Three axes have different unit lengths and are not mutually orthogonal.

TABLE 3-4 Minimum Symmetry Elements for Each Crystal System

System	Minimum symmetry elements
Isometric (cubic)	Four diagonal triads
Hexagonal	One hexad or rotoinversion hexad
Trigonal	One triad or rotoinversion triad
Tetragonal	One tetrad or rotoinversion tetrad
Orthorhombic	Three perpendicular diads
Monoclinic	One diad or mirror
Triclinic	None

a crystal structure to conform crystallographically with other members of a group having similar structures or for other compelling reasons.)

All point groups with a unique tetrad (4 or $\bar{4}$ see Table 3-4) are assigned to the tetragonal crystal system. The tetrad defines the **c** crystallographic direction with two equal and mutually orthogonal axes, $\mathbf{a}_1$ and $\mathbf{a}_2$, at right angles to **c**. A second element, if present, in a tetragonal point-group symbol designates the symmetry of **a**. A third element refers to symmetry of coplanar axes bisecting the **a** directions. The symmetry $4/m\ 2/m\ 2/m$ is holohedral, and lattice parameters are **c** and **a**.

A unique triad or hexad refers a point group or lattice to the trigonal or hexagonal crystal system, respectively. The unique axis defines crystallographic **c**. Trigonal and hexagonal lattices are derived by orthogonal stacking of 120° rhombic nets, the edges of which define $\mathbf{a}_1$ and $\mathbf{a}_2$ axial directions. Operation of either the triad or the hexad generates a third coplanar $\mathbf{a}_3$ axis. A second element, if present, in a point-group symbol gives symmetry of **a** axes, and a third in the hexagonal crystal system gives symmetry of the three bisectors of **a**. In both systems, lattice parameters are **c** and **a**. The holohedral classes are $\bar{3}\ 2/m$ and $6/m\ 2/m\ 2/m$.

(This simple assignment of all lattices and point groups characterized by a unique triad to the trigonal system and all by a unique hexad to the hexagonal system is not universally followed. Some mineralogists assign all such lattices and point groups to the hexagonal system, which they then divide into hexagonal and trigonal or hexagonal and rhombohedral subsystems.)

All point groups and lattices characterized by four diagonal triads are collected in the isometric (also cubic) crystal system. This system is recognized by the appearance of 3 or $\bar{3}$ as a second element in its point-group symmetry. This diagonal triad provides the minimum symmetry necessary for this crystal system (Table 3-4). The first element in the symbol refers to symmetry of the crystallographic axes, $\mathbf{a}_1$, $\mathbf{a}_2$, and $\mathbf{a}_3$, which symmetry requires to be mutually orthogonal. A third element, if present, refers to six symmetry axes diagonally connecting midpoints of opposite edges of a unit cube. A unique lattice parameter **a** completely defines isometric minerals. The holohedral point group is $4/m\ \bar{3}\ 2/m$.

Each lattice, each point group and associated crystal class, and each space group belongs to one of seven crystal systems. Each mineral species has the symmetry of one of the point groups and is, therefore, a member of a crystal class and crystal system. Considerable inequality exists, however, in the numbers of minerals crystallizing in the 32 crystal classes and in the seven crystal systems (Table 3-5).

3-6 CRYSTAL FORMS

Given adequate time and appropriate physical and chemical conditions, a growing crystal develops crystal faces (see Sec. 7-2). Smooth surfaces have less surface area than rough ones and, therefore, expose fewer ions to high-energy states characteristic of surfaces (see Sec. 4-6). Arrangements at surfaces are generally planes that have a dense packing of ions, as compared with other possible planes in crystals, since more ions per unit area are required to advance that surface by a given distance during crystal growth than for any other surface. Hence, these planes grow more slowly (see Chap. 7).

Crystal Faces Planes that offer densest packing of ions are those that have a rational set of intercepts in an appropriate space lattice (Fig. 3-12). Crystal faces, therefore, have rational intercepts with coordinate axes. Indeed, Miller indices were first derived from observation of crystal faces and crystal forms. It was a century later that these same planes were observed to diffract X rays. Although not all mineral samples have crystal faces, those that do have them permit assignment of minerals to crystal classes.

A crystal form is a set of symmetrically related crystal faces. In any crystal class one or more crystal faces may be equivalent by symmetry operations that define the point group for that class. Conventionally, Miller indices of a crystal face are set in parentheses, such as (001), and a form has the indices of the most positive face set in braces, such as {001} (see Table 3-2). Each crystal class has forms in common with other classes, but most classes have a form or combination of forms unique to that class: the more complicated the symmetry of a class, the more faces that make up a given form.

Open Forms The least symmetrical forms are open forms (Fig. 3-38; Prog. 3-6). Open forms do not by themselves fully enclose space. A pedion

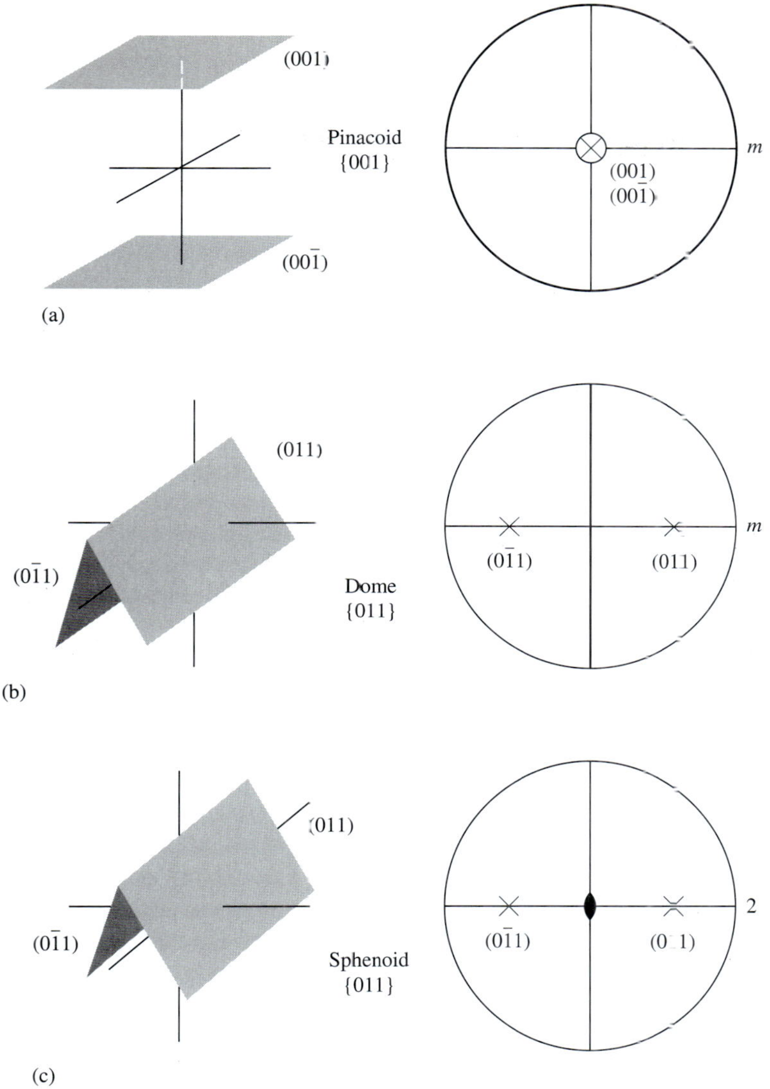

FIGURE 3-38 Open crystal forms. Symmetrically related faces and reference coordinates are shown at left. Name and form index are in the middle. Stereogram and symmetry are to the right. (a) Pinacoid. (b) Dome. (c) Sphenoid.

is a form consisting of only one face and is possible only in crystal classes that lack a center of symmetry. A pinacoid is a form consisting of two parallel faces related by a center of symmetry, by a mirror, or by a diad. A base is a unique pinacoid that intersects only the **c** axis. Sphenoids and hemidomes are two intersecting planes parallel to a crystallographic axis

TABLE 3-5 Common Minerals Classified According to Crystal Class and Percentage of Minerals in Each System

System (percent) class symmetry	Example
Isometric (cubic) (12)	
$4/m\ \bar{3}\ 2/m$	Copper, gold, platinum, iron, argentite, pentlandite, galena, cuprite, uraninite, pyrochlore group, microlite group, halite, sylvite, fluorite, chlorargyrite, bromargyrite, periclase, spinel group, garnet group, high leucite, analcime
$2/m\ \bar{3}$	Pyrite, skutterudite
$\bar{4}/\ 3\ m$	Diamond, sphalerite, lazurite, tetrahedrite, tennantite, sodalite
432	Cuprite
23	High cristobalite
Hexagonal (8)	
$6/m\ 2/m\ 2/m$	Graphite, pyrrhotite, nickeline, covellite, molybdenite, beryl, high tridymite
$6mm$	Wurtzite, zincite, ice
$6/m$	Apatite group
6	Nepheline, cancrinite
622	High quartz
$\bar{6}m2$	—
$\bar{6}$	—
Trigonal (10)	
$\bar{3}\ 2/m$	Arsenic, bismuth, corundum, hematite, brucite, magnesite, calcite group
$3m$	Tourmaline group, millerite, pyrargyrite, proustite
$\bar{3}$	Ilmenite, dolomite, ankerite, willemite, chabazite
32	Low quartz, cinnabar
3	—

Tetragonal (9)	
$4/m\ 2/m\ 2/m$	Rutile, cassiterite, pyrolusite, xenotime, torbernite group, autunite group, zircon, vesuvianite, apophyllite
$4mm$	—
$4/m$	Leucite, scheelite, wulfenite
4	—
$\bar{4}2m$	Bornite, chalcopyrite
422	Low cristobalite
$\bar{4}$	—
Orthorhombic (22)	
$2/m\ 2/m\ 2/m$	Sulfur, stibnite, marcasite, enargite, bournonite, lepidocrocite, boehmite, goethite, chrysoberyl, perovskite, columbite, tantalite, aragonite, strontianite, witherite, cerussite, anhydrite, celestite, barite, anglesite, olivine group, sillimanite, andalusite, topaz, zoisite, lawsonite, orthopyroxene group, orthoamphibole group, cordierite, diaspore, atacamite, carnallite
$mm2$	Chalcocite, hemimorphite, prehnite, natrolite
222	—
Monoclinic (31)	
$2/m$	Arsenopyrite, realgar, orpiment, manganite, romanechite, gibbsite, azurite, malachite, borax, kernite, vivianite, erythrite, annabergite, wolframite, cryolite, gypsum, monazite, lazulite, carnotite, sphene (titanite), clinozoisite, epidote, allanite, clinopyroxene group, clinoamphibole group, talc, pyrophyllite, mica group, chlorite group, kaolinite group, antigorite, clinochrysotile, sanidine, orthoclase, low tridymite, heulandite
2	—
m	Lizardite, antigorite, laumontite
Triclinic (8)	
$\bar{1}$	Amblygonite, turquoise, kyanite, axinite group, chlorite group, wollastonite, pectolite, rhodonite, kaolinite, microcline, plagioclase group
1	—

and related by a diad and a mirror, respectively. A prism has three or more faces enclosing space around the maximum-order axis of a crystal class, but is open-ended. A dome is similar but is open ended in another crystallographic direction. Pyramids intersect the axis of maximum order and one or more others.

Closed Forms Closed forms consist of symmetrically related faces that enclose a volume of space (Prog. 3-6). Disphenoids and bipyramids are closed forms (Fig. 3-39). Faces of trapezohedra are trapezia or quadrilaterals with no parallel edges. Faces of scalenohedra are scalene triangles—triangles with edges all of unequal length.

Some common tetragonal forms are illustrated in Fig. 3-40, some trigonal forms in Fig. 3-41, some hexagonal forms in Fig. 3-42, and isometric forms in Fig. 3-43. Note that all isometric forms are closed because the crystallographic axes $\mathbf{a}_1$, $\mathbf{a}_2$, and $\mathbf{a}_3$ are equivalent. Not all isometric forms occur in all isometric classes (Table 3-6).

Twin Forms Periodically perfect crystals exist only in a mineralogist's mind, and many kinds of chemical and physical defects occur in real minerals. Crystal twinning is a special kind of defect wherein two or more parts of a crystalline material have different orientations that are related by a symmetry element. This element may be a mirror, a glide plane, or an *n*-order rotation axis (Fig. 3-44). A twin element cannot belong to the point group of its crystal class, but generally it is one that is as angularly close as possible for a crystal structure. A twinned crystal may mimic a form of higher symmetry than it possesses internally and, thus, show pseudosymmetry. Merohedral crystal structures are commonly twinned.

Different kinds of twins develop by different means. Growth twins result when an adatom (see Sec. 7-1) takes up a slightly higher energy site on an accreting crystal face and thereby forces succeeding adatoms to follow suit. Transformation twinning results from polymorphic inversion through a phase transition (see Sec. 1-7). Generally, high-temperature polymorphs have higher symmetry than low-temperature ones. If high symmetry can be lost in more than one direction of structural change, different parts of a crystal may nucleate lower symmetry in different ways. A low-temperature polymorph then contains more than one geometry of inversion. For example, when high quartz (class 622) inverts to low quartz (class 32) at 573°C, different volumes of a single crystal nucleate this inversion simultaneously, resulting in quartz twinned according to the Dauphiné law. Glide twins result from mechanical deformation. Deformed calcite develops glide twinning across the $(01\bar{1}2)$ plane.

Contact twins have between them a common composition plane. In centric classes, this reflection across a composition plane is geometrically equivalent to a diad normal to the composition plane. An apparent twin axis need not be a rational direction in the monoclinic and triclinic crystal

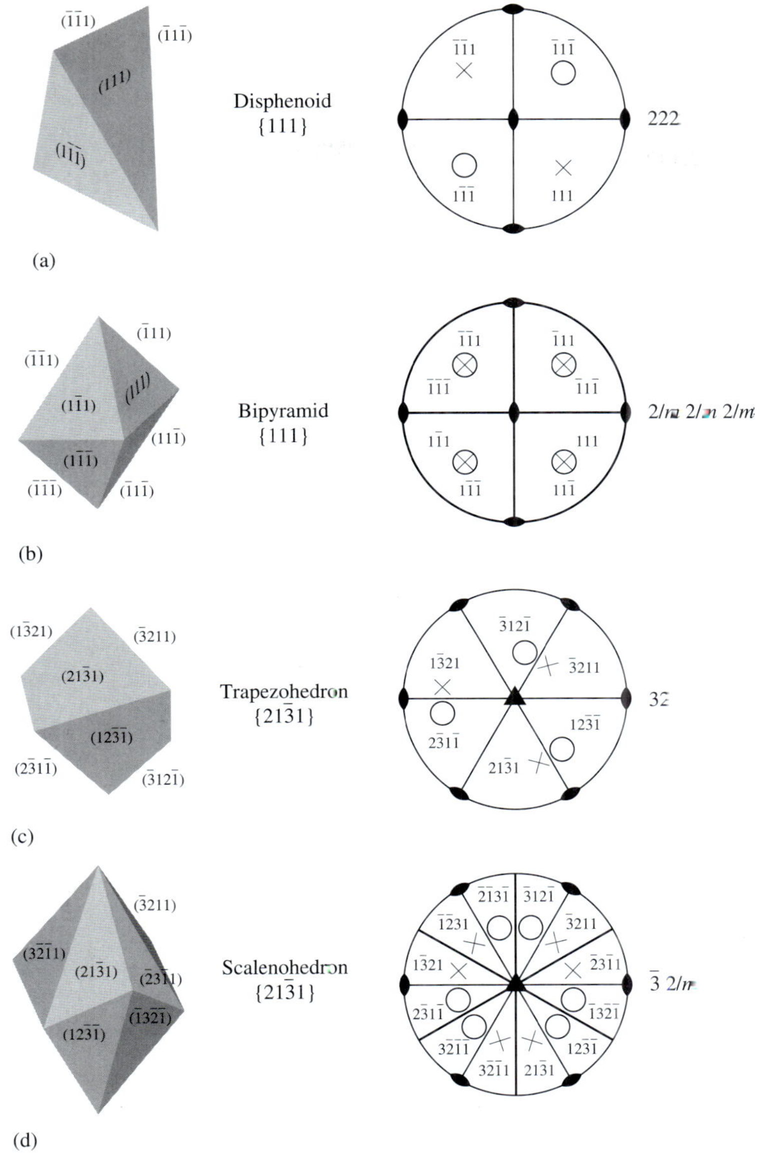

FIGURE 3-39 Closed crystal forms (notation as in Fig. 3-38). (a) Disphenoid. (b) Bipyramid. (c) Trapezohedron. (d) Scalenohedron.

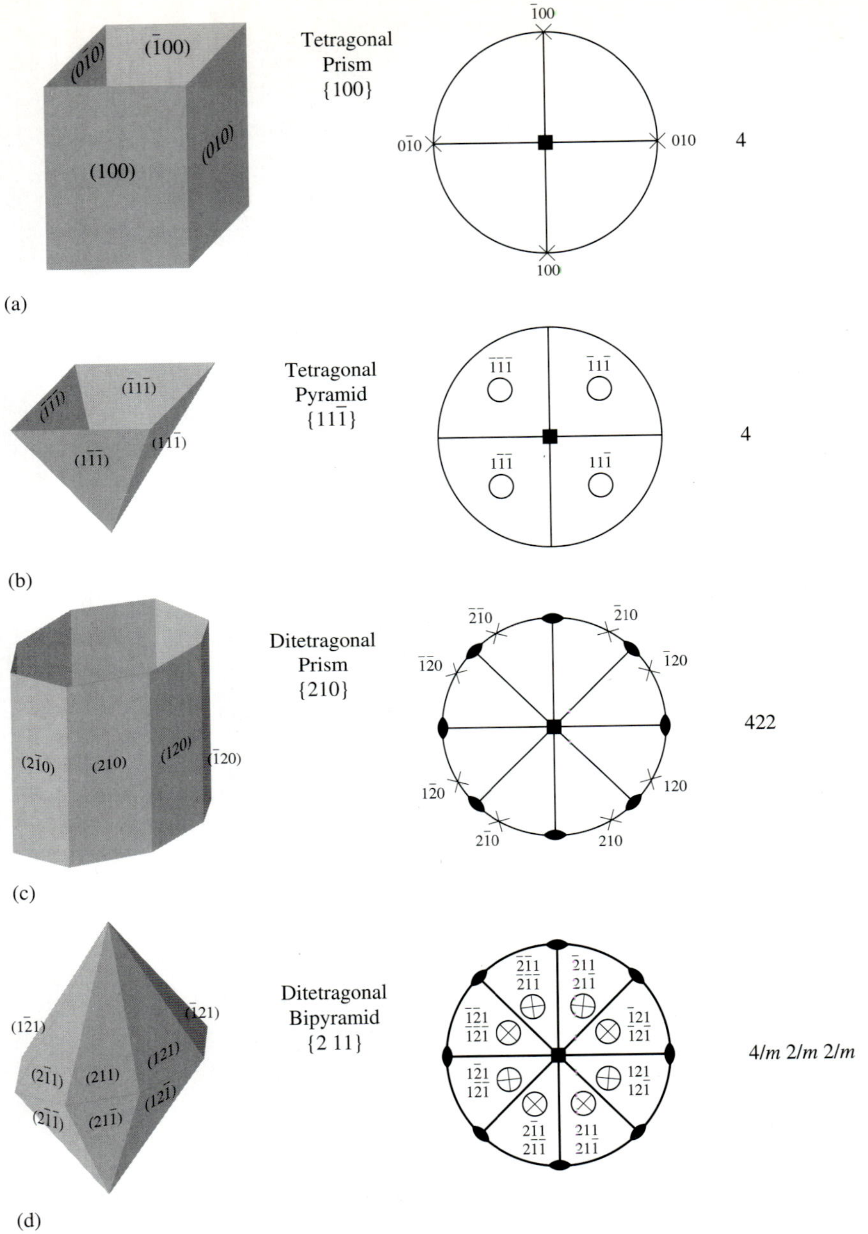

FIGURE 3-40 Tetragonal forms (notation as in Fig. 3-38). (a) Second-order tetragonal prism. (b) First-order tetragonal pyramid. (c) Ditetragonal prism. (d) Ditetragonal bipyramid.

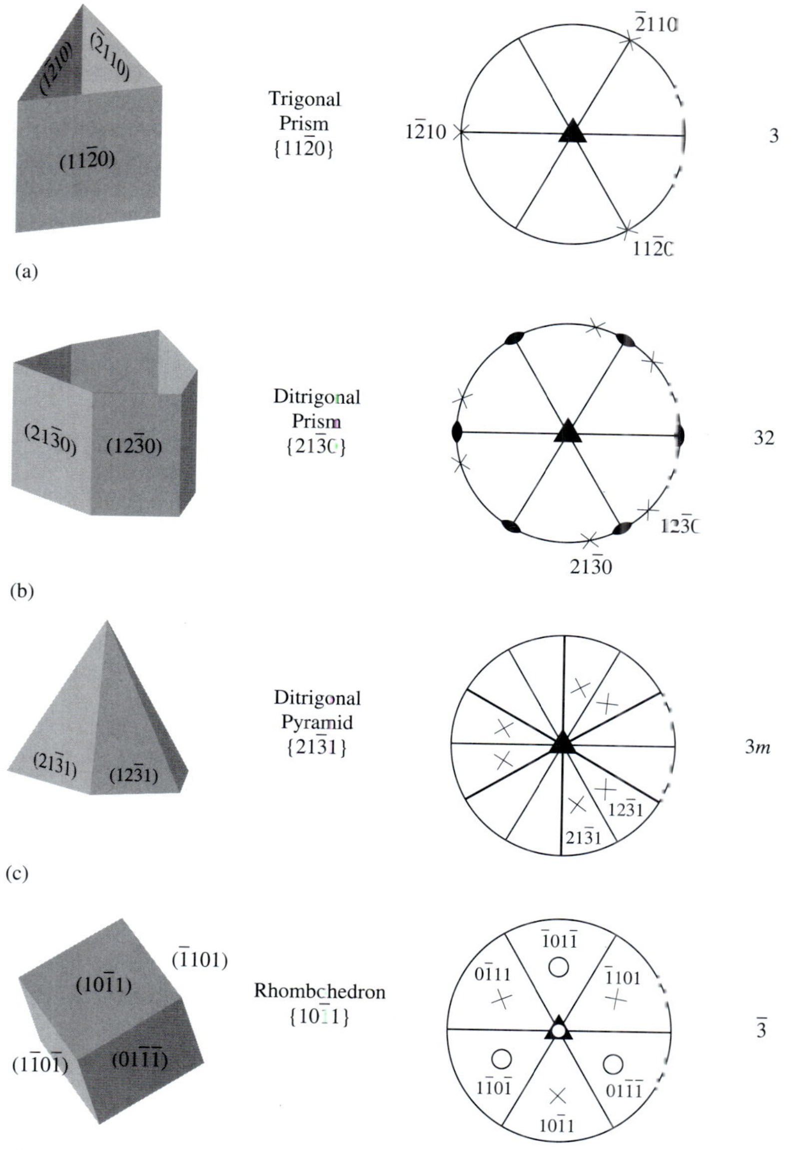

FIGURE 3-41 **Trigonal forms (notation as in Fig. 3-38). (a) Trigonal prism. (b) Ditrigonal prism. (c) Ditrigonal pyramid. (d) Rhombohedron.**

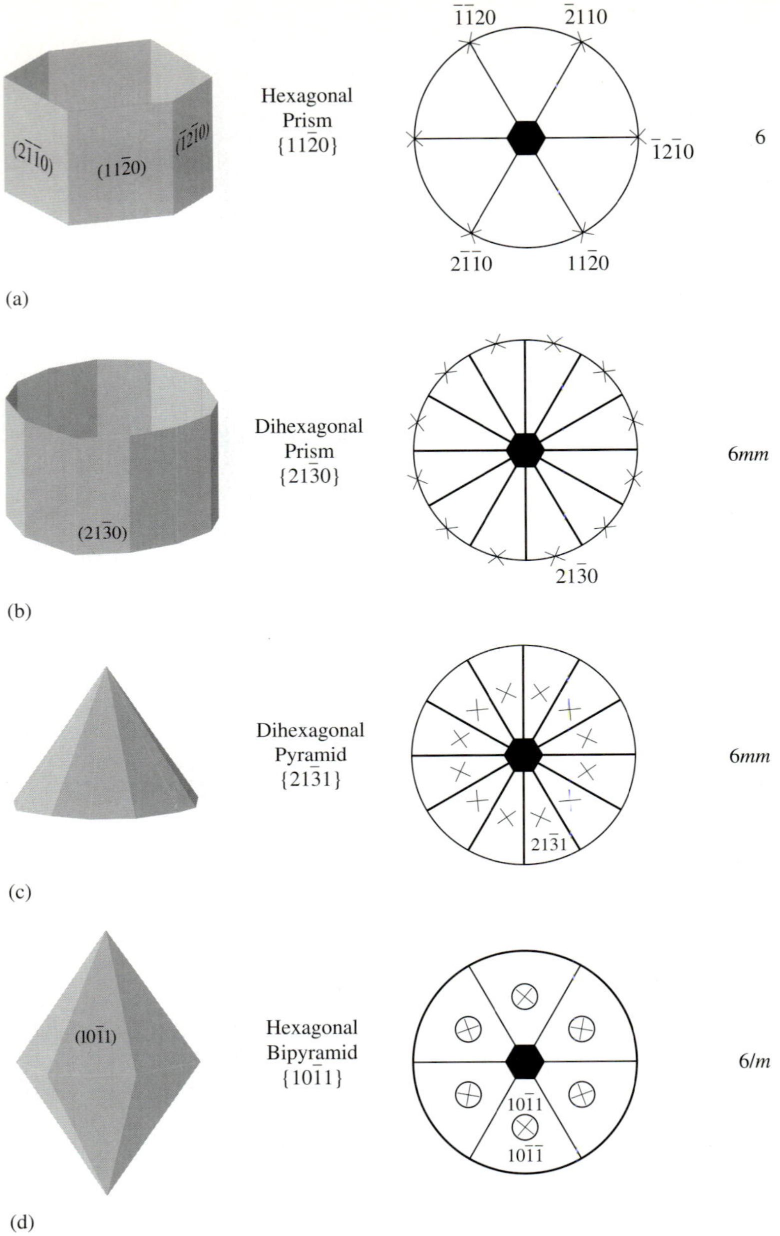

FIGURE 3-42 Hexagonal forms (notation as in Fig. 3-38). (a) Hexagonal prism. (b) Dihexagonal prism. (c) Dihexagonal pyramid. (d) Hexagonal bipyramid.

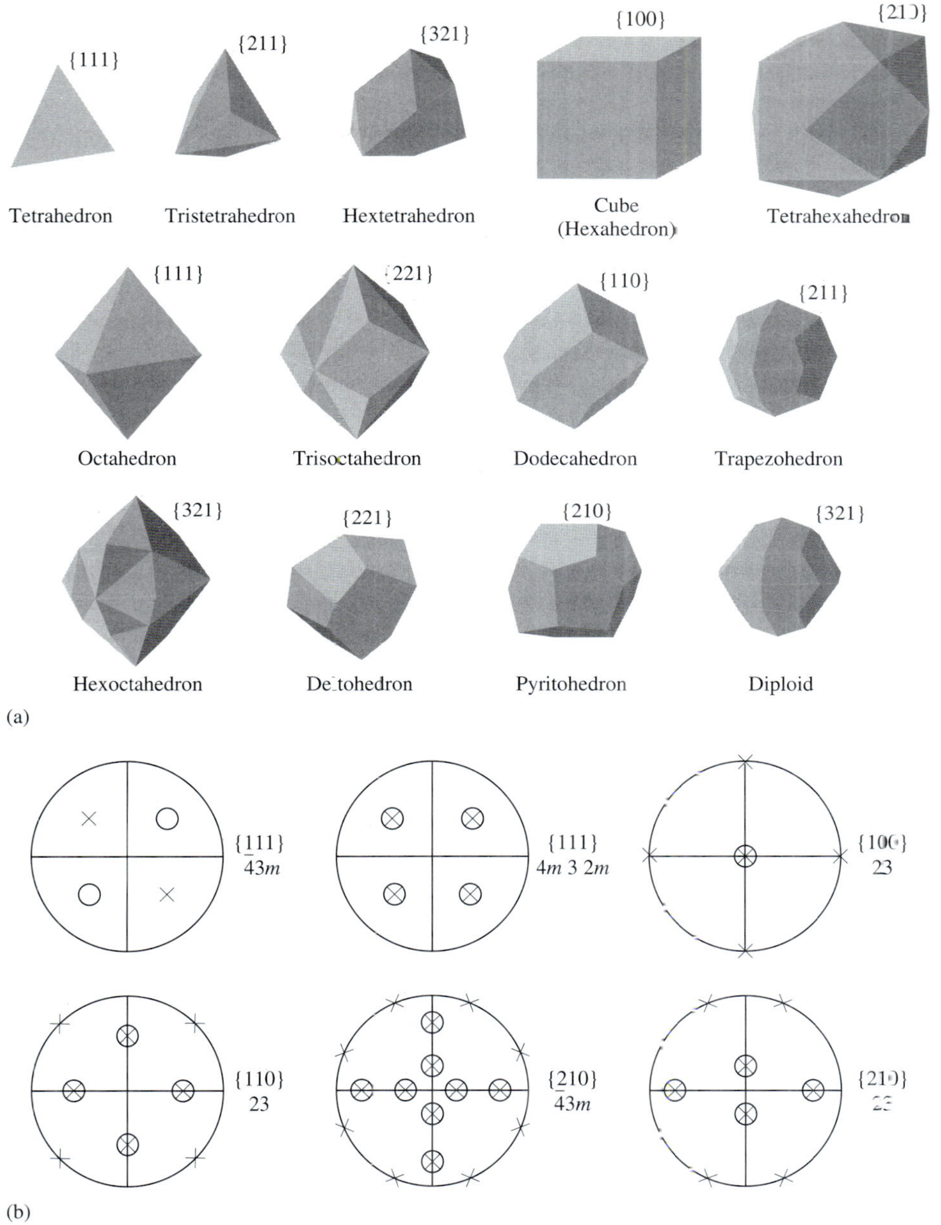

FIGURE 3-43 Isometric (cubic) forms. (a) Sketches of 13 forms with their names and indices. (b) Stereograms for six forms with form numbers and a point group that can produce them.

TABLE 3-6 Isometric (Cubic) Forms

Number of faces	Form	Class symmetry 23	432	$2/m\bar{3}$	$\bar{4}3m$	$4/m\ \bar{3}\ 2/m$
4	Tetrahedron	×			×	
6	Cube (hexahedron)	×	×	×	×	×
8	Octahedron		×	×		×
12	Dodecahedron	×	×	×	×	×
12	Pyritohedron	×		×		
12	Tristetrahedron	×			×	
12	Deltoid	×			×	
12	Tetratoid	×				
24	Tetrahexahedron		×		×	×
24	Trapezohedron		×	×		×
24	Trisoctahedron		×	×		×
24	Hextetrahedron				×	
24	Diploid			×		
24	Gyroid		×			
48	Hexoctahedron					×

systems. Therefore, some twin laws are defined by twin planes and some by twin axes, the latter requiring specification of a composition plane between twin members.

Crystal twinning is simple if two halves of a crystal are in twin relationship, such as Carlsbad twinning in feldspars. It is multiple if more than two twin-related parts are present, such as geniculate twinning in rutile. Polysynthetic twinning involves multiple twinning all with the same twin plane. Polysynthetic twinning in plagioclase according to the albite law produces lamellae ranging from easily visible striations on {001} cleavages to submicroscopic appearances. Interpenetration twins share a common volume (Fig. 3-45).

3-7 MINERAL HABITS

Recognition of crystal forms often leads to identification of a crystal class and, not infrequently, to identification of a mineral species or group. Since most minerals crystallize in holohedral classes of their crystal system, a review of all possible merohedral forms and combinations of forms is unnecessary for identification of most common minerals.

Minerals may nucleate and grow in a gaseous, liquid, or solid environment. Whether faces develop on a mineral grain depends on chemical and physical environment, growth medium, growth rate, and

FIGURE 3-44 Twin plane. One level in the feldspar structure (Fig. 2-27) depicts twinning according to the Baveno twin law. Dashed line denotes the trace of a glide (Fig. 3-35) plane (021) that relates two halves of this twin. Traces of mirrors with the feldspar structure are indicated by solid lines.

subsequent recrystallization. Structure and composition are also important; some minerals habitually display crystal faces (garnets, for example), whereas others rarely do (turquoise, for example).

Isometric Habits Isometric minerals typically display forms with simple indices, cubes {100}, dodecahedra {110}, and octahedra {111}. Halite [NaCl], sylvite [KCl], periclase [MgO], galena [PbS], and fluorite [CaF_2] mostly display cube faces, in some specimens modified at their extremities by dodecahedral, octahedral, or hexoctahedral {321} faces (Fig. 3-45). Interpenetration twins of cubes with [111] twin axis are also found (Fig. 3-45). Spinel group minerals typically crystallize in octahedra, some of which are modified by dodecahedral faces. Cuprite [Cu_2O] octahedra may be modified by cubes and dodecahedra. Garnet group minerals typically occur as dodecahedra or trapezohedra {210}, singly or in combination. Leucite [$KAlSi_2O_6$] and analcime [$NaAlSi_2O_6$] crystals are typically trapezohedra.

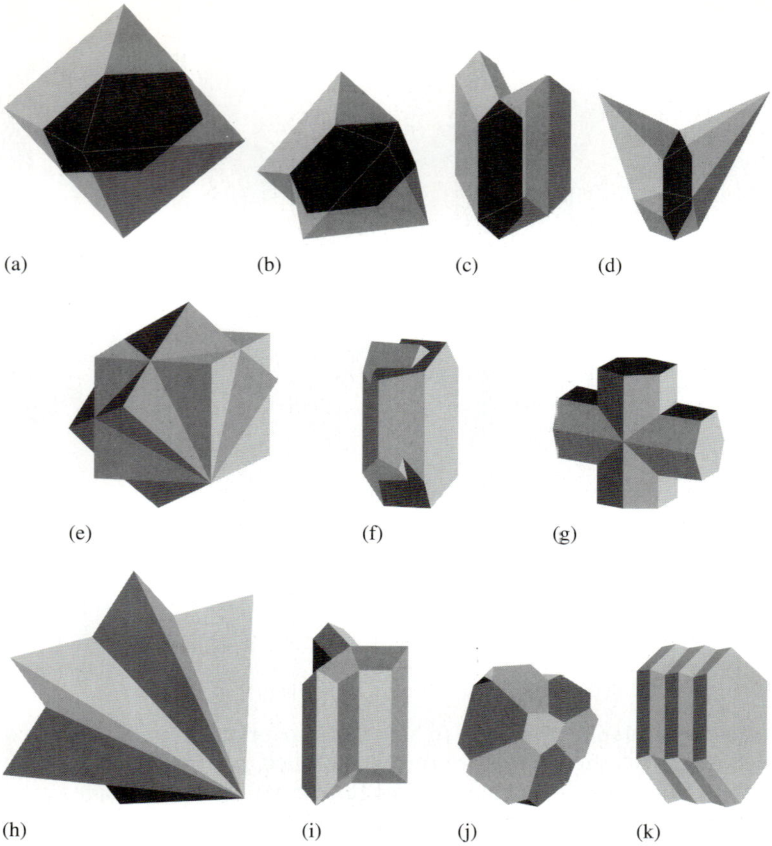

FIGURE 3-45 Crystal twinning. (a) Octahedron with octahedral twin plane. (b) Spinel twin from (a). (c) Swallowtail twin (gypsum) by twinning across the c axis. (d) Calcite with rhombohedral twin plane. (e) Iron cross (pyrite) with a dodecahedral twin plane. (f) Carlsbad twin (orthoclase) with c as twin axis. (g) Staurolite (fairy cross) with (031) twin plane. (h) Multiple twin of tetrahedrite. (i) Multiple twin of aragonite with (110) twin plane. (j) Multiple twin of pyroxene with (122) twin plane. (k) Polysynthetic albite twinning with [010] twin axis.

Pyrite [FeS_2] is the most common mineral to crystallize in class $2/m\ \bar{3}$. Most pyrite crystals are cubes, although pyritohedra {210} occur in many deposits. Striations seen on many pyrite cube faces represent oscillatory repetition of pyritohedral faces, which can occur only in classes with diads as the **a** axes. Skutterudite's [$CoAs_{2\text{-}3}$] habit is similar. Class $\bar{4}3m$ includes tetrahedrite [$(Cu,Fe)_{12}Sb_4S_{13}$], diamond [C], sphalerite [ZnS], and lazurite [$(Na,Ca)_{7\text{-}8}(Al,Si)_{12}(O,S)_{24}(SO_4,Cl_2(OH)_2)$]. Tetrahedrite, as its name implies, and tennantite [$(Cu,Fe)_{12}As_4S_{13}$] crystallize mostly in tetra-

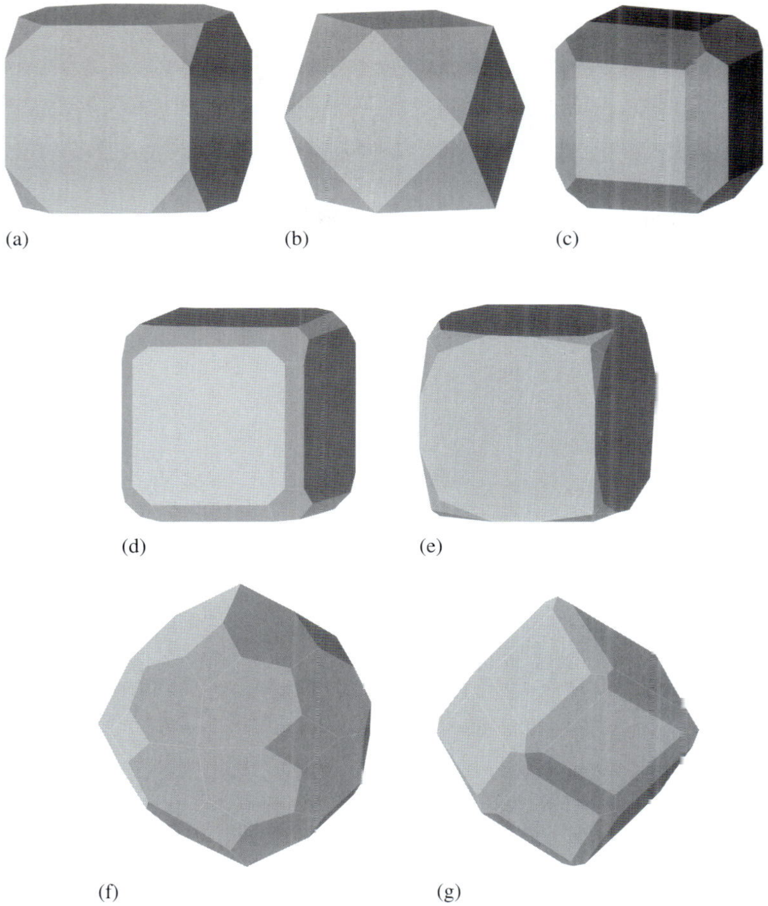

FIGURE 3-46 **Isometric (cubic) habits. (a) Cube modified by an octahedron. (b) Cube and octahedron equally developed. (c) Cube modified by dodecahedron. (d) Cube modified by octahedron and dodecahedron. (e) Cube modified by hexoctahedron (fluorite). (f) Trapezohedron modified by dodecahedron (garnet). (g) Dodecahedron modified by trapezohedron (garnet).**

hedra {111} or in combinations of positive and negative tetrahedra {111} and {$\bar{1}$11}. Diamond cubes are uncommon, but positive and negative tetrahedra equally developed to resemble octahedra are common. Sphalerite displays tetrahedra, although cube, dodecahedral, and tristetrahedral {211} faces are present on some specimens. Lazurite displays cubes and dodecahedra when faces are present. Cristobalite [SiO_2] (class 23) shows equal development of positive and negative tetrahedra resembling minute octahedra.

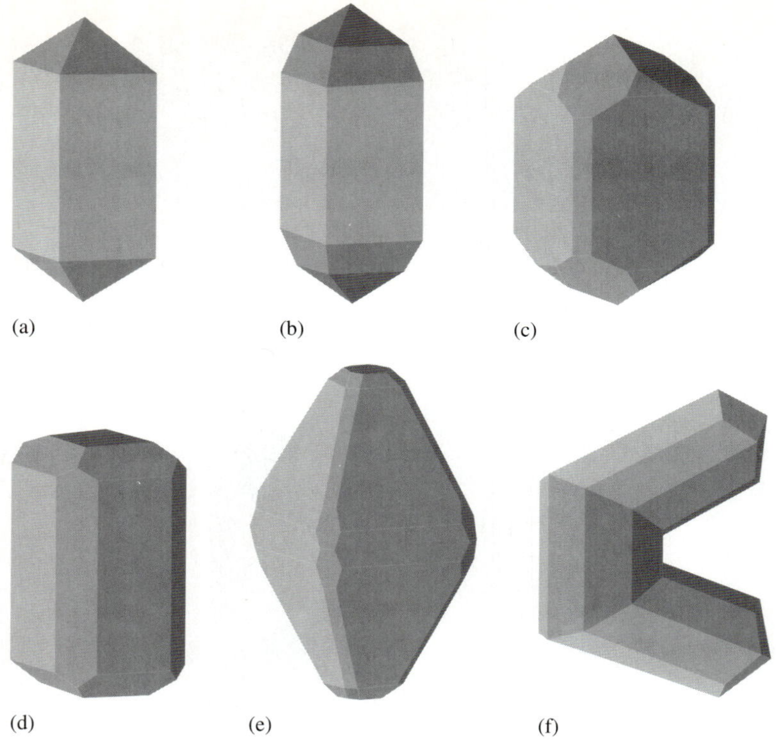

FIGURE 3-47 Tetragonal habits. (a, b) First-order prisms and bipyramids (zircon). (c) First- and second-order prisms and bipyramids (rutile). (d) First- and second-order prisms, first-order bipyramid, and base (vesuvianite). (e) First-order prism, two first-order bipyramids, three second-order bipyramids, and base (anatase). (f) Geniculated twinning with (101) twin plane (rutile).

Tetragonal Habits The point group for the holohedral class of the tetragonal system is $4/m\ 2/m\ 2/m$. Common forms include first- and second-order prisms, {110} and {100}, first- and second-order pyramids, {111} and {101}, and basal pinacoids, {001} (Fig. 3-47, Table 3-6). Minutely alternating first- and second-order prism faces produce striated prisms exhibited by rutile [TiO_2] and cassiterite [SnO_2]. Simple combinations of first- and second-order prisms terminated by first- and second-order pyramids typify cassiterite, rutile, zircon [$ZrSiO_4$], and vesuvianite [$Ca_{10}Mg_2Al_4(SiO_4)_5(Si_2O_7)(OH)_4$]. Basal pinacoids modify some pyramids. Octahedrite (anatase) [TiO_2] and braunite [$Mn^{2+}Mn_6^{3+}SiO_{12}$] occur mostly in bipyramids closely resembling octahedra. Torbernite [$Cu(UO_2)_2(PO_4)_2\cdot 8\text{–}12(H_2O)$], autunite [$Ca(UO_2)_2(PO_4)_2\cdot 10\text{–}12(H_2O)$], and apophyllite [$KCa_4(Si_4O_{10})_2F\cdot 8(H_2O)$] commonly occur in tabular prisms terminated by basal pinacoids. Simple or multiple contact twinning with (101) as composition plane is not uncommon on crystals of zircon, rutile, and cassiterite. Leucite (class $4/m$), which is isometric above 625°C, typically retains its trapezohedra. Scheelite [$CaWO_4$] and wulfenite [$PbMoO_4$] (class $4/m$) occur as pseudo-octahedral bipyramids {111}. The most common habit for chalcopyrite [$CuFeS_2$] (class $\bar{4}2m$) is a disphenoid {112} or {$1\bar{1}2$} closely approaching a tetrahedron in shape.

Hexagonal Habits The point group for the holohedral class of the hexagonal system is $6/m\ 2/m\ 2/m$. Beryl [$Be_3Al_2Si_6O_{18}$] develops large hexagonal prisms generally lacking distinct terminations. Crystals of molybdenite [MoS_2], graphite [C], and tridymite [SiO_2], when they do occur, are generally hexagonal plates dominated by basal pinacoids. Ice [H_2O] (class $6mm$) develops skeletal basal crystals (snowflakes) and dendrites (frost). Apatite [$Ca_5(PO_4)_3F$] (class $6/m$) occurs as hexagonal prisms ranging from acicular to stubby, terminated by pyramids or by basal pinacoids. Isostructural mimetite [$Pb_5(AsO_4)_3Cl$] and vanadinite [$Pb_5(VO_4)_3Cl$] show similar forms. Nepheline [$(Na,K)AlSiO_4$] (class 6) crystals are commonly short prisms. High-temperature quartz [SiO_2] (class 622) paramorphs, found as phenocrysts in some lavas, generally exhibit hexagonal bipyramids with or without short prism faces.

Trigonal Habits The holohedral class ($\bar{3}\ 2/m$) of the trigonal system contains the calcite group, hematite [Fe_2O_3], corundum [Al_2O_3], and brucite [$Mg(OH)_2$]. Calcite [$CaCO_3$] crystals exhibit a greater variety of forms and habits than any other mineral species (Fig. 3-48). The most frequently encountered forms include rhombohedra {$h0\bar{h}\ell$} ranging from obtuse to acute; prisms ranging from short to long with a variety of terminations; and scalenohedra {$hki\ell$} of many types (dogtooth spar). Twinning, commonly polysynthetic, occurs with twin planes ($01\bar{1}2$) or (0001). Siderite [$FeCO_3$] develops curved rhombohedra {$10\bar{1}1$} or {$11\bar{2}1$}, commonly built of subindividuals. Crystals of hematite display rhombohedra, some modified by basal pinacoids. Corundum typically occurs as barrel-shaped hexagonal prisms. Exsolution planes in the basal and rhombic directions cause parting in some crystals.

Class $3m$ of the trigonal system contains one important mineral group, tourmaline (borosilicates). Hexagonal prisms {$11\bar{2}0$} are commonly modified by trigonal prisms {$10\bar{1}0$} yielding nine-sided crystals ranging from stubby to slender and terminated by combinations of pyramidal forms. Rounded three-sided prisms with striations are trigonal prisms modified by abundant minute hexagonal prism faces. Pyrargyrite [Ag_3SbS_3] and proustite [Ag_3AsS_3] crystals occur as hexagonal prisms terminated by acute trigonal and ditrigonal pyramids. Class $\bar{3}$ contains dolomite, ankerite, ilmenite, willemite, and chabazite. Dolomite crystals [$CaMg(CO_3)_2$] are commonly saddle-shaped composites of rhombohedral faces. Ilmenite [$FeTiO_3$] rhombohedra are commonly modified by basal

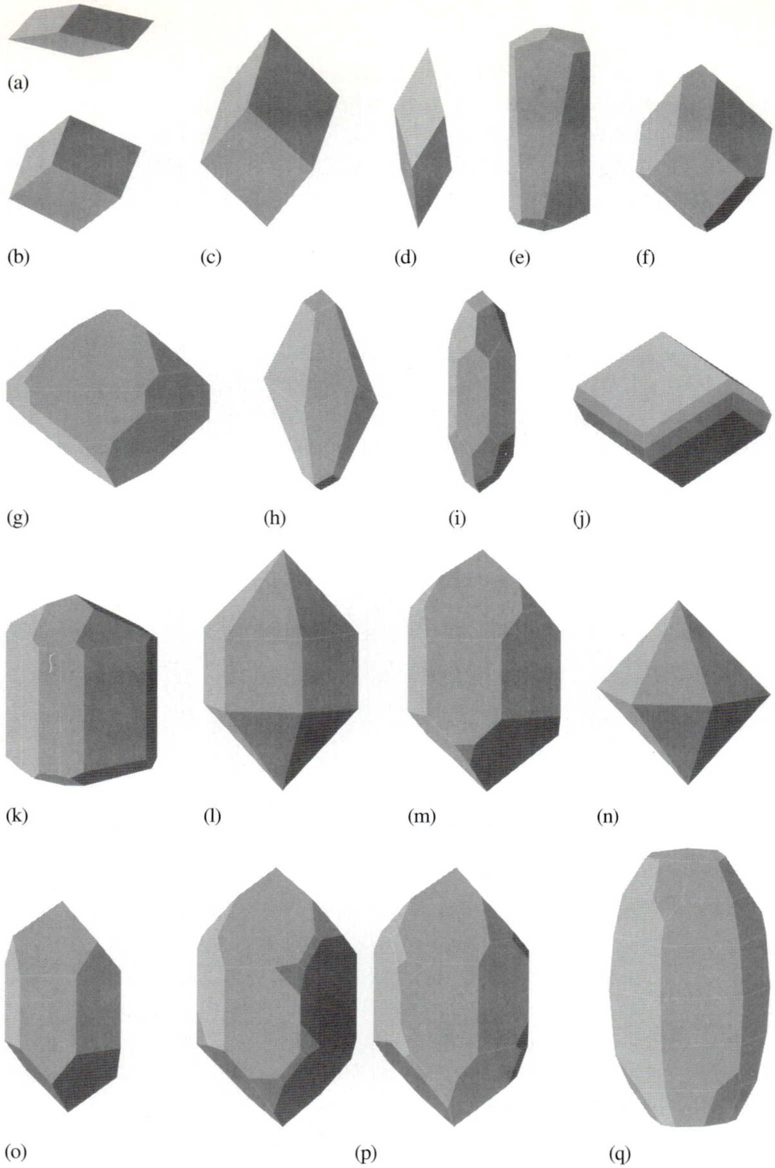

FIGURE 3-48 Trigonal habits. (a)–(d) Varieties of rhombohedra (calcite). (e)–(g) Combinations of rhombohedra (calcite). (h) Scalenohedron modified by rhombohedron (calcite). (i) Prism terminated by rhombohedron and scalenohedron (calcite). (j) Rhombohedron modified by scalenohedron. (k) Trigonal and ditrigonal prisms terminated by pyramids (tourmaline). (l)–(m) Hexagonal prism modified by positive and negative rhombohedra (quartz). (n) Positive and negative rhombohedra forming a pseudobipyramid. (o) Hexagonal prism terminated by a rhombohedron (quartz). (p) Right- and left-handed quartz. (q) Three hexagonal bipyramids terminated by a rhombohedron and base (corundum).

pinacoids or hexagonal prisms. Willemite [Zn_2SiO_4] displays hexagonal prisms with rhombohedral terminations. Chabazite [$CaAl_2Si_4O_{12} \cdot 6H_2O$] rhombohedra have internal angles so near to right angles that they resemble cubes.

Class 32 contains quartz [SiO_2], the mineral perhaps most frequently encountered with crystal faces in nature. Quartz crystals are generally prismatic $\{10\bar{1}0\}$ with faces striated at right angles to the triad axis by alternating positive and negative rhombohedral faces. Prisms are terminated by two rhombohedra, $\{10\bar{1}1\}$ and $\{01\bar{1}1\}$, which give the appearance of a hexagonal pyramid when equally developed. Angles between rhombohedral faces are close enough to 90° to give a distorted cubic appearance to single forms. Twin crystals are fairly common on quartz, including twin axis parallel to **c** (Dauphine law), twin planes parallel to **c** and one of the **a** axes (Brazil law), twin plane $(11\bar{2}2)$ (Japan law), and other rarer types. Quartz is enantiomorphous, and crystals may be right- or left-handed, depending on the apparent twist of the helices (Sec. 2-6). This difference may be recognized if either a right trigonal pyramid face $\{11\bar{2}1\}$ or a positive right trapezohedral face $\{51\bar{6}1\}$ is present These faces are to the right of the hexagonal prism face below the dominant positive rhombohedral $\{10\bar{1}1\}$ face on right-handed quartz, and oppositely on left-handed quartz (Fig. 3-49). Right and left enantiomorphs occur equally in quartz.

Orthorhombic Habits Most important orthorhombic minerals crystallize in the holohedral class ($2/m\ 2/m\ 2/m$) of this system. Most habits are various combinations of prisms, domes, and pinacoids (Fig. 3-49). Prisms of sillimanite [Al_2SiO_5] and andalusite [Al_2SiO_5] are very nearly square, as is one prism {110} of topaz [$Al_2SiO_4(F,OH)_2$]. Aragonite [$CaCO_3$] and witherite [$BaCO_3$] develop multiple twinning on {110} to give a pseudohexagonal habit, as does cordierite [$Mg_2Al_4Si_5O_{18}$] with its {110} and {130} twin planes. Crystals of staurolite [$(Fe,Mg,Zn)_2Al_9(Si,Al)_4O_{22}(OH)_2$] (fairy crosses) are interpenetration twins with a cruciform shape of simple prisms and basal pinacoids. These twins are at right angles if the twin plane is (031), and at 60° if the twin plane is (231). Multiple twinning across (110) gives crystals of bournonite [$PbCuSbS_3$] their typical cogwheel appearance.

Many orthorhombic crystals are typically prismatic in habit (stibnite [Sb_2S_3], columbite [$FeNb_2O_6$], goethite [$FeO(OH)$], aragonite, strontianite [$SrCO_3$], cerussite [$PbCO_3$], anglesite [$PbSO_4$], zoisite [$Ca_2Al_3)(SiO_4)(Si_2O_7)O(OH)$]), and topaz; others are more often found to be distinctly tabular (marcasite [FeS_2], chrysoberyl [$BeAl_2O_4$], cerussite, celestite [$SrSO_4$], barite [$BaSO_4$], and olivine [$(Mg,Fe)_2SiO_4$]); and some are pyramidal (sulfur [S] and cerussite). Perovskite [$CaTiO_3$] is pseudocubic. Enargite [Cu_3AsS_4] and lawsonite [$CaAl_2Si_2O_7(OH)_2 \cdot H_2O$] may be either prismatic or tabular. In class $mm2$, natrolite [$Na_2Al_2Si_3O_{10} \cdot 2H_2O$] forms slender prisms with

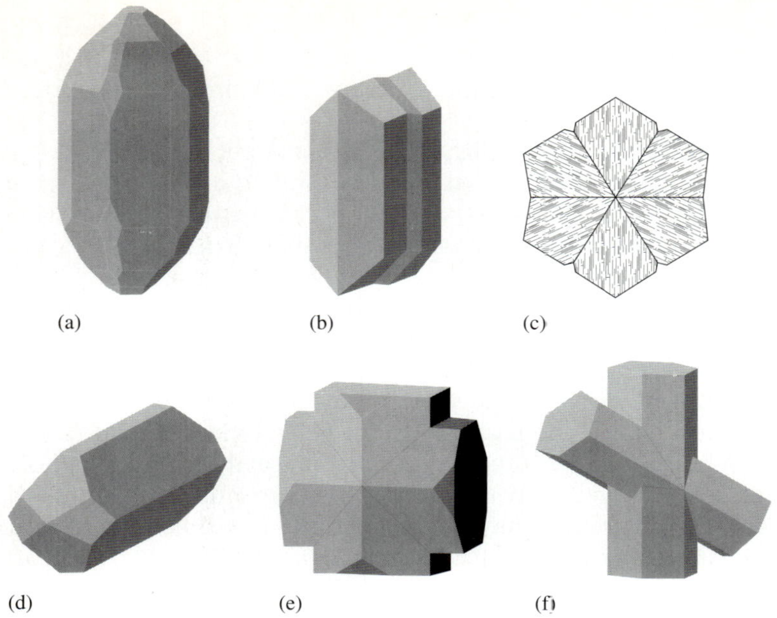

FIGURE 3-49 Orthorhombic habits. (a) Prisms, pyramids, domes, and pinacoids (topaz). (b) Multiple twinning with (110) twin plane (aragonite). (c) Multiple twinning across (110) to give pseudohexagonal basal section (aragonite). (d) Prisms, domes, and base (barite). (e) Fairy-stone twin with (031) twin plane (staurolite). (f) Fairy-stone twin with (231) twin plane (staurolite).

pyramidal terminations and hemimorphite [$Zn_4Si_2O_7(OH)_2 \cdot H_2O$] may be either prismatic or tabular.

Monoclinic Habits The holohedral class ($2/m$) of the monoclinic system contains all the important minerals in this system. Amphiboles, clinopyroxenes, and orthoclase are the most important rock-forming minerals in this group. Crystals of clinopyroxenes are generally stubby prismatic shapes composed of pinacoids {100} and {010} at right angles or prisms {110} at near right angles. Combinations of these forms give eight-sided habits. Crystals are terminated with domes, some of which are modified by pyramids (Fig. 3-50). Amphibole crystals are commonly prismatic with or without pinacoidal modifications. Termination is mostly by the low dome {011} or two domes {011} and {101}, which resemble a rhombohedral form. Prismatic orthoclase [$KAlSi_3O_8$] derives from combinations of pinacoids modified or terminated by domes. Carlsbad twinning of orthoclase is across the (100) plane.

Tabular gypsum [$CaSO_4 \cdot 2H_2O$] crystals are pinacoids terminated by domes. Twinning across (100) gives the familiar swallow-tail twin. Sphene

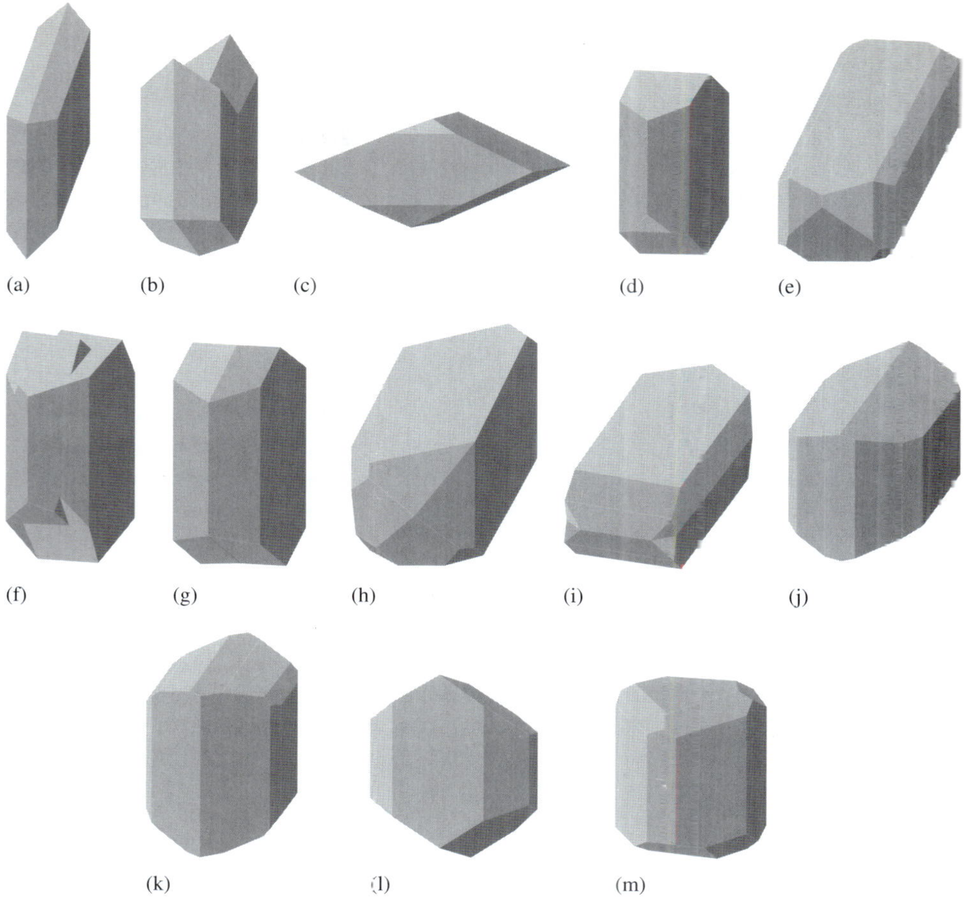

FIGURE 3-50 Monoclinic habits. (a) Prism, dome, and pinacoid (gypsum). (b) Swallowtail twin with (100) twin plane (gypsum). (c) Domes and pinacoid (sphene). (d) Prism, domes, and pinacoid (orthoclase). (e) Prisms, domes, and pinacoids (orthoclase). (f) Carlsbad interpenetration twin with (100) twin plane (orthoclase). (g) Carlsbad contact twin with (010) as composition face (orthoclase). (h) Baveno twin with (021) as twin plane (orthoclase). (i) Manebach twin with (001) twin plane (orthoclase). (j) Prisms, pinacoids, and domes (clinopyroxene). (k) Prisms, pinacoids, and domes (clinopyroxene). (1) Prisms, pinacoids, and domes (amphibole). (m) Prism, domes, and pyramid (amphibole).

(titanite) [$CaTiSiO_5$] got its name from its wedge-shaped habit resulting from a combination of slightly acute to highly acute domes. Epidote [$Ca_2(Al,Fe)_3(SiO_4)(Si_2O_7)O(OH)$] is generally prismatic parallel to b with domal terminations, typically at one end only. Spodumene [$LiAlSi_2O_6$] crystals occur as nearly square prisms, commonly striated, which range up to 15 m in length and 2 m in diameter. Other monoclinic crystals are prismatic (arsenopyrite [FeAsS], realgar [AsS], monazite [$REPO_4$], manganite [MnO(OH)], vivianite [$Fe_3^{2+}(PO_4)_2 \cdot 8H_2O$], erythrite [$Co_3(AsO_4)_2 \cdot 8H_2O$], and borax [$Na_2B_4O_5(OH)_4 \cdot 8H_2O$]); some are typically tabular (azurite [$Cu_3(CO_3)_2(OH)_2$], monazite [$REPO_4$], heulandite [$(Na,Ca)_{2-3}Al_3(Al,Si)_2Si_{13}O_{36} \cdot 12H_2O$], and the micas). Muscovite [$KAl_2(Si_3Al)O_{10}(OH,F)_2$] may develop pseudohexagonal tabular crystals, whereas chlorites and biotite [$K(Mg,Fe)_3(Al,Fe)Si_3O_{10}(OH,F)_2$] may be pseudorhombohedral. Tridymite typically occurs as minute paramorphic hexagonal platelets. Wolframite [$(Mn,Fe)WO_4$] may be either prismatic or tabular. Cryolite [Na_3AlF_6] crystals are commonly pseudocubes. In class m, laumontite [$CaAl_2Si_4O_{12} \cdot 4H_2O$] occurs as prismatic crystals with oblique terminations.

Triclinic Habits Two of the most important rock-forming minerals, microcline [$KAlSi_3O_8$] and plagioclase, crystallize in the holohedral class ($\bar{1}$) of the triclinic system. Because of this low symmetry, only pinacoids occur in this class. Habits of triclinic feldspars, however, are quite similar to those of orthoclase, and mineralogists frequently use monoclinic form names for these feldspars. Indeed, microcline got its name from the fact that the angle between {010} and {001} ranges down to 89.5°, whereas the same angle in orthoclase is 90° as required by symmetry. In plagioclases, this angle varies from 86.4° in albite [$NaAlSi_3O_8$] to 85.8° in anorthite [$CaAl_2Si_2O_8$]. In addition to Carlsbad twinning, triclinic feldspars habitually display polysynthetic twinning according to the albite (twin plane (010)) and pericline (twin axis [010]) twin laws. Albite twinning in plagioclase produces visible striations on {010} cleavage planes of many specimens of this mineral.

Kyanite [Al_2SiO_5] most commonly occurs as long-bladed crystals of pinacoids that are rarely terminated by a form. Wollastonite [$CaSiO_3$] and rhodonite [$(Mn,Fe,Mg,Ca)SiO_3$] form tabular crystals, whereas pectolite [$NaCa_2(OH)Si_3O_8$] is acicular parallel to **b**. Axinites (a borosilicate group) occur in axe-shaped wedges, whence the group name.

Recognizable and therefore identifiable crystal forms are far more encountered in mineral museums and laboratories than they are in any general run of rocks in the earth's crust. Nevertheless, recognition of distinctive forms is a powerful tool in identification of mineral species.

FURTHER READINGS

Bloss, F. D., *Crystallography and Crystal Chemistry.* New York: Holt, Rinehart and Winston, 1971.

Boisen, M. B., Jr., and G. V. Gibbs, *Mathematical Crystallography.* Washington, DC: Mineralogical Society of America, 1985.

Buerger, M. J., *Elementary Crystallography.* New York: Wiley, 1963.

Hahn, T. (ed.), *International Tables for Crystallography, vol. A, Space-Group Symmetry.* Dordrecht, Holland: Reidel, 1983.

Henry, N. F. M., and K. Lonsdale (eds.), *International Tables for X-ray Crystallography.* Birmingham, England: Kynoch Press, 1968.

Megaw, H. D., *Crystal Structures: A Working Approach.* Philadelphia: Saunders, 1973.

Palache, C., H. Berman, and C. Frondel, *Dana's System of Mineralogy,* vol. I, 7th ed. New York: Wiley, 1944.

Phillips, F. C., *An Introduction to Crystallography,* 4th ed. New York: Wiley, 1972.

Smith, J. V., *Geometrical and Structural Crystallography.* New York: Wiley, 1982.

Strunz, H., *Mineralogische Tabellen,* 5. Auflage. Leipzig: Akademische Verlagsgesellschaft, 1970.

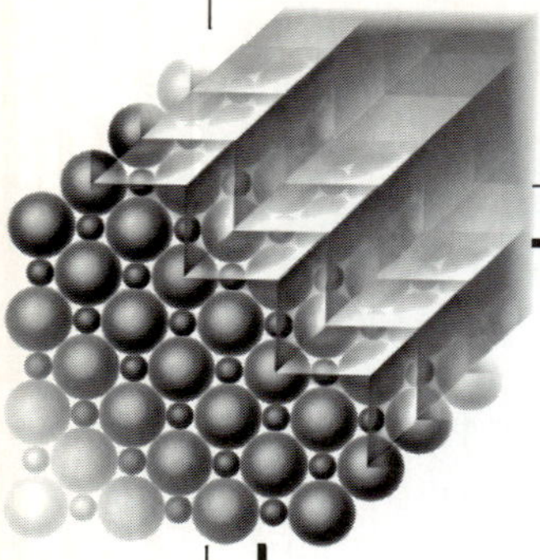

4

PHYSICAL PROPERTIES OF MINERALS

Physics is a branch of science that deals with the inanimate part of the universe, and mineralogy is a branch that deals with the crystalline part, specifically naturally occurring materials. Overlap between these two sciences—the interaction of energy and crystalline matter—is the subject of Chaps. 4 and 5. Two kinds of energy of concern to mineralogists are mechanical energy (Chap. 4) and radiant energy (Chap. 5). How a mineral reacts to application of either form of energy depends on its chemical composition and crystal structure. Physical properties of minerals, as they are observed in a laboratory or in the field, relate directly to chemical and structural characteristics set forth in Chaps. 1–3.

One of the first things you are likely to notice about an object is its weight, especially its weight compared with other objects of similar size, shape, and appearance. Consider three objects about the size and shape of a brick. One is silvery metallic, one is dull and reddish, and a third is brown and grainy. Most people would decide, purely on the basis of appearance, that the metallic block is heaviest and the woody (grainy) one lightest. If this wooden block were teak and the metallic one were aluminum, most people would consider the wooden one to be exceptionally heavy and the metallic one to be exceptionally light, even though relative weight remains the same. And most people would feel tricked somewhat if the reddish block was not the brick they expected, but instead a block of iron disguised by rust. This thought experiment should demonstrate to you that correlation of appearance of solid objects with other physical properties is subliminal, and the anticipated responses just given are really common knowledge. Density is associated with appearance, and both are related to crystal chemistry and structure.

4-1 DENSITY AND SPECIFIC GRAVITY

How much mass a given volume can accommodate depends on atomic masses of chemical elements present, atomic or ionic radii, the packing of atomic particles, temperature, and pressure. This quantity may be measured as density or specific gravity. Density is mass per unit volume; therefore units, commonly g cm^{-3}, must be stipulated. Specific gravity is a ratio of weight of material to weight of an equal volume of water at 4°C. Specific gravity is, therefore, dimensionless. Since pure water has a density of 1 g cm^{-3} at 4°C and a specific gravity of 1 these two measures are commonly (and erroneously!) interchanged.

Ionic size depends on electronic structure, but ionic radii vary only by a factor of 2 or 3 (Chap. 1). Atomic mass depends on total nucleons (neutrons plus protons) and varies by two orders of magnitude. Hence, mineral densities depend on atomic mass (Table 4-1) and on ionic size (Table 4-2). When a mineral is heated, some heat energy is converted to thermal oscillation, making ions effectively larger and a mineral less dense. Under pressure they become smaller without change in mass, thereby increasing mineral density. Polymorphic changes result in density changes (Fig. 4-1). High-pressure polymorphs tend to have higher densities, and high-temperature polymorphs tend to have lower densities with few exceptions.

Density may be measured directly on a mineral sample, or it may be calculated from results of chemical analysis and X-ray diffraction. Unit-cell volume can be calculated from diffraction data, and unit-cell mass from chemical data. These two quantities yield a theoretical density, which can be compared with measured densities (generally obtained by converting specific gravity measurements). Chemical and structural defects may be measured in terms of deviation of sample density from theoretical density. Pyrrhotite ($Fe_{1-x}S$, x = 0–0.17) always has lower than theoretical density because of omission of ferrous iron from its structure (Fig. 1-14). Metamict minerals (Sec. 1-8) are less dense than the theoretical density of their crystalline reconstitutions because of displacement of ions from equilibrium locations.

Density of an object is related to appearance as demonstrated at the beginning of this chapter. This observation can be traced to the kinds of chemical bonds present in a mineral. Most native metals crystallize in one of two close-packed arrays (Sec. 1-5). This packing gives a maximum

TABLE 4-1 Dependence of Density on Atomic Mass

Mineral	Composition	Atomic mass		Density ($g\ cm^{-3}$)
Olivine				
Forsterite	Mg_2SiO_4	Mg 24.31		3.22
Fayalite	Fe_2SiO_4	Fe 55.85		4.41
Carbonate				
Calcite	$CaCO_3$	Ca 40.08		2.71
Magnesite	$MgCO_3$	Mg 24.31		2.98
Rhodochrosite	$MnCO_3$	Mn 54.94		3.70
Siderite	$FeCO_3$	Fe 55.85		3.96
Smithsonite	$ZnCO_3$	Zn 65.37		4.45
Feldspar				
Orthoclase	$KAlSi_3O_8$	K 39.10 Si 28.09	67.19	2.56
Celsian	$BaAl_2Si_2O_8$	Ba 137.34 Al 26.98	164.32	3.37
Spinel				
Spinel	$MgOAl_2O_3$	Mg + 2Al =	78.27	3.55
Chromite	$FeOCr_2O_3$	Fe + 2Cr =	159.85	5.09
Magnetite	$FeOFe_2O_3$	3Fe =	167.55	5.20
Franklinite	$ZnOFe_2O_3$	Zn + 2Fe =	177.07	5.34

number of atoms per unit volume, and, furthermore, metal atoms are not diluted by the presence of low-mass anions. Associated metallic luster (Sec. 5-4) also results from bond type. You expect minerals with metallic luster to have higher than average density.

Covalent bonds are directional (Sec. 1-3), which results in inefficient packing. Nonmetallic topaz with its anionic close packing is distinctly denser than similar-appearing quartz with its open framework because of more efficient filling of space with constituent ions.

TABLE 4-2 Dependence of Density on Bond Length

Mineral	Formula weight	*d* (pm)	Density ($g\ cm^{-3}$)
Sylvite	74.6	31.4	2.0
Halite	58.5	27.5	2.2
Periclase	40.3	20.7	3.6

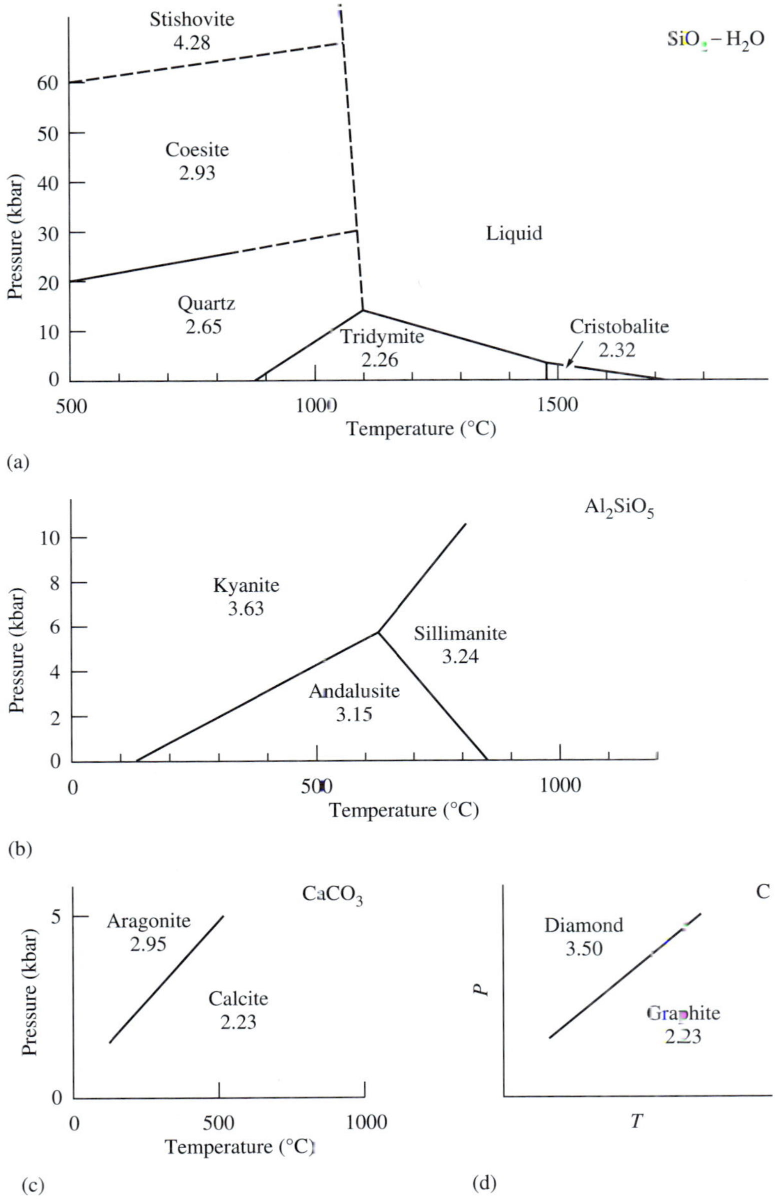

FIGURE 4-1 Density differences in isochemical matter. Temperatures and pressures of equilibrium crystallization of various polymorphs and their densities (g cm^{-3}) under laboratory conditions are shown. High-pressure polymorphs tend to be denser and high-temperature ones less dense than those formed at low pressures and temperatures.

4-2 ELASTIC AND THERMAL PROPERTIES

Mechanical behavior of crystalline materials may be conveniently divided into two categories: breaking chemical bonds or not breaking chemical bonds. The latter is generally reversible, whereas the former is irreversible. For example, shrinking a mineral sample by compression or cooling can be reversed by decompression or heating. A scratched or broken mineral, however, cannot be unscratched or unbroken. Elastic and thermal properties of crystal structures are important to geologists in interpretation of all the earth not visible for inspection, as well as some of its visible characteristics.

Strain (deformation) is produced in a mineral when stress (force) is applied to it. On an atomic scale, this stress means that forces other than those of chemical bonding are present. Ions are moved from their equilibrium positions (strained) if stresses are great enough. Note that stress and strain are different kinds of things. Stress is a force measured as force per unit area (Pa = N m^{-2}, 1 bar = 10^6 dynes cm^{-2}, 1 bar = 10^5 Pa). Strain is measured as a dimensionless number of deformation in terms of the original size, that is, length change/unit length.

Hooke's Law Elastic deformation of crystalline materials follows Hooke's law: Strain is proportional to stress with a constant of proportionality, an elastic stiffness coefficient (bulk modulus = reciprocal compressibility), having units of pressure. Stress involves both tension-compression and torsion-shear components. Strain deformation, which is anisotropic in nonisometric structures, may also depend on crystallographic directions in isometric structures. For example, chemical bond density in halite structures differs between {100} and {111} planes (Figs. 1-9, 2-2). Polycrystalline aggregates may be treated as though they are isotropic if individual crystals are oriented randomly.

Elastic stiffness coefficients in minerals are related to kinds and strengths of chemical bonds. In general, the shorter and stronger the chemical bonds in a crystal, the greater is its stiffness and the less its strain for a given stress. A pressure of 1 GPa (10 kbar) reduces the volume of periclase from its value at room pressure by approximately 0.6%, whereas that of halite reduces by 3.6% (Table 4-2). Strain may bring adjacent ions closer together, but in open framework structures, strain also may cause rotation of parts of a structure. Thus, at a pressure of 1 GPa (10 kbar), olivine volume reduces by approximately 0.8%, whereas that of quartz reduces by 2.4% (compare Figs. 2-11 and 2-22).

In silicates, which make up most of the earth's crust and upper mantle, stiffness is controlled largely by how silica tetrahedra share polyhedral elements. Quartz and olivine both have bond distributions nearly equal in all directions; their elastic stiffness coefficients vary from an average value by about 10% with crystallographic direction. Micas, with their layers of corner-shared tetrahedra bonded by alkali ions, have elastic stiffness coefficients three times as great parallel to sheets as normal to them. Feldspars are more anisotropic than quartz. Chain silicates are stiffer parallel to chains than perpendicular to them.

Volume compressibility represents volume decrease (density increase) resulting from pressure. Stiff bonding correlates with low volume compressibility. Pressure is hydrostatic when equal in all directions. Laboratory experiments with minerals obtain hydrostatic pressure by using a fluid or an easily deformed solid, such as halite, as a pressure-transmitting medium. Within the earth, hydrostatic pressure results from plastic deformation of crystalline materials over long periods of time.

Pressure Dependence Elastic stiffness coefficients increase with increase in pressure and decrease with increase in temperature. The smaller the initial elastic stiffness coefficient, the smaller its change with increase in pressure since the stiffest bonds are least sensitive to pressure change.

At atomic levels, structures approaching closest packing of oxygen ions yield to hydrostatic pressure by shrinkage of edge-sharing polyhedra; that is, *M*—O bonds shorten. Framework structures also shrink by tetrahedral rotation with bending of chemical bonds. Initial compression upon burial in the earth is greater in the latter than in the former. Thus, quartz, which initially shrinks 2.4% on going to 1 GPa (10 kbar), shrinks by only an additional 1.3% between 3 and 4 GPa (30 and 40 kbar). For comparison, olivine, with its initial shrinkage of 0.8% on going to 1 GPa, shrinks by 0.7% between 3 and 4 GPa.

Temperature Dependence Temperature dependence of elastic stiffness coefficients is negative because increased thermal vibration increases bond lengths, thereby decreasing stiffness. Since temperature and pressure increase with depth within the earth, negative temperature change partially offsets positive pressure change in elastic stiffness coefficients of deeply buried minerals. Changes in stiffness in minerals upon progressive burial in the earth show up in changes with depth of velocities of seismic waves. Indeed, much information about mantle mineralogy comes from seismic data and comparison of these data with experimentally determined information about mineral elasticity.

Anelastic Deformation Although mineral stiffness with respect to short-term stresses such as seismic waves increases with depth, long-term stresses such as those associated with plate tectonics produce anelastic deformation, which is irreversible. Once a mineral undergoes anelastic deformation, it has no tendency to return to its original state. Plastic deformation of minerals occurs along well-defined crystallographic planes in specific directions. For example, quartz has 11 crystallographically oriented slip planes, each plane having one or more slip directions. (Any quartz specimen, however, will display only a few directions of deformation lamellae.) This kind of deformation is analogous to shifting a deck of cards so that each card slips a little with respect to adjacent cards.

Under mantle conditions, olivine develops slip planes $\{0k\ell\}$ that permit glide in the [100] direction along several intersecting planes analogous to a pile of pencils slipping past one another. Such plastic deformation may be preserved as thin deformation lamellae or as deformation twinning; it may be annealed out by recrystallization.

Anelastic deformation, as discussed in preceding paragraphs, occurs in brittle materials subjected to differential stresses under high confining pressure. Native metals and alloys, on the other hand, may be irreversibly deformed without loss of cohesion in the field or laboratory. These materials are malleable in that you can flatten them with a hammer. Many of them are also ductile since you can extrude them as wire. Yellow iron sulfide minerals are truly "fools' gold," since none of them are the least bit malleable, as is the real item.

Thermal Conductivity Temperature rises when a material is heated. Crystalline materials express this heat through atomic vibrations. At room temperature this vibration is about 3–7% of interatomic spacing. Empirical observations backed by theoretical considerations indicate that each chemical element in a crystal contributes about 6 kcal deg^{-1} mol^{-1}. The specific heat of native silver is 5.8, halite 12, and fluorite 17.1 kcal deg^{-1} per formula weight.

How warm or cool a mineral feels at a particular temperature depends on how efficiently it conducts heat. Minerals conduct heat principally by two mechanisms: electron transport and phonon waves. (Phonons are units of elastic vibrational energy analogous to photons, the units of electromagnetic energy.) Although all crystalline materials conduct heat by phonons, only metals have large quantities of free electrons. Hence, metals have thermal conductivities on the order of 10–100 cal m^{-1} sec^{-1} deg^{-1}, compared with nonmetals with values around 1 cal m^{-1} sec^{-1} deg^{-1}. Metals thus feel warmer or cooler to touch at a given temperature than do nonmetals.

Thermal conductivities in nonmetals are limited to scattering of phonons at atomic sites in ionic structures. Increase in temperature increases atomic vibration amplitudes, thus increasing phonon scattering and decreasing thermal conductivity as a consequence of this limitation. Disordered structures scatter phonons more effectively than crystalline as another consequence. A glass bauble at room temperature feels warmer on a trained tongue than does the crystalline gem it is designed to imitate because of differences in thermal conductivities. Diamond, with its low thermal expansion, low impurity levels, and low number of defects, has an extremely high thermal conductivity, even higher than some metals.

Thermal Anisotropy Thermal expansion and thermal conductivity are controlled by crystallographic direction in anisotropic crystals. An extreme example of this dependence occurs in graphite, which has thermal conductivity in its **a** direction four times its conductivity in its **c** direction. This property makes graphite useful in manufacture of rocket heat shields, because heat buildup is dissipated laterally and not transmitted across layers.

The greater the vibrational amplitude of an atomic particle in a crystal, the larger is its effective radius. Hence, specific volume (reciprocal density) increases with increasing temperature. Linear expansion coefficients of crystals are a measure of their change in length per unit length per degree of temperature:

$$\alpha = \frac{1}{\Delta T}\,\frac{\Delta \ell}{\ell}.$$

A corresponding volume expansion coefficient is the sum of three mutually perpendicular linear coefficients.

Closest-packed structures have large linear expansions on the order of 8–10 $\times$ 10^{-6} deg^{-1}. As a generalization, the stronger the chemical bonds in a crystal, the lower its thermal expansion. Strong C—C bonds in diamond give it great hardness and extremely low thermal expansion. Layered structures, as might be expected, have much greater thermal expansion perpendicular to than parallel to layers. In closest-packed structures, atomic vibration must operate against nearest neighbors in these structures. In framework silicates, however, additional thermal vibration may be directed toward open structural channels resulting in values for thermal expansion that are much less than for closest-packed structures. On the other hand, structural units such as silica tetrahedra may rotate as a unit, thereby contributing to high thermal expansion values as in quartz.

Anomalous increase in density upon temperature increase occurs in β-eucryptite [$LiAlSiO_4$], a stuffed derivative of the quartz structure. The Li^+ occupies four- and sixfold sites in the helical channels parallel to **c** in this structure. Heating increases the size of Li^+, causing progressive shift of Li^+ from tetrahedral to octahedral sites, which in turn causes the unit cell to shrink on heating. This anomalous behavior of β-eucryptite may be compared with volume expansion of quartz. Upon heating from 20 to 400°C, quartz expands 0.73% normal to **c** and 0.43% parallel to **c** for a volume expansion of 1.89%. Over the same temperature range, β-eucryptite expands 0.28% normal to **c**, but −0.70% parallel to **c**, which results in a volume change of −0.14%.

4-3 HARDNESS AND TENACITY

Hardness is a mineral's resistance to surface scratching; toughness is its resistance to breaking. They are different kinds of things, although both require rupture of chemical bonds. Friedrich Mohs proposed, in 1820, a series of 10 common minerals with the property that each mineral higher on his scale could scratch all those minerals lower on his scale. From softest to hardest, these minerals are

1. talc
2. gypsum
3. calcite
4. fluorite
5. apatite
6. orthoclase
7. quartz
8. topaz
9. corundum
10. diamond

Intervals on this hardness scale are roughly equal on a logarithmic scale, except that the gap between corundum and diamond is considerably greater than other intervals. In addition to this excessive gap, well-crystallized gypsum is softer than massive gypsum, calcite is about half a point softer on its basal {0001} pinacoid than on its rhombohedral $\{10\bar{1}1\}$ faces, and apatite is a group with variable composition and hardness. A. S. Povarennykh proposed, in 1963, a modified Mohs scale that defines each point more precisely because its compounds (not all of them occurring naturally) vary less in composition and because crystallographic direction is specified:

1. talc [001]
2. halite [100]
3. galena [100]
4. fluorite [111]
5. scheelite [111]
6. magnetite [111]
7. quartz $[10\bar{1}0]$
8. topaz [001]
9. corundum $[11\bar{2}0]$
10. TiC
11. BN
12. B_4C
13. $B_{12}C_2$
14. carbonado diamond
15. bort diamond [111]

Some useful secondary hardness standards for the Mohs scale are your fingernail (2+), a copper coin (3), a knife blade (5+), window glass (5½), and file steel (6½).

Crystallographic Controls One difficulty in relating hardness to bonding and crystal structure arises because structure depends on the strongest bonds present, whereas hardness depends on the weakest bonds. All silicate minerals are built of silica tetrahedra with little variation in Si—O bond strength. The Mohs hardness of silicates ranges from talc (1) to topaz (8) because of other chemical bonds in silicates. Even in materials with only one kind of chemical bond, numbers of bonds per unit area varies with crystallographic direction. Diamond is harder on {111} than on all other directions.

Double bonds are shorter and stronger than single bonds in covalent crystals. Ionic bonds are also stronger for higher charges; monovalent halite [NaCl] has hardness 3, whereas isostructural periclase [MgO] has hardness 6. Longer bonds resulting from larger ions are weaker than

TABLE 4-3 Dependence of Hardness on Octahedral Radius

Mineral	Composition	Radius (pm)	H
Olivine	M_2SiO_4		
Forsterite	Mg	80	7
Fayalite	Fe	86	$6\frac{1}{2}$
Corundum	M_2O_3		
Corundum	Al	61	9
Hematite	Fe	73	6
Halite	MCl		
Halite	Na	110	$2\frac{1}{2}$
Sylvite	K	146	2

shorter bonds from smaller ions (Table 4-3); corundum is harder than isostructural hematite. High-pressure polymorphs with more ions and more chemical bonds per unit volume are harder than low-pressure polymorphs; aragonite has hardness 4 and calcite 3. These materials are all brittle, and the Mohs scale of hardness applies best to brittle materials (hardness of a malleable mineral is characterized by indentation with a stylus).

Characteristically, metallic bonds yield to stress by deforming plastically. Whereas movement of one ionic diameter juxtaposes oppositely charged ions in ionic structures, metals have their metal ions neutralized by an electron gas. As a result, metal ions in a metal can move past one another without causing electrostatic repulsion, so that metals are characteristically malleable.

Covalent bonds being directional tend not to fill space efficiently; diamond, again, is an exception to the rule. Covalent bonds can yield to external stress by bending, a phenomenon most readily seen in layered silicates. Thin cleavage sheets of mica are elastic and snap back after considerable bending. Chlorite sheets are flexible and do not snap back after bending. Mica layers are held together by K^+ ions in large well-defined coordination polyhedra that deform when layers are bent only to reform when an external stress is removed. Chlorite layers are talclike with a net negative charge and brucitelike with a net positive charge. Bending is permanent as one layer slides past another.

Fracture If strain in a crystalline material exceeds its elastic limit, this material breaks. Actual mechanisms of breakage are complicated and poorly understood at best. Breakage involves concentrations of stresses at ends of microfractures and near structural defects. Actual mechanisms are less important in mineralogy than are resulting rupture patterns. These patterns depend on orientation and distribution of chemical bonds in a crystal structure.

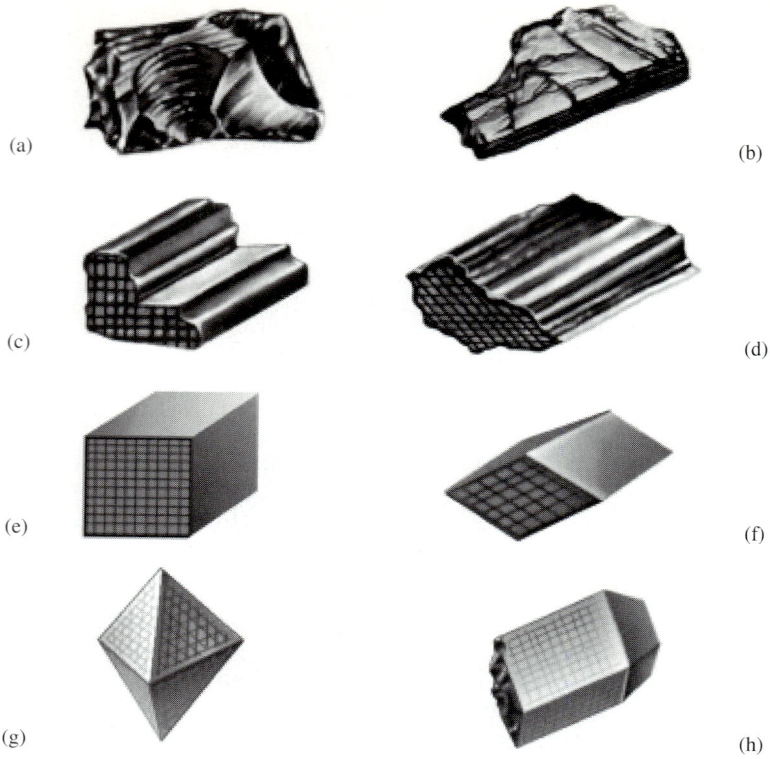

FIGURE 4-2 Fracture and cleavage. (a) Conchoidal fracture as in quartz and olivine. (b) Basal cleavage as in micas and chlorites. (c) Prismatic cleavage as in pyroxenes and feldspars. (d) Prismatic cleavage as in amphiboles. (e) Cubic cleavage as in halite and galena. (f) Rhombohedral cleavage as in calcite. (g) Octahedral cleavage as in fluorite. (h) Dodecahedral cleavage as in sphalerite.

Some crystal structures, notably quartz, garnet, and olivine, have bond strengths approximately equal in all crystallographic directions. Fracture follows no particular crystallographic pattern in these cases. These minerals fracture in a pattern resembling broken glass, that is, conchoidal (Fig. 4-2). Other fracture patterns are fibrous, smooth, rough, or splintery. Differences in fracture pattern depend on propagation patterns, which in turn depend on microfractures and other defects.

Cleavage Some crystal structures have different kinds of bonds or different bond densities arranged crystallographically. In these minerals cleavage follows preferential crystallographic planes. Layered silicates all have strong Si—O—Si chemical bonds in layer planes and weak bonds between these layers. They have basal cleavage. Similarly, strong Mo—S bonds within molybdenite layers and strong C—C bonds within graphite layers with weak bonds between them produce basal cleavage (Fig. 4-2).

Two intersecting sets of crystallographic planes with systematically weak chemical bonds produce prismatic cleavage. Chain silicates have strong Si—O—Si bonds in chains parallel to **c**, but weaker *M*—O bonds between chains. Pyroxene {110} cleavage is at 87° because **a** and **b** unit-cell edges are approximately equal in length (Fig. 2-17). Amphiboles with **b** roughly twice the length of **a** have {110} prismatic cleavage at approximately 56° (Fig. 2-18). Feldspar prismatic cleavage on {001} and {010} results from fewer, not different, chemical bonds in those pinacoidal directions (Fig. 2-27).

When cleavage occurs in crystals because of fewer, mostly homodesmic, bonds in certain crystallographic directions, electrostatic neutrality exists on each side of these cleavage planes. This observation applies to {100} cubic cleavage in halite structures, analogous $\{10\bar{1}1\}$ rhombohedral cleavage in calcite structures, to {111} octahedral cleavage in fluorite, and to {110} dodecahedral cleavage in sphalerite. Diamond has {111} cleavage.

Parting In some mineral species, breakage in some specimens produces crystallographic surfaces, and in other specimens only fracture occurs. This parting depends on individual histories. Contact twinning, especially if followed by hydration or other chemical alteration along a twin plane, may cause basal and rhombohedral parting of some corundum crystals. Parting planes are finite macroscopic distances apart and cannot be further parted, whereas cleavage planes can be further cleaved to sizes below microscopic detection. If a crystal solution series is complete only at high temperatures and restricted at low temperatures, exsolution may occur preferentially at certain favored crystallographic planes. Thus, parting may occur at these nascent crystal faces.

Toughness Just as hardness refers to a mineral's resistance to scratching, toughness refers to its resistance to breakage. Single crystals of diamond, the hardest known mineral, are exceeded in toughness by quartz, corundum, and two jades, jadeite and nephrite, a variety of tremolite-actinolite. Although no commonly accepted toughness scale exists, relative toughness of several gem minerals have been determined. Some tough minerals (with their Povarennykh hardnesses) are, in order, carbonado diamond (14) (toughest), nephrite (6½), jadeite (7), chrysoberyl (8½), corundum (9), quartz (7), diamond (15), forsterite (7), beryl (8), garnet (6–7½), zircon (7½), topaz (8), orthoclase (6), and spodumene (6½–7) (least tough).

Jadeite has pyroxene cleavage, but is normally composed of randomly oriented microscopic crystallites that force any transgranular breakage to change direction at each crystallite boundary. Carbonado diamond is tougher than single-crystal diamond for the same reason. Nephrite is an asbestiform amphibole with a fibrous microstructure of randomly oriented interlocking fibers. Polycrystalline materials appear to be tougher than single crystals, especially when cleavage is present in the crystals. Broken surfaces of toughest minerals have the highest surface area per unit of cross-sectional area.

4-4 ELECTRICAL PROPERTIES

Crystal structures have symmetry; thus structural properties have symmetry. This symmetry of properties may be the same as that of a structure, or, because of directional character of a property, some elements of point-group symmetry may be suppressed. Symmetry of polar properties may be less than structural symmetry, but it can never be greater.

Electric and magnetic properties are polar; that is, they point in a direction like an arrow. An electrostatic charge has positive and negative directions, and a magnet has north-seeking and south-seeking poles. These properties are dipolar; they are not centrosymmetric. These properties may be intrinsic to a structure, or they may be induced by an external force.

Symmetrically, any property that has one value at [*uvw*] and an opposite value at [$\bar{u}\bar{v}\bar{w}$] is a polar property, giving the structure a unique polar axis in that direction. Therefore, polarity is symmetrically impossible in any point group having a center of symmetry ($\bar{1}$). There are 11 centrosymmetric point groups and 11 more that lack a center of symmetry but are nonpolar because of combinations of other symmetry elements (Table 4-4).

Acentric Symmetry In eight of the acentric point groups, the principle axis of rotation (2, 3, 4, or 6) gives the polar direction. In *m*, a polar direction must lie in the mirror plane, but it is unrestricted in point group 1.

Crystals with a unique polar axis contain a built-in spontaneous polarization that generally changes with temperature. If heated or cooled, these crystals develop an electrostatic charge on opposite ends of their polar axes; they are pyroelectric. (Tests for pyroelectricity must be made quickly after a temperature change, since electrostatic charges rapidly dissipate or leak away, although enough residual charge may remain to cause these minerals to pick up dust preferentially on certain crystal faces.) Pyroelectric minerals include the axinite group (point group 1), boracite (*mm*2 below 265°C), greenockite (6*mm*), hemimorphite (*mm*2), the tourmaline group (3*m*), wurtzite (6*mm*), and zincite (6*mm*). Some

TABLE 4-4 Point Groups by Center of Symmetry

Centric point groups	Acentric nonpolar point groups	Acentric polar point groups
$4/m\ \bar{3}\ 2/m$	$\bar{4}3m$	
$2/m\ \bar{3}$	432	
	23	
$4/m\ 2/m\ 2/m$	$\bar{4}2m$	$4mm$
$4/m$	$\bar{4}$	4
	422	
$6/m\ 2/m\ 2/m$	$\bar{6}m2$	$6mm$
$6/m$	$\bar{6}$	6
	622	
$\bar{3}\ 2/m$	32	$3m$
$\bar{3}$		3
$2/m\ 2/m\ 2/m$	222	$mm2$
$2/m$		2
		m
$\bar{1}$		1

specimens of topaz also are pyroelectric because (F,OH) ordering reduces their symmetry from centric ($2/m\ 2/m\ 2/m$) to acentric (2, m, or 1).

Pyroelectric crystals are also piezoelectric, in that electrostatic polarity may be induced by pressure changes. In addition, acentric nonpolar structures may display piezoelectricity when stress is applied in certain crystallographic directions. Quartz (32) and sphalerite ($\bar{4}3m$) develop polarity when stressed. Because of helices of silica tetrahedra parallel to **c** in quartz, compression in the **a**-axis direction induces polarity (Fig. 2-22). Shearing about an **a** axis in sphalerite causes differential displacement of S^{2-} and Zn^{2+} ions, leading to induced polarity (Fig. 2-3). Conversely, electric charge applied to a polar axis of a piezoelectric crystal causes dimensional change at right angles to its polar axis. Thus, electric current oscillation can be converted to acoustic vibrations and vice versa, leading to a variety of uses for quartz oscillators in electronics.

Quartz also shows pyroelectric effects, indicating an apparent polarity of its **a** axes. Such polarity is anomalous, since it is not permitted by symmetry 32. A possible mechanism is that stress from nonuniform heating induces piezoelectric effects on temperature change.

In most insulators (i.e., nonconductors of electricity, which includes most nonmetallic minerals), imposition of an external electric field displaces electric charge in a crystal and creates polarization within a structure. Four contributors to total polarizability within a structure are ionic, electronic, dipolar, and space charge (Fig. 4-3).

In crystals where bonding is best described as ionic, an external electric field displaces anions and cations in opposite directions from their equilibrium positions. Electronic polarizability is displacement of an electron cloud with respect to its atomic nucleus. A dipole, such as OH^- and its H proton embedded in the O electron cloud, may be randomly oriented with respect to a crystal structure, but aligned by an electric field to contribute dipolar polarization to total charge. Space-charge polarization arises when charge carriers, which may be impurity ions, are displaced as a result of an external field, cations toward a cathode and anions toward an anode. Induced electric fields in boreholes may be correlated with rock lithology and mineralogy.

Band Model Characteristically, insulators are materials with low electrical conductivity, whereas metals have high conductivity. In developing electronic configurations of atoms (Sec. 1-1), we conceptually added electrons to isolated atomic nuclei according to certain rules.

In an idealized band model, we conceive these same atomic nuclei at their equilibrium lattice positions in a crystal structure. Rather than add electrons to an individual nucleus, in this formalism we add electrons to an entire periodic array of nuclei (Fig. 4-4; Prog. 4-1). Energy levels from each individual nucleus combine to form energy bands in a crystal structure. Since each nucleus can accept two electrons of opposite spin in each suborbital, a band in a structure of N nuclei can accept $2N$ electrons. But the Pauli exclusion principle permits no more than two electrons to have the exact same energy level. Thus, a sharp orbital energy level of an atom broadens to a narrow, but finite, energy band in a crystal structure. Each atomic orbital contributes to one band in a structure.

Imagine each atomic nucleus to represent an energy well and add electrons N at a time to a structure of N atomic particles. Given a periodic array of N Na nuclei, for example, $2N$ electrons exactly fill its $1s$ band. An additional $2N$ electrons fill its $2s$ band, and $6N$ more fill its $2p$ band. These bands are deep within energy wells created by our periodic array of N Na^+ nuclei.

Its $3s$ band, however, overlaps barriers between energy wells. Add N more electrons to create electrostatic neutrality, and but slight energy is required to excite these conduction electrons into the unfilled half of its $3s$ band where they may flow from nucleus to nucleus. Crystalline Na^0 thus is metallic. Had our energy wells been created by Mg nuclei, an additional N electrons into its $3s$ band would have created electrostatic neutrality. In this case, however, the energy range of the $3s$ band overlaps that of the $3p$ band. Hence, slight excitation energy pushes a $3s$ electron from nucleus to nucleus by way of a vacant $3p$ orbital. Crystalline Mg^0 is also metallic.

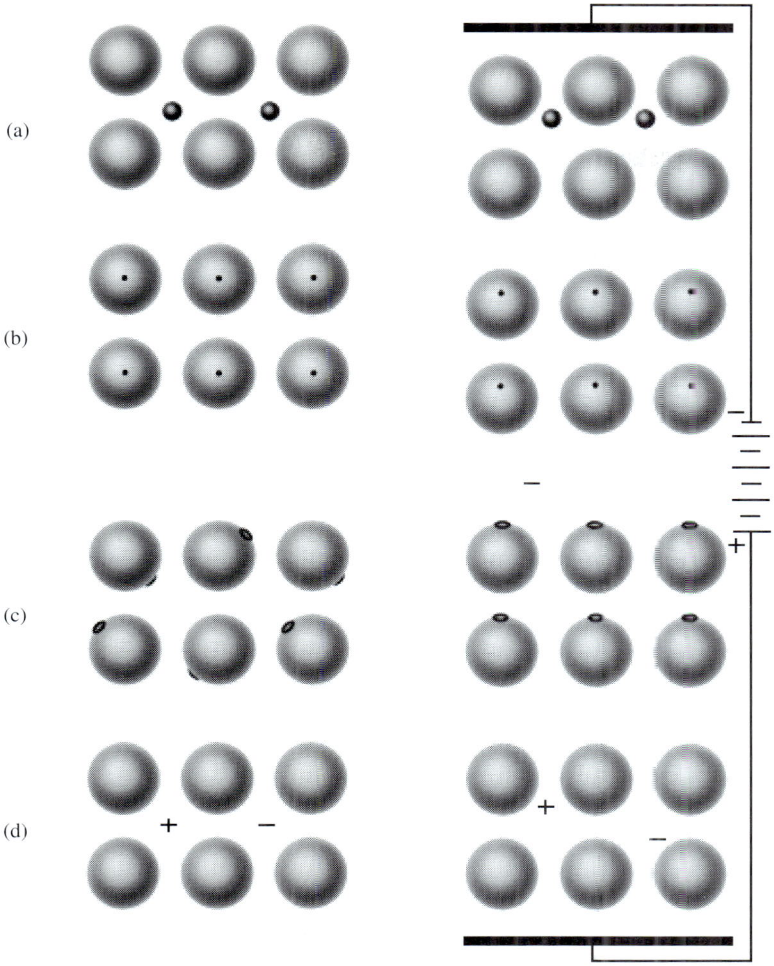

FIGURE 4-3 Polarizability. Schematic representation of crystal structures (left) are depicted with their response to an external electric field (right). (a) Ionic response finds anions displaced toward the anode and cations toward the cathode from their equilibrium positions. (b) Electric response occurs as electron clouds of ions are displaced toward the anode with nuclei displaced slightly toward the cathode. (c) Dipolar radicals or molecules rotate so that their positive end points toward the cathode and their negative end toward the anode. (d) Charge carriers are displaced from their equilibrium positions by an external electric field.

With an idealized band model, metallic conductors have partly filled valence bands or have overlapping vacant conduction bands. Insulators have a full valence band within an energy well but separated from a next higher energy conduction band by a large energy gap (E_g) (forbidden

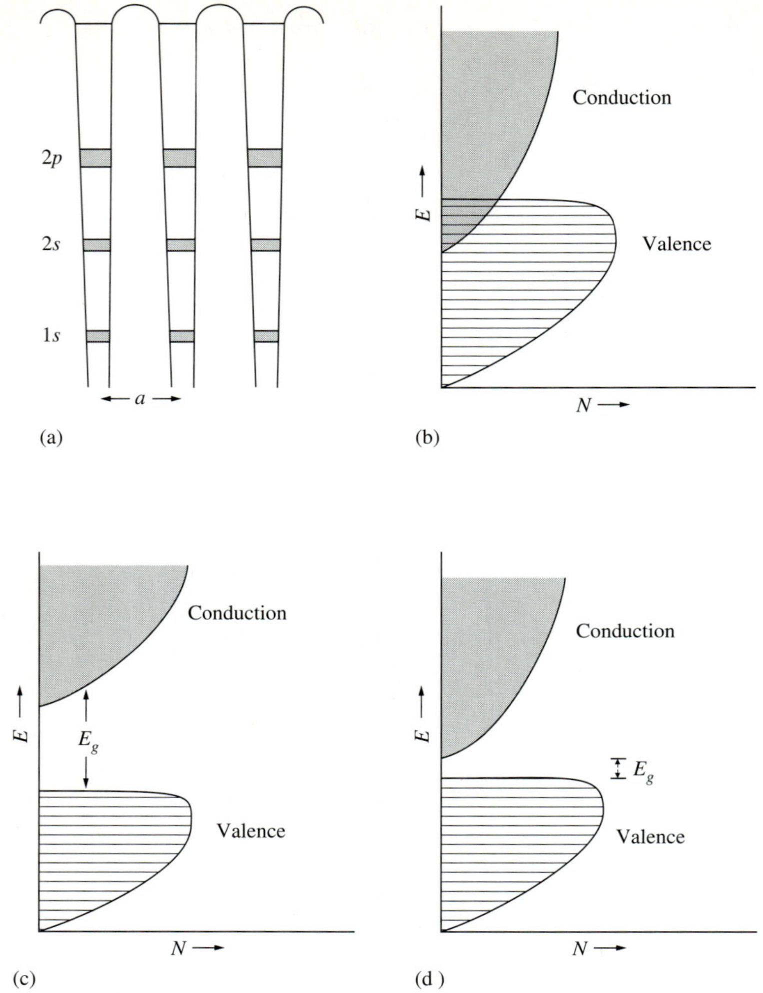

FIGURE 4-4 Band model. (a) Three energy "wells" in a section of a sodium crystal are depicted. Energy bands with electrons are shaded. (b) Band model of a metal shows overlap between valence bands (ruled) and conduction bands (shaded). (c) Band model of an insulator shows a large energy gap (E_g) between filled valence band and empty conduction band. (d) Band model of an intrinsic semiconductor has a small energy gap (E_g) between valence and conduction bands.

zone). Metals have delocalized electrons that can be readily excited to pass from nucleus to nucleus, whereas insulators have localized electrons.

When an external electric field is applied to a metal, conduction electrons initially accelerate in a direction opposite to this external field. Since metal ions make up the bulk of the volume of a metal, however, collisions between conduction electrons and metal ions limit free paths of these electrons. Although a net drift of conduction electrons parallel to an external field gradient occurs, collisions limit conductivity (its reciprocal is resistivity) of a metal to a finite value that is a characteristic of each pure metal. Since thermal vibrations increase effective ionic size as temperature rises, collision frequency also increases and conductivity decreases.

For metallic crystals with isometric symmetry and for randomly oriented aggregates of nonisometric crystals, conductivity is independent of crystallographic direction. For anisotropic metallic crystals, electrical conductivity depends on crystallographic orientation with respect to an external field. Conductivity parallel to **c** of metals with hexagonal close-packed structures may differ from that in the plane containing **a** by an amount ranging from a few percent to more than 20%.

Hybrid Orbitals In graphite, a nonmetal, electrical conductivity parallel to **c** is two orders of magnitude less than in the basal plane. To account for this crystallographically controlled difference in electrical properties of graphite, we must introduce a concept involving molecular orbitals. Atomic *s* orbitals are illustrated as spherical shells, and *p* orbitals as dumbbell-shaped surfaces (Fig. 1-2). Carbon structures and properties require an idealized bond that combines characteristics of *s* and *p* orbitals into hybrid *sp* (Prog. 4-2) orbitals.

Since electrostatic repulsion separates *p* electrons into two of three available *p* orbitals, the electronic structure of C may be expanded to $1s^22s^22p^12p^12p^0$ (compare Sec. 1-1). Electron-spin repulsion then moves one 2*s* electron to the vacant 2*p* orbital, thereby creating four hybrid $2(sp^3)$ orbitals with one electron each oriented toward corners of a tetrahedron (Fig. 4-5). Tetrahedral bonding in diamond results from shared electrons in each of these four hybrid $2(sp^3)$ orbitals for the diamond structure (Fig. 2-1); this structure is stable at high pressures.

In graphite structure, two 2*p* orbitals hybridize with the 2*s* orbital to form three coplanar $2(sp^2)$ hybrid orbitals at 120° to each other with the remaining 2*p* orbital at right angles to the plane of the hybrid orbitals (Fig. 4-5). The four valence electrons of C distribute themselves one each to three hybrid $2(sp^2)$ orbitals and one to the remaining 2*p* for a hybrid configuration of $1s^22(sp^2)^32p^1$. Each $2(sp^2)$ orbital overlaps and shares its electrons with the three neighboring C ions in the basal sheet of six-membered rings with strong covalent bonding (Prog. 4-2). The remaining *p* orbitals at right angles to the basal sheet overlap to create π bonds. Thus, π electrons are free to move from ion to ion in each sheet to account for the good electrical conductivity of graphite parallel to its basal plane. Adjacent sheets in graphite structure are bonded only by van der Waals forces in the **c** direction, accounting for much lower conductivity parallel to [0001] and for the easy basal cleavage in graphite.

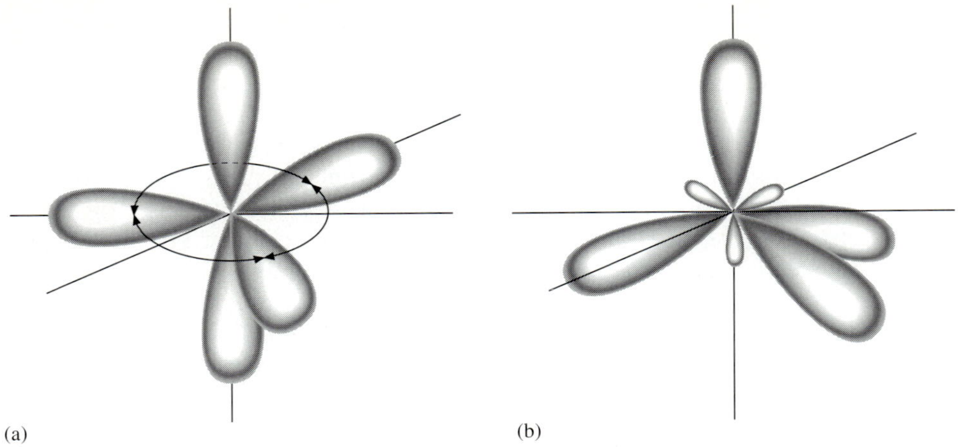

FIGURE 4-5 Hybrid orbitals. (a) Two 2 *p* orbitals hybridize with one 2 *s* orbital to form three coplanar 2 (sp^2) orbitals at 120°. The remaining *p* orbital is normal to the plane of the hybrid orbitals (compare Figs. 1-1 and 3-6). (b) 2 *p* orbitals hybridize with 2 *s* orbitals to form four 2 (sp^3) orbitals directed at the apices of a tetrahedron (compare Fig. 2-1).

Semiconductivity Band formalism, thus far, adds little to descriptions of metals and insulators in terms of idealized ionic, covalent, and metallic bond models (Sec. 1-3) beyond unifying them. Minerals exist, however, with chemical bonding that is predominantly covalent but partly ionic; they are capable of conducting electricity; they are semiconductors. Pyrite and other sulfides fall into this class of minerals with electrical properties that are used in exploration for them.

In an intrinsic semiconductor, a band gap with energy E_g between a filled valence band and an empty conduction band is so narrow that thermal excitation alone can excite an appreciable number of electrons from valence band to conduction band (Prog. 4-3). Each electron excited into a conduction band leaves behind a positively charged hole in a valence band. Negatively charged electrons (n) and positively charged holes (p) migrate when an electric field is applied, and both contribute to conduction in intrinsic semiconductors.

Since the number of thermally excited electrons depends on temperature, conductivity increases with increasing temperature. An intrinsic semiconductor may become an insulator upon sufficient cooling, and some insulators become semiconductors upon heating. Thus, a band model formalism serves to relate idealized ionic and covalent bonding with localized electrons to idealized metallic bonding with mobile electrons in addition to making sense out of brittle minerals with metallic luster, which includes many sulfides.

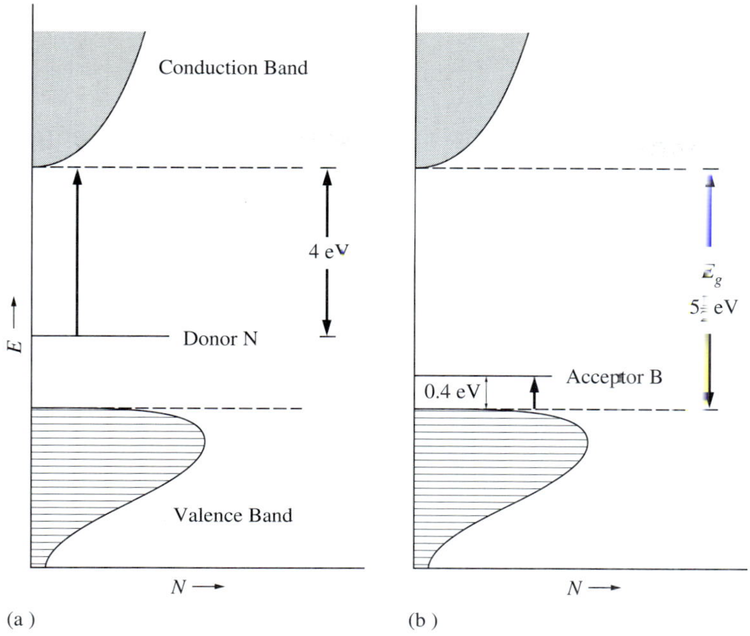

FIGURE 4-6 Diamond impurity semiconductor. (a) Impurity nitrogen ions replacing carbon ions cause a donor level to occupy the energy gap for diamond. (b) Impurity boron ions replacing carbon ions cause an acceptor level to occur within the energy gap for diamond.

Even a mineral with large E_g—an insulator—may display semiconduction if impurity ions are present. Impurity or doped semiconductors result from a presence of foreign atoms with greater or fewer electrons than a host and provide energy levels within a band gap or forbidden zone of that host.

For example, pure diamond has large E_g; it is an insulator. Wherever a N atom replaces a C atom in the diamond structure, the third $2p$ electron of N has an energy level that lies within its band gap between valence and conduction bands for pure diamond (Fig. 4-6). A photon of violet light has just enough energy to excite this donor electron (n) into the empty diamond conduction band. Diamond with as little as 10 ppm N impurity in it is an n-type impurity semiconductor at high temperature, is yellow in color (see Sec. 5-3), and is harder.

On the other hand, an atom of B with one fewer p electron than host C may substitute in a diamond structure. This B substitution leaves a p-orbital vacancy (a hole) within the band gap. Ambient temperature provides sufficient energy to excite a C valence-band electron into this acceptor level. Elevation of a p electron from C to the B impurity acceptor level leaves a mobile positive hole in the diamond valence band. Thus, diamonds with as little as 1 ppm B substitution for C are *p*-type impurity semiconductors that conduct electricity at room temperature and are blue because of associated light absorption (Fig. 4-6).

In both intrinsic and impurity semiconductors, increase in temperature increases the number of excited electrons and the number of positive holes. Thus, in distinct contrast to metallic electrical conduction, conductivity of semiconductors increases with increasing temperature.

4-5 MAGNETIC PROPERTIES

Magnetic characteristics of minerals arise from interactions of electron spins among ions within a crystal structure and between these spins and any external magnetic field. Response of a mineral to a magnetic field may be positive or negative, indicating that it may be attracted to or repelled by a magnetic field gradient.

When electrons are spin-paired, magnetic polarity associated with each electron is canceled. Unpaired electrons, however, give a net magnetic polarity to ions with which they are associated; the strength of this polarity is determined by the number of unpaired electrons. Transition-metal and rare-earth ions can have one or more unpaired electrons.

Magnetic Susceptibility Response of a mineral to an external magnetic field may be expressed in terms of a dimensionless quantity, the magnetic susceptibility $\bar{\chi}$ (chi bar), which ranges from 10^{-5} for weak responses to 10^{+6} for strong responses. Values of $\bar{\chi}$ for minerals may be sensitive to temperature change and show abrupt changes at magnetic transition temperatures.

In many minerals, all electrons are paired by chemical bonding between constituent ions, thus canceling magnetic properties associated with each electron. An external magnetic field causes small changes in electron orbitals, which results in a small negative value for $\bar{\chi}$. This diamagnetism is common to, among others, colorless rock-forming minerals.

Ferromagnesian minerals, among others, contain relatively small amounts of Fe and other transition-metal ions. Since these metal ions with their unpaired *d* electrons are separated one from another by other ions with paired electrons, unpaired electrons can interact only weakly, leaving their spin directions randomly oriented. An external magnetic field causes alignment of spins of unpaired electrons, resulting in a positive value for $\bar{\chi}$. This response of transition-metal ions in dilute solution is paramagnetism. Paramagnetic effects decrease with increasing temperature since thermal vibrations inhibit magnetic alignment of ions with unpaired electrons.

Some semiconductors, such as pyrite, also are paramagnetic. An external magnetic field causes a slight energy change in conduction bands such that unpaired electrons of opposite spins are unequal in number. This type of paramagnetism is relatively insensitive to temperature changes.

Magnetic Domains When spins of unpaired electrons interact appreciably among neighboring ions, ordered magnetic configurations form within a crystal structure. A magnetic domain is that part of a structure with one possible magnetic configuration; a single crystal may consist of several domains. Above a certain temperature, which is characteristic for each mineral species, a nonstructural phase transformation occurs to destroy these ordered configurations, and these minerals become paramagnetic. As a mineral cools through this transformation temperature, magnetic ordering occurs spontaneously.

Three kinds of magnetic order occur in minerals. In native iron, nickel, and their natural alloys, separation between nearest-neighbor atoms is relatively short so that unpaired *d* electrons align with parallel spins. This type of magnetic order is ferromagnetism (synthetic ferromagnets need not contain iron). The critical temperature above which thermal vibration destroys magnetic order is the Curie point. Ferromagnets have large and positive values for $\overline{\chi}$.

Each domain in a ferromagnet is magnetically polar, parallel to one $\langle 100 \rangle$ in the case of native iron. Hence, in a single crystal six directions of spontaneous magnetic polarization (easy magnetization) yield six possible domain orientations. Iron is structurally isometric holohedral ($4/m\ \bar{3}\ 2/m$), but polarity along one of its **a** axes reduces its magnetic symmetry to tetragonal ($4mm$).

Superexchange In many transition-metal oxides and sulfides, spins on adjacent ions with unpaired electrons are aligned antiparallel to one another. This alignment is brought about by a superexchange interaction operating through each intervening anion effectively to pair ionically unpaired electrons (Prog. 4-4). Magnetic order by superexchange interaction of this type is antiferromagnetism, which gives small positive values for $\overline{\chi}$.

Superexchange interaction may be visualized with a small portion of an antiferromagnetic structure consisting of two metal ions separated by an anion. Chemical bonding with ionic and covalent characteristics makes this interaction possible. Valence electrons of transition-metal ions are not fully ionized but exist simultaneously as *d* electrons on a metal cation and as *p* electrons on an intervening anion.

If *d* orbitals of a cation are less than half-filled, a valence electron has its lowest energy when it occupies a vacant *d* orbital with spin aligned parallel with other *d* electrons. This same electron, however, partially

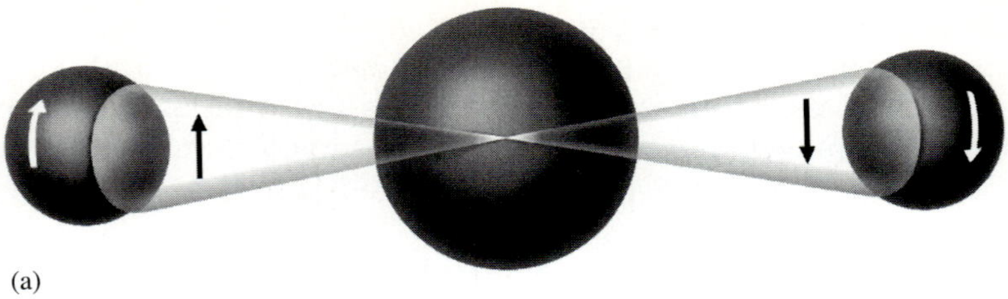

(a)

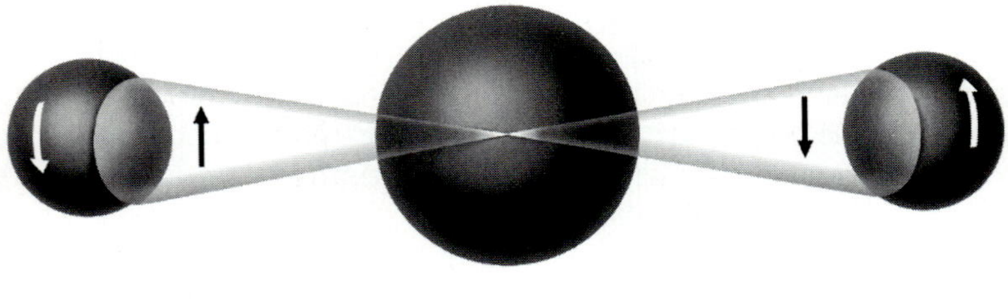

(b)

FIGURE 4-7 Superexchange interaction. A portion of a ferrimagnetic crystal structure is represented schematically by two transition-metal cations and one intervening anion. The "dumbbell" shape represents a *p* orbital of the anion (compare Fig. 1-2), and arrows represent electron spins. Electron transfer from cation to anion is not complete, as depicted by overlap of an anion *p* orbital with cation *d* orbitals. (a) When cation *d* orbitals are less than half full, an incompletely transferred valence electron aligns itself spin parallel to other *d* electrons in a high-spin state. As a *p* electron on the anion, however, its spin must be opposite to the other *p* electron as required by the Pauli exclusion principle (Sec. 1-2). Thus, *d* electrons on the opposite cation must also be aligned oppositely. (b) When cation *d* orbitals are half or more full, the incompletely transferred valence electron is paired with a *d* electron of opposite spin. This pairing, coupled with pairing of *p* electrons on the anion, causes *d* orbitals on cations on opposite sides of an anion to have opposing net spins.

occupies a *p* orbital on an adjacent anion. The other electron in that *p* orbital has its spin antiparallel to the first in accordance with the Pauli exclusion principle (Sec. 1-1). This second *p* electron, in turn, partially occupies a vacant *d* orbital on the next adjacent transition-metal ion. Since all *d* electrons on each cation with less than half-filled *d* orbitals have parallel spins, *d* electrons on opposite sides of an anion, therefore, must have antiparallel spins (Fig. 4-7).

If, on the other hand, *d* orbitals are more than half-filled with electrons, the result is the same. A valence electron pairs itself with a *d* electron in direction opposite to the net spin of unpaired electrons. But as a *p* electron on the next adjacent anion, this electron has spin opposite to the other *p* electron in that orbital. The second *p* electron of this intervening anion must pair itself with a *d* electron on the next adjacent cation, again forcing opposite spins on opposite sides of a bonding anion in an antiferromagnetic structure. Repetition of this alternation of cation spin polarity throughout a three-dimensional crystal structure leaves no net polarity on it.

Ferrimagnetism Antiferromagnetism occurs where spins of electrons on adjacent transition-metal cations are aligned antiparallel and are equal in number. If neighboring cation spins are unequal in number, net magnetic polarity is imparted on a crystal structure. Small to moderate positive χ values characterize this ferrimagnetism. The most important natural ferrimagnet is magnetite, although pyrrhotite and maghemite (cubic defect Fe_2O_3) also exhibit this property.

Magnetite has an inverse spinel structure (Sec. 2-3) in which all Fe^{2+} and half of Fe^{3+} are in octahedral coordination, with the remaining half of Fe^{3+} in tetrahedral coordination. Superexchange interaction aligns all spins of octahedrally coordinated Fe^{2+} and Fe^{3+} antiparallel to spins of tetrahedrally coordinated Fe^{3+}. Spins of octahedral Fe^{3+} pair with spins of tetrahedral Fe^{3+}, thus, canceling their magnetic polarity. Spontaneous magnetization of one Fe^{2+} per formula unit remains in this structure (Fig. 4-7).

Directions of spontaneous magnetic polarity in magnetite are $\langle 111 \rangle$, which results in eight possible domain orientations in each crystal. Structural symmetry of magnetite is isometric holohedral ($4/m\ \bar{3}\ 2/m$), but polarity of a single triad axis reduces its magnetic symmetry to trigonal ($3m$).

When all possible domains of a magnetic mineral (ferromagnetic or ferrimagnetic) are equal in number and size, no spontaneous magnetization occurs, such as is exhibited by a bar magnet or a specimen of lodestone magnetite. Polarities of different domains effectively cancel one another by forming closed flux loops in this state of lowest magnetic energy. For a sample to have a net polarity, domains of one magnetic polarity must predominate in size or number over all others.

Application of an external magnetic field to a magnetic mineral raises energy levels of different domains differently; those domains with polarities most favored by an external magnetic field may grow at the expense of all other domains. Increase in strength of an external magnetic field eventually causes each crystal in it to become a single magnetic domain having as direction of magnetic polarity a single polar axis angularly closest to this external field, a $\langle 100 \rangle$ direction in native iron or a $\langle 111 \rangle$ direction in magnetite. Magnetic saturation occurs when an external magnetic field is so strong that magnetic polarity of a specimen rotates away from a polar crystallographic direction and becomes parallel to the external field direction in totality (Fig. 4-8).

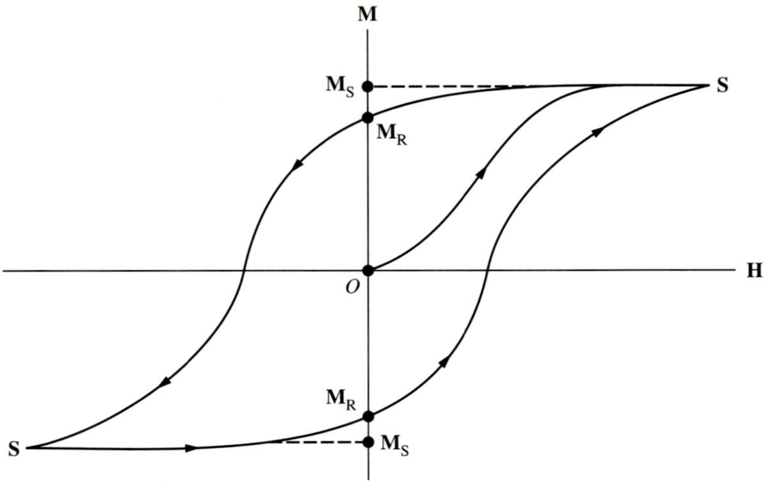

FIGURE 4-8 Magnetic response of magnetic minerals. H represents an external magnetic field, M the magnetization of a mineral, and point *O* no spontaneous magnetization. M_R represents remanent magnetization, and M_S magnetic saturation. Application of an external magnetic field (H) to a magnetic mineral with no spontaneous magnetization eventually leads to magnetic saturation. Reduction of an external field to zero permits magnetic alignments to relax to the nearest crystallographic direction of easiest magnetization leaving remanent magnetism (M_R). Reversal of an external magnetic field first reduces remanent magnetization to zero, then reaches saturation in the opposite direction.

Natural Remanent Magnetism Upon reduction of magnetic field strength below magnetic saturation of a mineral, magnetic polarity spontaneously reverts to the nearest polar crystallographic direction. Further reduction in magnetic field strength, however, promotes little, if any, immediate domain growth since new domains require additional energy to nucleate and grow (Sec. 7-1). Such a sample exhibits remanent magnetism. Although considerably weaker than saturation strength, earth's geomagnetic field does impart natural remanent magnetism to magnetite and to other magnetic minerals.

Natural remanent magnetism occurs in igneous rocks when those magnetic minerals present cool through their Curie temperatures and develop spontaneously oriented magnetic domains with a preference for those closely parallel to the geomagnetic field at the time of magnetic inversion. During formation of sedimentary clastic rocks, settling grains with natural remanent magnetism preferrentially align themselves with the existing geomagnetic field. Any crystallization or recrystallization at temperatures below the Curie inversion temperature may also produce natural remanent magnetism. Natural remanent magnetism can be destroyed or altered by subsequent recrystallization, by heating above the

Curie temperature, or by shock waves such as may be generated by meteorite impact or by blasting for construction.

Studies of natural remanent magnetism (paleomagnetism) have led to conclusions that the geomagnetic dipole has decayed and reversed itself repeatedly through geologic time and that it has wandered with respect to lithospheric tectonic plates in our geologic past. These conclusions led to construction of a geomagnetic time scale that may be locally more precise than radiometric or paleontologic time scales. These studies confirm that the earth's crust is composed of lithotectonic plates that move with respect to one another over geologic time.

4-6 RADIOACTIVITY

Some atomic nuclei are not stable but alter spontaneously to a different species of nucleus. Causes for this instability are poorly understood and quite beyond the scope of mineralogy. Certain properties and consequences of radioactive decay (spontaneous nuclear change), however, are mineralogically important. When or how a particular unstable nucleus will decay is impossible to predict. Given a sufficiently large number of such nuclei (any chemically measurable quantity is sufficiently large), however, decay rate is a quantity that is proportional to the number of nuclei present. This constant of proportionality, known as the decay constant, is unique for each radioactive isotope. This decay constant may be used to calculate a half-life of an isotope, which is the length of time required for half the nuclei present to decay spontaneously.

Decay Processes Radioactive isotopes change their chemical identity by one or more of four processes. A nucleus may emit an α particle, a He^{2+} ion with mass 4. Alpha decay produces a daughter nucleus that is two elements lower in the periodic chart of chemical elements and 4 mass units lighter (Fig. 4-9). Thus, a U ion or atom, atomic number 92 and atomic mass 235 or 238, transmutes by α-particle decay to a Th ion or atom, atomic number 90 and mass 231 or 234, respectively.

A second decay scheme involves emission of a β particle (an electron) from an atomic nucleus. Effective mass does not change with β emission, but daughter elements are one atomic number higher in the periodic chart of chemical elements. The Rb isotope with mass 87 decays by β emission to ^{87}Sr. In effect, a neutron emits a nuclear electron to become a proton, thereby increasing atomic number by one. A third mode of transmutation involves nuclear capture of a K electron. This K capture converts a proton to a neutron with a resulting daughter isotope one element lower in the periodic chart; for example, K capture converts ^{40}K to ^{40}Ar.

Spontaneous nuclear fission is a fourth mode of atomic transmutation. In this process, an unstable nucleus splits into two or more atomic nuclei

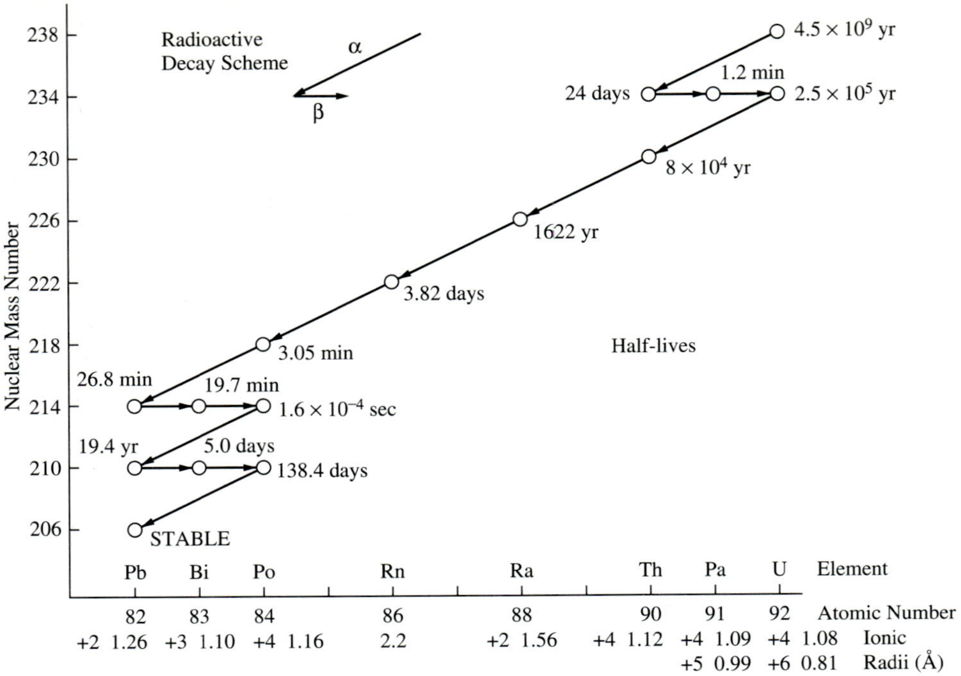

FIGURE 4-9 Radioactive decay of ^{238}U. Uranium decays to daughter elements, the ions of which have sizes and charges different from U^{4+} or U^{6+}. Change in size and charge of cations breaks up coordination polyhedra, causing metamictization. Decay schemes of ^{235}U and ^{232}Th differ in detail, but changes in charge and radius are just as drastic.

that may or may not be stable isotopes. Spontaneous nuclear fission may be accompanied by α, β, or γ radiation.

Metamictization Decay of a radioactive isotope of an ion in a crystal structure may alter it profoundly. Partial destruction of a crystal structure may result in metamictization (Sec. 1-7). Direct transmutation of U^{4+} with radius 108 pm (1.08 Å) to Pb^{4+} with radius 86 pm (0.86 Å) might not by itself destroy a coordination of O^{2-} polyhedra, but intermediate daughter elements have a much wider range of radii and different valence states (Fig. 4-9). This radius change along with recoil from particle emission knocks ions out of equilibrium structural positions with loss of X-ray diffraction crystallinity when about 20% of structural ions are displaced. Most minerals with essential U or Th, such as uraninite and thorite, are metamict and minerals in which these elements substitute, such as zircon, become partially metamict over geologic time periods.

Radioactive decay of ^{40}K to ^{40}Ar by K capture or to ^{40}Ca by β decay results in substantial change in size and valence. Structural damage to K-bearing minerals is slight since radioactive ^{40}K constitutes only about 0.01% of total natural K. In spite of constituting about one third of natural Rb, decay of ^{87}Rb does little structural damage to minerals since it is dispersed mostly in K minerals (see Chap. 7).

Alpha particles, becoming He^{2+} once liberated from a nucleus, are very strong oxidizing agents. One result of α decay is oxidation of reduced metal ions such as Fe^{2+} to Fe^{3+} in surrounding ferromagnesian minerals, producing a discoloration halo around minerals containing α emitters. Another result is recoil sufficient to knock ions out of their structural positions.

Autoradiography Emission of radiation by decaying radioactive nuclei permits their detection and, when compared with suitable calibrated standards, measurement of their concentrations. Since radiation affects photographic emulsions, attaching a sheet of photographic film to a polished surface of a mineral or mineral aggregate in darkness for a sufficient length of time yields, upon development, a picture of distribution of radioactive elements, an autoradiograph. Since each nuclear decay yields ionizing particles of characteristic mass and energy, detailed analysis of autoradiographs reveals the identity and locations of radioactive nuclei.

Autoradiographic analysis indicates that in most rocks trace amounts of U and Th are not dispersed uniformly but are concentrated in a few, commonly microscopic, crystals or metamict materials. In granitoid rocks, many of these radioactive grains are enclosed in biotite, which develops colored aureoles of oxidized and partially metamict material. These aureoles, called pleochroic halos, display concentric color variations, the radius of each being characteristic of an individual radiation emitter. Biotite and other minerals that develop pleochroic halos are thus natural autoradiographic materials.

Radiometric Ages Spontaneous nuclear transformations also permit measurement of time elapsed since a mineral containing radioactive isotopes became a closed system, that is, crystallized or recrystallized to retain daughter isotopes. This elapsed time is a radiometric age of a mineral or rock specimen. Measurement and interpretation of radiometric ages is the science of geochronology.

To a first approximation, differences in electronic charge and ionic radius between parent and daughter isotopes generally prevent entry of a daughter element into a crystal structure of a parent element. Where a nonradiogenic daughter isotope is present during crystallization, detailed isotopic analyses may be needed to reveal its presence. For instance, ^{204}Pb

has no radiogenic parent, and its presence may be used to compute total nonradiogenic Pb in a zircon crystal containing U and Th.

Amounts of parent and daughter isotopes are measured, generally with a mass spectrometer, to compute radiometric ages. Rate of radioactive decay is proportional to amount of parent isotope present according to $dN/dt = -\lambda N$, which integrates to $N/N_0 = \exp -\lambda t$, where N_0 represents the number of atoms initially present; N is the number remaining after time t for a decay constant λ. Thus, N is calculated from the number of daughter atoms ($N_0 - D = N$ for a closed system). Decay constants for each transmutation have been measured, permitting calculation of t, a radiometric age.

A half-life of a radioactive isotope is commonly given in place of its decay constant. When $N/N_0 = \frac{1}{2}$, the half-life $t_{1/2} = -(\ln \frac{1}{2})/\lambda = (\ln 2)/\lambda$. Radiometric ages, when combined with other geologic data, permit construction of a geochronologic time scale for earth history.

4-7 SURFACE PROPERTIES

In all preceding discussions, we have assumed explicitly that atoms or ions under consideration were in a crystalline environment and that crystal structures extended infinitely in all directions. Possibilities of slightly irregular environments were noted as structural defects (Sec. 1-6). Taken in this context, a surface of a crystalline solid might be considered the ultimate defect; no continuation of structure and associated lattice crosses a surface. In a polycrystalline aggregate a surface may have the same structure on either side of the boundary, but in entirely different and unrelated crystallographic orientations. A surface exposed to a liquid, a gas, or a vacuum has across it no crystalline environment whatsoever. The forces involved in crushing a mineral grain are sufficient to disturb the crystalline environment to depths of several atomic diameters.

A surface is that outer portion of a crystal structure where constituents no longer are in uniform crystal fields. Depth of surface disturbance (a surface phase) may range from one to several atomic layers into a crystal structure. Surface concentrations of constituent atomic particles are on an order of 10^{15} cm^{-2}, compared with bulk concentrations on an order of 10^{22} cm^{-3}. Hence, methods of surface analysis must be able to discern structure and composition of 10^{15} atoms from a background of 10^{22} atoms.

Surface Structure An ion in a crystal interior in an absence of defects is in a uniform crystalline environment. An ion at a surface is subject to a net attraction toward the bulk of a crystal that is not compensated by an equal attraction from whatever lies across that surface. This imbalance tends to strain surface atoms or ions into positions somewhat different from those that they occupy in the interior. Surface atoms are said to relax into new equilibrium positions. Depending on composition and crystallographic direction, this relaxation may be negligible (some metals), it may involve contraction of a few percent toward the crystal interior (some metals and alkali halides), or it may involve reconstruction to an order and unit cell completely different from crystal interiors (some oxides).

Structures of crystal surfaces, especially those created by crystal growth, display several characteristic phenomena (see Sec. 7-1). Surfaces represented by the smallest Miller indices, hence by highest atomic densities, may have large areas of perfect surface order at the atomic scale. There exist, however, terraces from a few to many atoms wide, steps that are commonly monatomic in height between terraces, kinks in steps, vacancies in terraces, and mobile adatoms (adsorbed atoms or clumps of atoms) on steps and terraces. Clearly, bulk chemical and structural characteristics of a surface are composed of some mix of different characteristics of atoms at these different sites.

Surfaces with high Miller indices tend to consist of a repetitious pattern of steps and kinks, each step and kink having low Miller indices That is to say, a surface that grossly may be assigned h, k, and l numbers of 4s, 5s, 6s, . . . at an atomic scale is a composite of terraces, kinks, and steps with h, k, and l numbers of 0s, 1s, and 2s. Specially prepared crystal surfaces may have up to one third of their atoms located on an ordered array of step sites (Fig. 4-10).

Surface Chemistry In addition to structural irregularities, chemical stoichiometry of a surface may differ from that of a crystal interior. One ion may be in excess on a surface, generally an anion except on some alkali halides where a cation may concentrate at a surface. Furthermore, unusual oxidation states may occur on surfaces. For instance, rutile [TiO_2] may have Ti^{3+} and corundum [Al_2O_3] may have Al^{2+} or even Al^{1+} at a surface. Electrostatic neutrality is maintained by ordered surface vacancies or by adsorbed impurities in these cases.

Surfaces are electrically polar, the strength of this polarity being a function of structure and chemical composition on its two sides. This surface polarity, or electrical double layer, may be fixed at a crystal-crystal interface or mobile at a crystal-fluid interface. Surface polarities determine wettability of mineral species. Degree of wetting by different fluids is determined by whether a molecule on a surface reduces or increases the overall surface energy.

Surface atoms, ions, or molecules are in a higher energy state than the same atomic particles in a crystal interior. Hence, where sufficient energy is available to break chemical bonds, recrystallization takes place to reduce surface areas; a crystal with no bounding surface would have the lowest energy of all. High-energy states of clean surfaces cause most

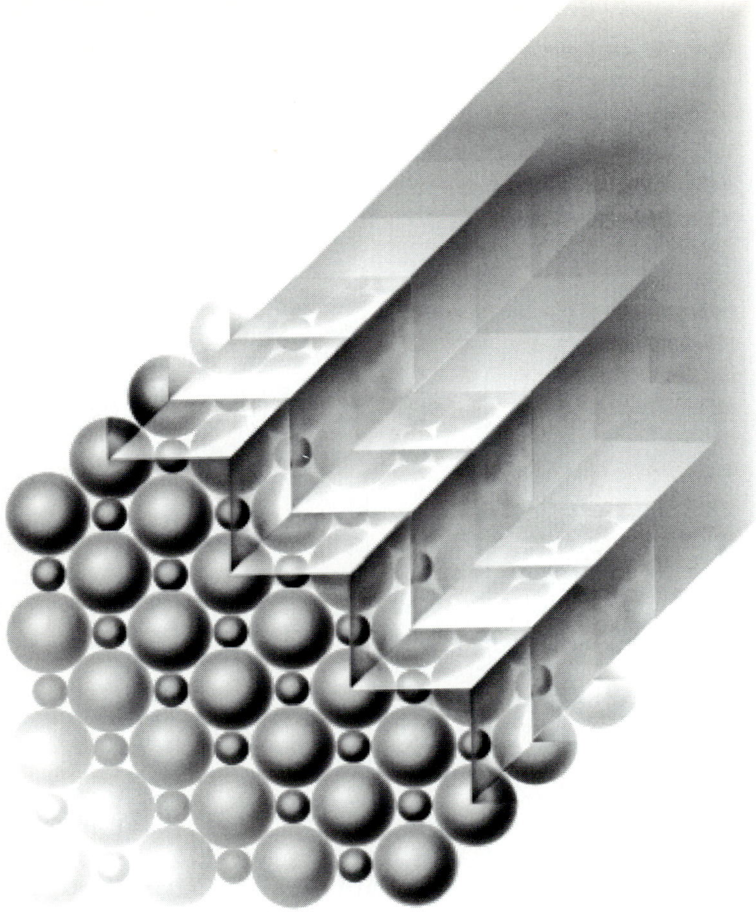

FIGURE 4-10 Composite crystal faces. A schematic representation of a dodecahedral (011) crystal face on a halite structure exists at the atomic level as alternating cube faces (010) and (001). Actual steps and terraces are larger than depicted but commonly below microscopic resolution.

mineral surfaces to coat themselves with a monolayer of adsorbed water, oxygen, sulfur, carbon, or hydrocarbon, which may be either atomic or molecular. This adsorbed monolayer strongly influences reactivity of a surface, including friction, wettability, solubility, crystal growth, oxidation and reduction kinetics, and other catalytic effects.

Mineral Separation Although crystal surfaces, whether generated by crystal growth, mechanical breakage, or chemical solution, are structurally and chemically different from crystal interiors, surfaces are just as

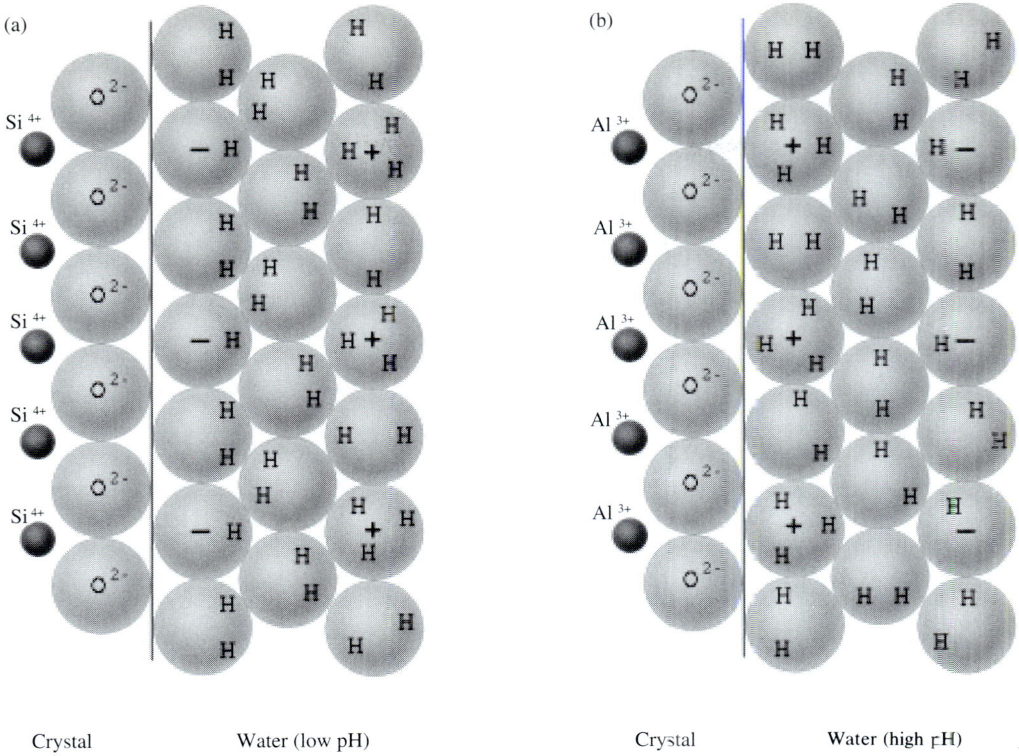

FIGURE 4-11 Polar surfaces. Highly charged cations distort their coordination polyhedra near a crystal surface in such a manner that these surfaces are composed wholly of anions. (a) Intergranular water with low pH caused by repulsion of H_3O^+ by Si^{4+} cations. (b) Intergranular water with high pH caused by attraction of H_3O^+ by anionic surface.

characteristic of a mineral species as are its internal structure and composition. Differences in surface properties are of considerable importance in procedures of mineral separation.

Water is a polar molecule, and many hydrocarbons are nonpolar. Diamonds separate readily from silicate gangue minerals with which they are found based on surface properties. Crushed diamond ore flushes down a grease table as an aqueous slurry. Silicate gangue minerals, well wetted by water, pass on, while poorly wetted diamonds stick in the grease on this table. Other poorly wetted minerals include zircon, beryl, topaz, spinel, corundum, and rutile, which are all less wetted than diamond.

Sulfide minerals separate from silicate and carbonate gangue minerals by flotation on a basis of wettability. Mix crushed ore and gangue with water and a small amount of fatty acid and a foaming agent. Sulfides are wetted by fatty acids, and gangue minerals are wetted by water. Even though sulfide ore minerals are denser than most gangue minerals, when air bubbles up through this slurry, oily sulfide particles ride up with the foam, while gangue minerals sink to the bottom.

Mutual repulsion between polarized surfaces can exceed the force of gravity on fine particles with high surface-to-volume ratios. Water between particles in colloidal suspension is forced by these polar surfaces to assume an almost crystalline arrangement, which at least temporarily prevents colloidal particles from sinking. Add salt with ions to balance these surface charges and colloids flocculate and sink. Fine clay particles rain out and choke harbors where fresh water mixes with seawater.

A slurry of freshly crushed mineral in distilled water develops an acidity, an abrasion pH, which is characteristic of a mineral species. For example, quartz concentrates H_3O^+ toward centers of interstices, thereby lowering the pH of slurry water (Fig. 4-11). On the other hand, corundum or hematite tend to collect H_3O^+ near their surfaces, rendering intergranular water less acidic. Silicates containing Al or Fe have intermediate abrasion pH, which depend on relative proportions of these elements. Unfortunately, abrasion pH is not reliably diagnostic for mineral identification because other factors, such as impurities, adsorbed matter, and particle size, can overwhelm this effect.

Surface polarities explain why mud pies and sand castles are possible. Water molecules next to clay and quartz grains are oriented with their positive, proton sides away from these surfaces. This polarization results in an electrostatic attraction between water near silicate surfaces and water central in intergranular space, an attraction that binds particles together (Fig. 4-11). Compare the quality of a castle built of moist quartz sand with one built of moist magnetite sand of the same size.

FURTHER READINGS

Azaroff, L. V., *Introduction to Solids.* New York: McGraw-Hill, 1969.

Clark, S. P., Jr. (ed.), *Handbook of Physical Constants*, Memoir 97. New York: The Geological Society of America, 1966.

Frye, K. (ed.), *The Encyclopedia of Mineralogy*. New York: Van Nostrand Reinhold, 1981.

Kieffer, S. W., and A. Navrotsky, *Microscopic to Macroscopic. Atomic Environments to Mineral Thermodynamics*. Washington, DC: Mineralogical Society of America, 1985.

Kittel, C., *Elementary Solid State Physics: A Short Course*. New York: Wiley, 1962.

Newnham, R. E., *Structure-Property Relations*. New York: Springer-Verlag, 1975.

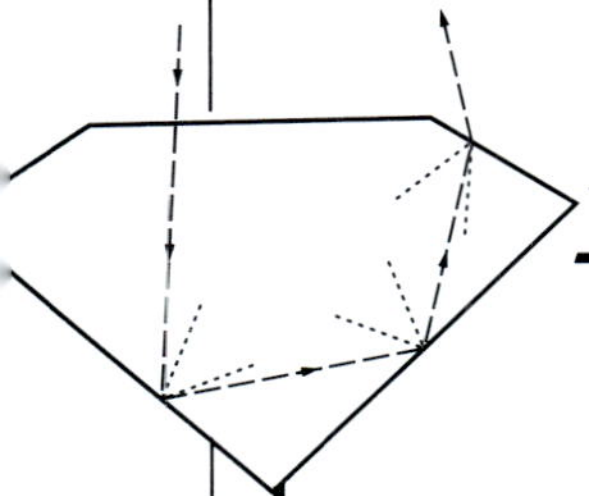

5

RADIANT ENERGY AND CRYSTALLINE MATTER

What is the nature of light? This question provoked scientific and philosophic controversy from the seventh decade of the 17th century until the third decade of the 20th century, a period of 250 years. Isaac Newton (1675) held that light was corpuscular based on its rectilinear propagation. Christiaan Huygens (1678) proposed that light traveled as waves analogous to waves on water. This issue was temporarily settled in favor of wave theory by Augustin Fresnel and Thomas Young (between 1800 and 1820), who observed that under certain conditions light bends around sharp edges and produces interference.

A wave theory of light received strong theoretical basis by James Clerk Maxwell (1856) when he demonstrated that light had properties in congruence with all other electromagnetic radiation. Thus, light waves were postulated to be perturbations of a luminiferous ether that pervaded our universe. Certain experimental results—photoemission of electrons from metal surfaces, long-wavelength shift in Compton scattering, even exposure of photographic emulsions—remained intractable to electromagnetic radiation theory.

Around the turn of the last century, Max Planck and other physicists sought to explain these otherwise inexplicable observations with a quantum theory, thereby reopening this old controversy over light's nature.

This question of the nature of electromagnetic radiation became even more unsettled when C. J. Davisson and L. H. Germer (between 1923 and 1927) demonstrated that electrons could be diffracted by crystal structures and, therefore, behaved as waves. Soon thereafter He atoms and H_2 molecules were diffracted. What theory could include electromagnetic radiation that behaved as ballistic particles and particulate matter that behaved like waves?

Light Resolved Resolution of the question of a dual nature of light appears in a theoretical argument set forth by Louis de Broglie in 1923. He observed that determination of positions of electrons on atoms involved integers (Sec. 1-1). At that time, the only other phenomena in physics that involved integers were light interference and harmonic vibrations. From these observations, de Broglie reasoned that periodicity—wave behavior—must be a property of electrons in orbitals about atoms. A de Broglie wavelength of electrons comes from the relationship

$$h\lambda = mv,$$

where h is Planck's constant, λ a wavelength associated with an electron, and mv is momentum (mass times velocity). This equation is analogous to one for the energy of a photon,

$$hc/\lambda = E,$$

where c is the velocity of light and E is its energy. The first equation describes diffraction of particulate matter; the second, quantum behavior of light.

These equations render meaningless that old question: Is light waves or particles? A similarly meaningless question would be: Is a billiards cue sporting equipment or lethal weaponry? Both questions can only be answered by describing what is being done at a particular time in a particular situation.

What, then, is the significance of using waves to describe motion of particles or quanta? Max Born answered that question in 1926. Certain experimental observations cannot be accounted for with an assumption that quanta and particles follow laws of Newtonian mechanics. Another fundamental law is required at this scale. You may now interpret wave equations as telling you the probability of finding non-Newtonian particles in any given place. Thus, de Broglie waves are not identical with matter, and electromagnetic waves are not identical with light. Rather, wave functions describe behavior. Note, this discussion does not mean that light is a special kind of matter. Light always travels at 3×10^{10} cm sec^{-1} in vacuo because it has zero rest mass; this is an impossibility for matter that has a finite rest mass.

Waves and Quanta Many interactions between radiant energy and minerals involve floods of energy that mask individual quanta and

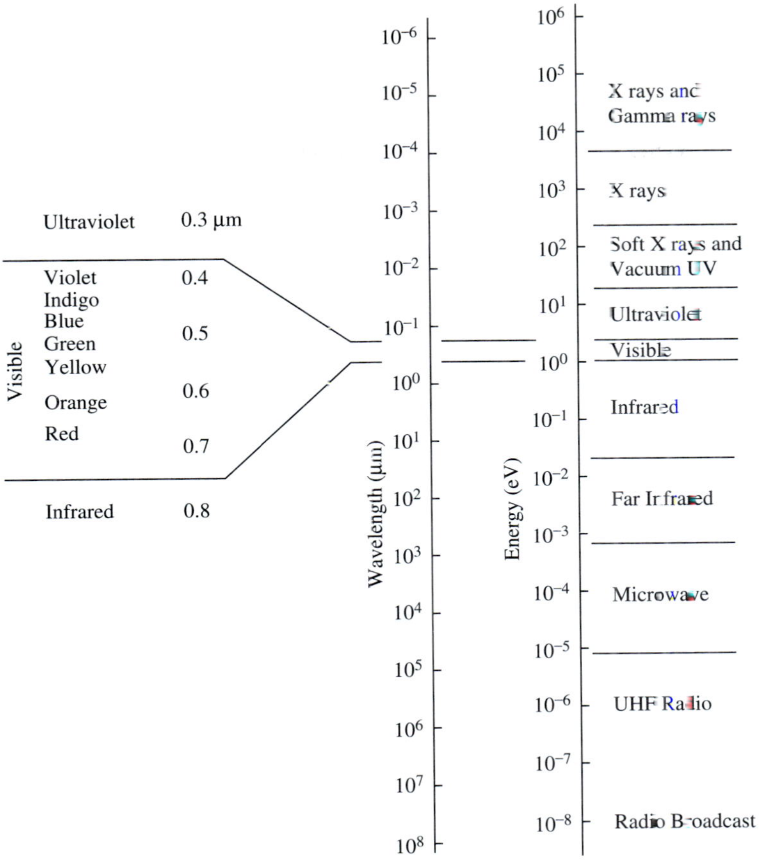

FIGURE 5-1 Electromagnetic spectrum. Different regions of the electromagnetic radiant energy spectrum are labeled with associated wavelength given in micrometers and quantum energy given in electron volts (1 eV = 1.24 μm).

involve no energy transfer. For these interactions, wave theory is entirely satisfactory; interactions involving energy transfer require quantum theory. The beauty of a cut and polished pale blue diamond requires wave theory to account for its fire and quantum theory to account for its color (Sec. 5-4). Focus of an ordinary camera requires reference to light waves, while exposure of its photosensitive emulsion requires reference to photons.

The electromagnetic spectrum (Fig. 5-1) ranges from radio frequencies at its long-wavelength end to cosmic radiation at its short-wavelength end. Divisions within this spectrum derive from methods of generation and detection, so boundaries overlap. Visible light (400–700 nm, 4000–

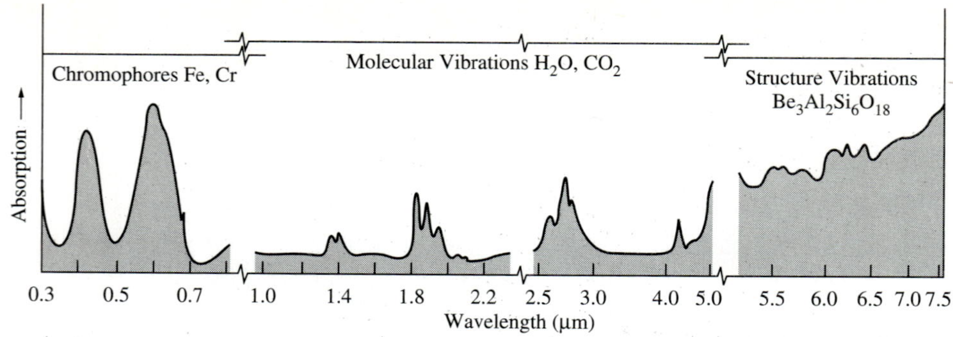

FIGURE 5-2 Absorption spectrum of beryl, emerald variety. Energy absorption of a crystal varies with wavelength of radiant energy incident upon it. Maximum transparency (minimum absorption) in the visible range is at 0.5 μm, and maximum absorption (minimum transparency) is at 0.43 and 0.60 μm. Thus, both red and violet light are absorbed, and this mineral appears green to the eye. [After D. L. Wood and K. Nassau, *Amer. Mineral.* 53 (1968): 778.]

7000 Å) is that limited part of this electromagnetic spectrum detected by a normal human eye.

Light incident upon a mineral may be transmitted, refracted, reflected, or absorbed. Absorption and emission spectral phenomena require a quantum description of light. Color and luster of minerals result from absorption of visible light, but instruments extend spectral studies far beyond the visible range. An absorption spectrum of a mineral (Fig. 5-2) may be interpreted in terms of kinds of atomic particles, the kinds of chemical bonds present, and the defects in a mineral. Indeed, in modern laboratories spectra are used to identify mineral structures.

5-1 MINERAL SPECTRA

Electrons on atoms and ions occupy discrete orbitals with finite differences in energy separating these orbitals (Sec. 1-1). The Pauli exclusion principle limits numbers of electrons in a given orbital, and all available electrons occupy the lowest energy orbitals under equilibrium conditions; the lowest energy state of an atom with all its electrons is its ground state. If an electron is excited to an unoccupied orbital, the energy of the atom is higher than that of the ground state. Finite differences in energy between electrons in the ground state and those in the lowest excited state can be designated ΔE; intermediate energy states are forbidden in that intermediate energy quanta are not absorbable.

Whenever a quantum of radiation with energy equal to ΔE strikes an excitable electron, energy of this quantum transfers to that electron. This now-excited electron jumps to an orbital of the higher energy state. In a real crystal structure with many atoms with a particular energy state, all quanta with that energy and wavelength are absorbed (providing a sample is thick enough). A quantum with energy less than ΔE passes on, as does one with more, since it would place this electron at a forbidden (i.e., nonexistent) energy level (Fig. 1-1). Thus, ions with excitable electrons operate as a filter, removing from a stream of white light all quanta of energy and wavelength equal to ΔE.

In actuality, owing to various defects in crystal structures (Sec. 1-6) and local variations in ionic environment, energy absorbed by real minerals in this fashion has a finite and appreciable width in any electromagnetic spectrum (Fig. 5-2). Presence of more than one kind of ion with excitable electrons and existence of different excited states above ground state lead to many different bands of radiation being absorbed by any mineral.

A crystal structure can absorb radiant energy in ways other than simple excitation of an electron. All are quantized. Each mode of energy absorption adds to the complexity of absorption and transmission of quanta as a function of wavelength of radiation impinging on a crystal.

Some mineral coloration results from photon absorption. White light is a mixture of all wavelengths of light in the visible part of the electromagnetic spectrum (Fig. 5-1). Colors are narrow bands of light or mixtures of narrow bands of light within this visible range. Photons with energy corresponding to an energy gap are absorbed; photons that do not may be transmitted. If a mineral sample absorbs part of the visible spectrum, that mineral's color is a mixture of wavelengths of light that are transmitted or reflected. Thus, a crystal structure that contains ions that provide many energy gaps near 1.91 eV (wavelength near 650 nm, 6500 Å) absorbs strongly in the red part of the spectrum and appears blue. Similarly, strong absorption near 2.75 eV (450 nm, 4500 Å) in the blue part results in a red mineral.

Crystal Fields Although *s* orbitals are spherically symmetrical, *d* orbitals are directional in spatial orientation (Sec. 1-1). In a free ion, all five *d* orbitals have the same energy; they are fivefold degenerate in that none can be distinguished from any other in this environment. If an ion is in a crystal structure, however, electron clouds of ligands—anions of its coordination polyhedron—interact with its *d* electrons. Energy levels of *d* orbitals are split by electron-electron repulsion between *d* electrons and electrons of anions.

In octahedral coordination, d_{xy}, d_{xz}, and d_{yz} orbitals point between ligands while $d_{x^2-y^2}$ and d_{z^2} point directly at them (Fig. 5-3). Electrostatic repulsion thus raises energy levels of $d_{x^2-y^2}$ and d_{z^2} orbitals while lowering energy levels of d_{xy}, d_{xz}, and d_{yz} orbitals. This energy separation and partial removal of degeneracy of *d* orbitals is called crystal field splitting and is designated Δ_o (o stands for octahedral). Each electron in one of

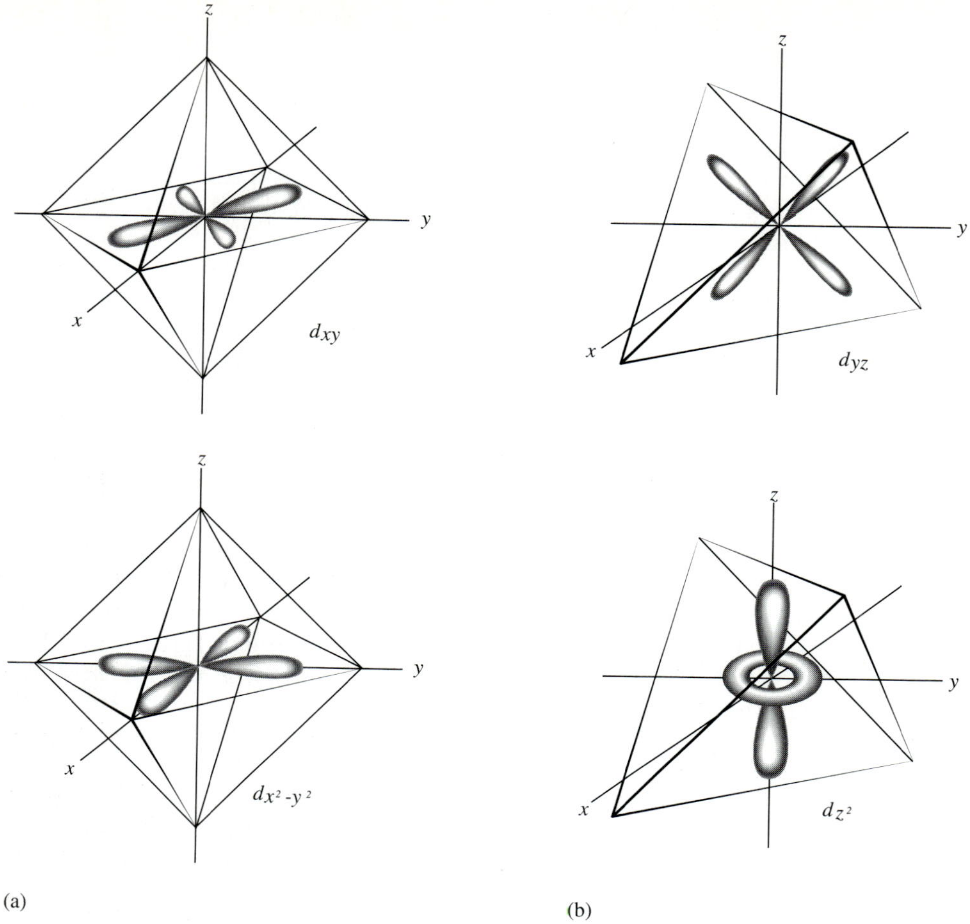

FIGURE 5-3 Coordination polyhedra and *d* orbitals. Electron-electron repulsions between *d* electrons and ligand electrons split these orbitals into separate energy states. (a) Octahedral coordination lowers the energy of a d_{xy} orbital but raises that of a $d_{x^2-y^2}$ because $d_{x^2-y^2}$ orbitals are directed toward ligands and d_{xy} orbitals are directed between ligands. (b) Tetrahedral coordination stabilizes d_{z^2} and destabilizes d_{yz} for the same reason. (After R. G. Burns, *Mineralogical Applications of Crystal Field Theory*. New York: Cambridge University Press, 1970.)

these lower three *d* orbitals stabilizes a transition-metal ion by $(2/5)\Delta_o$, and each electron in one of its upper two orbitals reduces stability by $(3/5)\Delta_o$ (Fig. 5-4). Summation of Δ_o terms gives crystal field stabilization energy (CFSE) for an ion in octahedral coordination (Table 5-1).

Ligands in tetrahedral and cubic coordination around a transition-metal ion energetically favor $d_{x^2-y^2}$ and d_{z^2} over d_{xy}, d_{xz}, and d_{yz} orbitals with CFSEs of Δ_t and Δ_c, respectively. Relative CFSEs are $\Delta_t = (-4/9)\Delta_o$

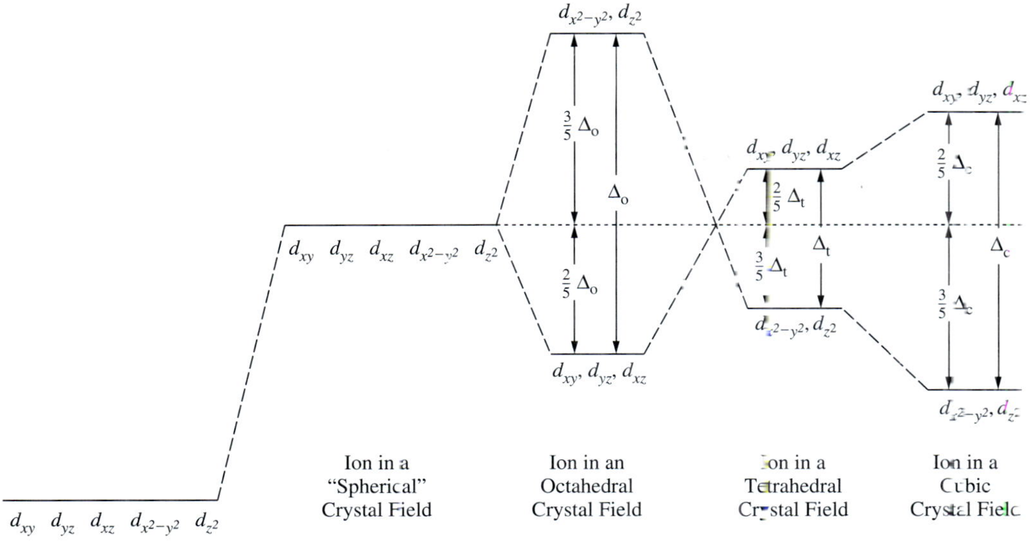

FIGURE 5-4 Crystal field splitting. A hypothetical "spherical" crystal field raises the energy state of *d* orbitals above a free-ion state. Octahedral, tetrahedral, and cubic crystal fields split *d* orbitals by an amount Δ. Mineral coloration occurs, in part, because Δ values lie in the visible and near-visible spectrum.

and $\Delta_c = (-8/9)\Delta_o$, partitioned as indicated in Fig. 5-4, when cations, ligands, and metal ligand distances are identical in the two coordinations.

In filling *d* orbitals, electrons fill the lowest energy orbitals first. Because of electron spin interactions, orbital electrons tend not to pair up but to maintain parallel spins in orbitals with little difference in energy. The first three *d* electrons on octahedrally coordinated transition-metal ions enter three lower energy orbitals, d_{xy}, d_{xz}, and d_{yz}. A fourth *d* electron may enter one of these lower energy orbitals by pairing spins with its other electron or one of the higher energy orbitals to maintain spin parallel to the other *d* electrons. The former is a low-spin configuration, and the latter is a high-spin configuration. Ions with high-spin configurations have larger ionic radii than the same ion with a low-spin configuration. Since spin-coupling energy is greater than CFSE in oxide and silicate structures, only high-spin radii are given (Table 1-5).

Reduction in ligand symmetry by distortion of octahedra further reduces degeneracy of *d* orbitals (Fig. 5-5). Depending on its number of *d* electrons, a transition-metal ion will seek out structural sites that give it a lowest possible CFSE, even to the extent of distorting a coordination polyhedron. Energy differences ΔE between *d* orbitals of transition-metal ions in crystal structure sites depend on atomic number, numbers of *d* electrons, coordination number of a cation, length of cation-anion bond, cation charge, and symmetry of coordinated ligands.

TABLE 5-1 Electron Distribution in *d* Orbitals and Crystal Field Stabilization Energies of Ions of the First Transition Series in Octahedral Coordination (High-Spin Configuration)

N_{total}	Ions	d_{xy}	d_{xz}	d_{yz}	$d_{x^2-y^2}$	d_{z^2}	N_{unpair}	CFSE
0	Ca^{2+}, Sc^{3+}, Ti^{4+}						0	0
1	Ti^{3+}	↑					1	(2/5) Δ_o
2	Ti^{2+}, V^{3+}	↑	↑				2	(4/5) Δ_o
3	V^{2+}, Cr^{3+}, Mn^{4+}	↑	↑	↑			3	(6/5) Δ_o
4	Cr^{2+}, Mn^{3+}*	↑	↑	↑	↑		4	(3/5) Δ_o
5	Mn^{2+}, Fe^{3+}*	↑	↑	↑	↑	↑	5	0
6	Fe^{2+}, Co^{3+}, Ni^{4+}*	↑↓	↑	↑	↑	↑	4	(2/5) Δ_o
7	Co^{2+}, Ni^{3+}*	↑↓	↑↓	↑	↑	↑	3	(4/5) Δ_o
8	Ni^{2+}	↑↓	↑↓	↑↓	↑	↑	2	(6/5) Δ_o
9	Cu^{2+}	↑↓	↑↓	↑↓	↑↓	↑	1	(3/5) Δ_o
10	Zn^{2+}, Ga^{3+}, Ge^{4+}	↑↓	↑↓	↑↓	↑↓	↑↓	0	0

*Also have low-spin configurations.

From R. G. Burns, *Mineralogical Applications of Crystal Field Theory*. New York: Cambridge University Press, 1970.

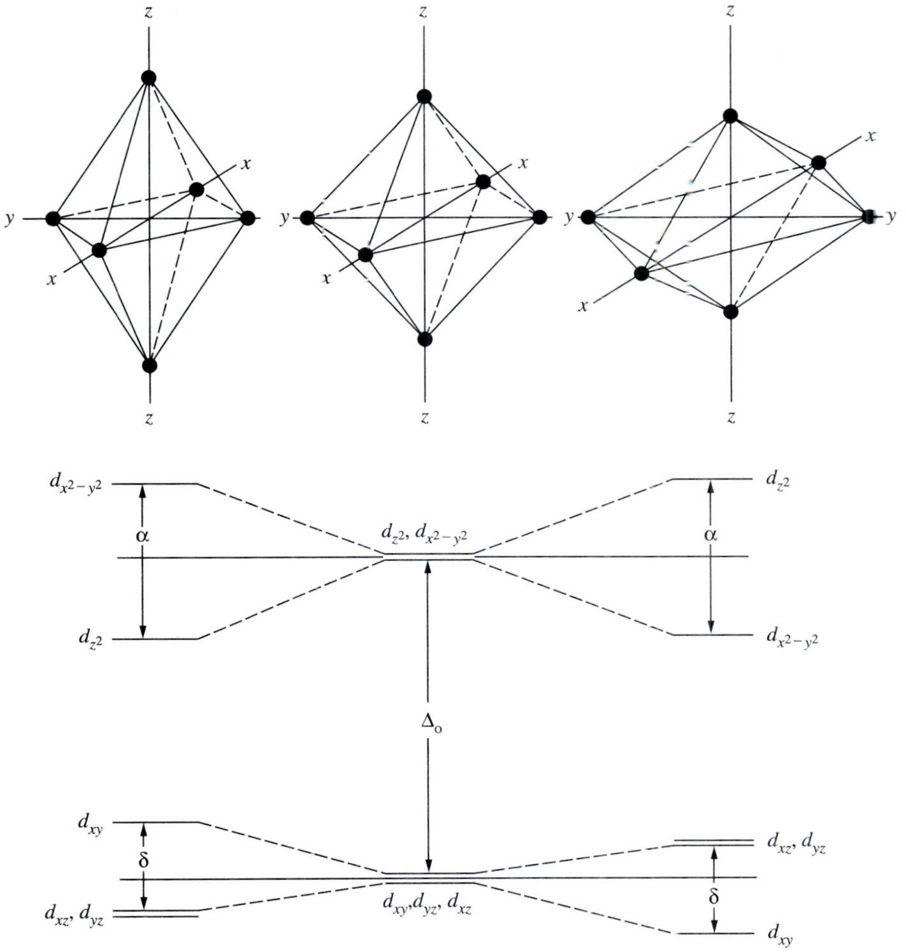

FIGURE 5-5 Distorted octahedral sites cause further splitting of *d* orbitals.

5-2 MINERAL COLORS

One mechanism by which colors develop in minerals results from transition-metal ΔE values that lie in visible and near-visible parts of the electromagnetic spectrum. Presence of transition-metal ions in a crystal structure thus causes selective absorption of some of the visible spectrum, that remaining imparting color to a mineral.

Mineralogists traditionally distinguish two classes of mineral coloration, idiochromatic and allochromatic. An idiochromatic (self-colored) mineral is one in which its chromophore (color bearer) is an essential constituent. Ferromagnesian minerals are mostly idiochromatic in that

TABLE 5-2 Idiochromatic Coloration by Transition Metals

Chromophore	Color	Mineral	Composition
Ce	Yellow	Parisite	$(Ce,La)_2Ca(CO_3)_3F_2$
Cr	Red	Phoenicochroite	$Pb_2O(CrO_4)$
	Orange	Crocoite	$PbCrO_4$
	Green	Uvarovite	$Ca_3Cr_2Si_3O_{12}$
Co	Pink	Erythrite	$Co_3(AsO_4)_2 \cdot 8H_2O$
		Roselite	$Ca_2(Co,Mg)(AsO_4)_2 \cdot 2H_2O$
		Sphaerocobaltite	$CoCO_3$
Cu	Red	Cuprite	Cu_2O
	Green	Dioptase	$CuSiO_2(OH)_2$
		Malachite	$Cu_2(CO_3)(OH)_2$
	Blue	Azurite	$Cu_3(CO_3)_2(OH)_2$
		Chrysocolla	$(Cu,Al)_2H_2Si_2O_5(OH)_4 \cdot nH_2O$
		Turquoise	$CuAl_6(PO_4)_4(OH)_8 \cdot 5H_2O$
Fe	Red	Almandine	$Fe_3Al_2Si_3O_{12}$
		Ludlockite	$(Fe,Pb)As_2O_6$
	Yellow	Cacoxenite	$Fe_9(PO_4)_4(OH)_{15} \cdot 18H_2O$
		Goethite	$FeO(OH)$
	Green	Olivine	$(Mg,Fe)Si_2O_4$
		Epidote	$Ca_2(Al,Fe)_3Si_3O_{12}(OH)$
	Blue	Lazulite	$(Mg,Fe)Al_2(PO_4)_2(OH)_2$
Mn	Pink	Rhodochrosite	$MnCO_3$
		Rhodonite	$(Mn,Fe,Ca)SiO_3$
	Orange	Spessartine	$Mn_3Al_2Si_3O_{12}$
	Yellow	Ganophyllite	$NaMn_3(OH)_4(Si,Al)_4O_{10}$
Ni	Green	Bunsenite	NiO
U	Orange	Curite	$Pb_2U_5O_{17} \cdot 4H_2O$
	Yellow	Autunite	$Ca(UO_2)_2(PO_4)_2 \cdot 10\text{–}12H_2O$
		Carnotite	$K_2(UO_2)_2(VO_4)_2 \cdot 3H_2O$

Data from K. Nassau, "The origins of color in minerals," *Amer. Mineral.* 63 (1978): 219–229.

Fe is an essential part of their composition. Table 5-2 lists some colored minerals with their chromophores.

An allochromatic (other-colored) mineral is one in which its chromophore is not an essential constituent, but something that may or may not be present, depending on specific genesis of a specimen. Many pale pastel-colored minerals, such as feldspars, quartz, and calcite, and even deeply colored ones such as ruby and emerald, owe their color varieties to traces of transition-metal cation impurities (Table 5-3).

Color Centers Presence of a transition metal is not necessarily required, however, for an unpaired electron to cause selective absorption of the visible spectrum by elevation into an excited energy state. A vacancy

TABLE 5-3 Allochromatic Coloration by Transition Metals

Chromophore	Color	Mineral	Composition
Cr	Red	Corundum (ruby)	Al_2O_3
		Spinel	$MgAl_2O_4$
		Topaz	$Al_2SiO_4(F,OH)_2$
	Green	Grossular	$Ca_3Al_2Si_3O_{12}$
		Spodumene (hiddenite)	$LiAlSi_2O_6$
		Beryl (emerald)	$Be_3Al_2Si_6O_{18}$
		Elbaite	$Na(Li,Al)_3Al_6Si_6O_{18}(OH)_4$
		Jadeite	$Na(Al,Fe)Si_2O_6$
	Green-red	Chrysoberyl (alexandrite)	$BeAl_2O_4$
Co	Blue	Spodumene	$LiAlSi_2O_6$
Fe	Yellow	Chrysoberyl	$BeAl_2O_4$
		Quartz (citrine)	SiO_2
		Vesuvianite	$Ca_{10}Mg_2Al_4(SiO_4)_5(Si_2O_7)_2(OH)_4$
		Orthoclase	$KAlSi_3O_8$
	Green	Beryl (aquamarine)	$Be_3Al_2Si_6O_{18}$
		Elbaite	$Na(Li,Al)_3Al_6Si_6O_{18}(OH)_4$
Mn	Pink	Beryl (morganite)	$Be_3Al_2Si_6O_{18}$
		Spodumene (kunzite)	$LiAlSi_2O_6$
		Elbaite	$Na(Li,Al)_3Al_6Si_6O_{18}(OH)_4$
	Green-yellow	Andalusite	Al_2SiO_5
V	Green	Apophyllite	$KCa_4Si_8O_{20}(F,OH)\cdot 8H_2O$
		Grossular	$Ca_3Al_2Si_3O_{12}$
		Beryl (emerald)	$Be_3Al_2Si_6O_{18}$
Pb	Green	Microcline (amazonite)	$KAlSi_3O_8$

Data from K. Nassau, "The origins of color in minerals," *Amer. Mineral.* 63 (1978): 219–229.

defect, such as a location where a F^- ion is missing from a fluorite structure, can preserve local electrostatic neutrality by trapping a single electron. This kind of defect creates an electron color center (Fig. 5-6). Quantized excitation of this trapped electron produces a purple color in some fluorite specimens.

A hole color center occurs when one electron of an orbital pair is missing from its expected location. Coupled substitution at a ppm level of Al^{3+} plus Na^+ (or H^+) for Si^{4+} in quartz does not, by itself, induce color. When such quartz, however, is irradiated either naturally or artificially, one electron of an O^{2-} ion on each alumina tetrahedron may be knocked from its orbital and trapped elsewhere in this quartz structure, for example $H^+ + e^- \rightarrow H$. This hole defect at the location of a missing electron has absorption transitions that give color to smoky quartz (Fig. 5-7). Glass slides used to mount samples for X-ray diffraction darken over time by the same mechanism.

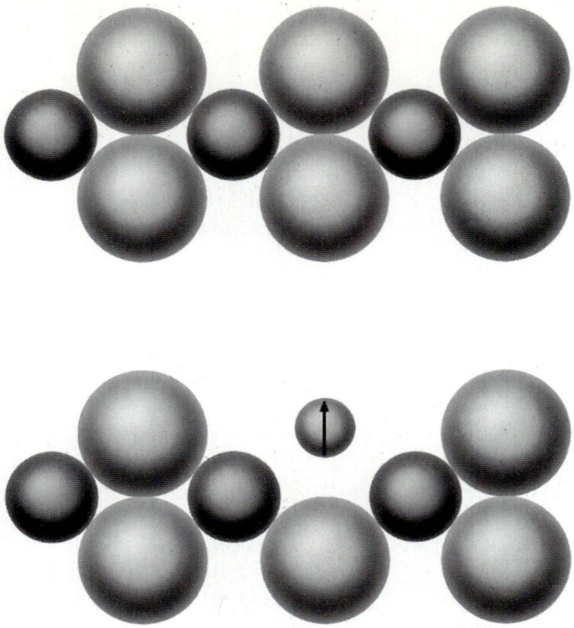

FIGURE 5-6 Electron color center. ***Top:*** **A part of fluorite structure is depicted schematically. Small spheres represent Ca^{2+} and large spheres F^- ions.** ***Bottom:*** **Missing F^- is shown replaced by a trapped electron (sphere with arrow). [After K. Nassau,** ***Amer. Mineral.*** **63 (1978): p. 223.]**

In the same way, amethystine quartz owes its purple color to a hole defect associated with Fe^{3+} substitution for Si^{4+} in quartz. This sort of color center may be recognized by heating smoky quartz or amethyst, thereby releasing trapped electrons so that they may again return to their original state and pair up to destroy hole defects and thus lose their color. Re-irradiation then may recreate both color centers and color. Such irradiation is one means by which gem dealers artificially enhance or alter colors of gems (a dangerous practice only if done improperly and stones remain radioactive, a shady practice if the stones soon bleach).

Molecular Orbitals Some quantized interactions between electromagnetic radiation and crystalline matter are not well described by this crystal field formalism, however, and other formalisms must be employed to gain insight into these interactions. Instead of adding electrons to individual nuclei (Sec. 1-1) or to a periodic array of nuclei (Sec. 4-4), you can envision a molecular array of atomic nuclei. In this formalism, individual atomic orbitals overlap and hybridize to become molecular orbitals (Sec. 4-4).

As with atomic orbitals, molecular orbitals are quantized into energy states, each state with its own set of quantum numbers and each accepting

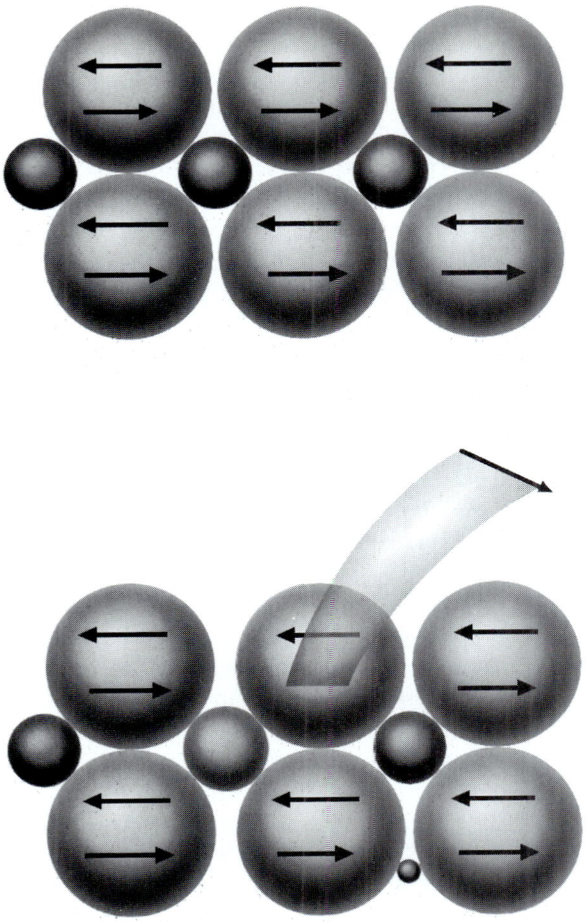

FIGURE 5-7 **Hole color center.** *Top*: **A part of quartz structure is depicted schematically. Small spheres represent Si^{4+} and large spheres O^{2-} ions. Paired electrons are denoted by arrows.** *Bottom*: **Coupled substitution of Al^{3+} (small light sphere) and Na^{+} (smallest sphere) for a Si^{4+} ion is shown. Irradiation knocks one electron (arrow) from one O^{2-} in an alumina tetrahedron, this electron to be trapped elsewhere in this structure. [After K. Nassau,** ***Amer. Mineral.*** **63 (1978): p. 223.]**

two electrons of opposite spin as required by the Pauli exclusion principle (Sec. 1-1). Again as with atomic orbitals, electrons may be energized from ground states to excited molecular orbital states by absorbing appropriate quanta of energy.

Atomic-orbital formalism would not predict color in rare, but highly prized, orange crocoite [$PbCrO_4$] since its ions form closed electron shells.

A CrO_4^{2-} radical, however, is a molecular unit in the crocoite structure; its electrons belong to this unit in molecular orbitals. Transfer of an electron from O^{2-} to Cr^{6+} by way of an excited molecular-orbital state results in absorption in the blue end of the visible spectrum and its resulting orange color. Orange to red vanadinite [$Pb_5(VO_4)_3Cl$] derives from similar charge transfers in VO_4^{3-} radicals. Electron charge transfer can also occur via molecular orbitals between transition-metal ions. Blue sapphire variety of corundum results from coupled substitution of impurity Ti^{4+} plus Fe^{2+} for $2Al^{3+}$. Charge transfer of an electron by photon absorption in the red end of the visible spectrum gives Ti^{3+} and Fe^{3+} and the resultant blue of sapphire. Blue color in kyanite has the same source.

In cordierite [$Mg_2Al_4Si_5O_{18}$], Fe^{2+} and minor Fe^{3+} substitute in different structural sites. Charge transfer between these Fe ion sites absorbs red, giving cordierite its typical, but allochromatic, blue color. Black magnetite [$FeOFe_2O_3$] and manganite [$MnO(OH)$] are colored idiochromatically from electron charge transfers. Fresh vivianite [$Fe_3(PO_4)_2 \cdot 8H_2O$] is colorless; exposure to air progressively oxidizes ferrous iron to ferric. With increase in opportunity for charge transfer, its color changes from pale blue to dark blue to black.

Band-Gap Colors Band theory is yet another formalism that must be brought to bear to describe visual appearances of some minerals (Sec. 4-4). Since excited states for electrons in conduction bands in metals are negligibly separated by small energy gaps, all wavelengths of light are absorbed and quickly reemitted at the surface giving a metallic luster. Differences in numbers of electrons allowed in conduction bands above a ground state for electrons give rise to different colors associated with specific metallic minerals.

Band-gap width (E_g) provides a basis for subdividing intrinsic semiconductors. If E_g is less than the energy of a photon at the red end of the visible spectrum, all wavelengths of light are absorbed giving a metallic luster. Galena [PbS], pyrite [FeS_2], and marcasite [FeS_2] are examples. If E_g is greater than the energy of photons at the violet end of the spectrum, absorption of visible light cannot occur and such minerals are colorless. Pure diamond [C], sphalerite [ZnS], and zincite [ZnO] are examples.

Band gaps with E_g in the visible range of the spectrum produce colored semiconductor minerals. Red cinnabar [HgS] results from E_g of 2.0 eV corresponding to a wavelength between red and yellow so that all wavelengths shorter than red are absorbed (Fig. 5-8). Native sulfur [S_8] and orpiment [As_2S_3] have E_g of about 2.6 eV; this is greater than the energy of green light but less than that of blue and violet, which are removed from the spectra of these minerals, the remaining part of the spectrum giving the complementary yellow color.

Even minerals with E_g greater than the energy of visible light may be colored semiconductors if impurity ions are present. Impurity-

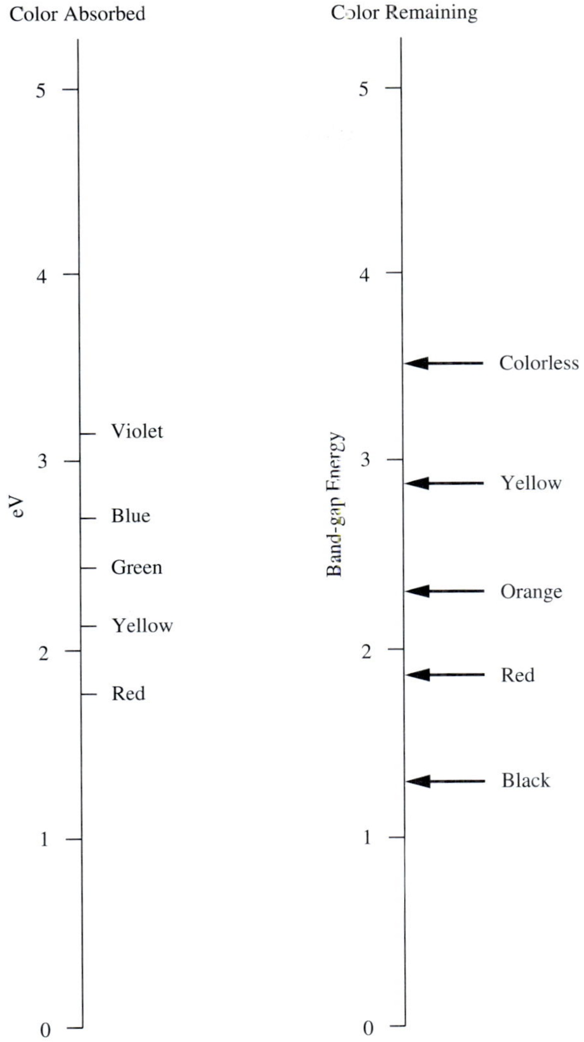

FIGURE 5-8 Band-gap colors. Spectral width of a band gap (E_g) determines colors absorbed by electrons excited from the valence band to the conduction band in semiconductors. All light with energy greater than E_g is absorbed, whereas that with less energy than E_g is transmitted or reflected.

containing (doped) semiconductors occur because foreign atoms with different numbers of electrons than the host provide available energy levels within a band gap (forbidden zone).

Pure diamond has a large E_g and is a colorless insulator. Replace C in diamond with as little as 10 ppm N, and the third $2p$ electron of N has an energy within this band gap. Since the energy to excite this donor

TABLE 5-4 Structural Colors in Minerals

Cause	Effect	Examples
Dispersion	Fire	Gems cut from diamond, rutile, zircon
Scattering	Chatoyancy	Quartz (cat's eye, tiger eye)
		Chrysoberyl (Oriental cat's eye)
	Asterism	Corundum (star sapphire and ruby)
		Garnet
		Quartz (sagenite, blue quartz)
	Aventurescence	Oligoclase (sunstone)
		Quartz (aventurine)
		Enstatite altered to serpentine (Schiller)
	Adularescence	Orthoclase (adularia)
		Opal (milky)
	Pearly luster	Aragonite (pearl)
		Talc
		Brucite
		Apophyllite
		Asbestiform minerals
		Gypsum (satin spar)
Interference	Iridescence	Chalcopyrite
		Columbite
		Bornite (peacock ore)
		Quartz (iris)
Diffraction	Fire	Opal (precious)
	Labradorescence	Labradorite

Data from K. Nassau, "The origins of color in minerals," *Amer. Mineral.* 63 (1978): 219–229.

electron (n) into the diamond conduction band is at the violet end of the visible spectrum, such a diamond is a yellow n-type semiconductor. Replace C in diamond with as little as 1 ppm B and get a vacant p orbital within its band gap. Ambient temperature provides sufficient energy to excite valence electrons into this acceptor level, leaving behind mobile positive holes (p) in the valence band. Diamonds, such as the Hope, are blue p-type semiconductors (Fig. 4-6).

Pseudochromatism In addition to colors produced by photon absorption, physical optics produces pseudochromatic colors and color plays, also called structural colors, in some minerals (Table 5-4). White light of the visible spectrum may be dispersed to produce flashes of color, called fire in the jewelry trade, in gems cut from diamond, zircon, or rutile (Fig. 5-17). Minute inclusions, which may be aligned in one or more crystallographic directions within a host crystal, scatter light in a variety of fashions (Table 5-3). Asterism of star sapphire results from rutile needles aligned along **a** axes of corundum. The blue of lazurite $[(Na,Ca)_8(Al,Si)_{12}O_{24}(S,SO_4)]$ results from scattering by atomic Na^0 atoms interstitial in its structure. Blue quartz gets its color from light scattered by minute inclusions of ilmenite, but its asterim from needles of rutile aligned along **a**.

Thin films of alteration material on surfaces of some minerals, for example, bornite $[Cu_5FeS_4]$, peacock ore in miners' jargon, may have thicknesses corresponding to wavelengths of visible light. These films cause optical interference and colors much like those produced by an oil slick on water. Periodic spacing of particles or layers of visible-wavelength thickness within a mineral may diffract visible light, giving colors only at certain angles to diffracting layers. Examples include precious opal, moonstone variety of albite, and labradorescent labradorite.

In summation, what a normal human eye and many optical devices detect are colors and lusters of minerals. Sources of these colors, however, derive from diverse mechanisms requiring several different kinds of formalisms.

5-3 QUANTUM EMISSION AND ABSORPTION

Some crystalline substances can be caused to emit visible light, to luminesce (quite apart from being heated to red or white heat). Luminescence results from electromagnetic radiation of one wavelength being absorbed in a crystal structure only to be reemitted as light, usually of a lower energy, that is, a longer wavelength. Energy is not created or destroyed during luminescence, but is absorbed or reemitted in stages, one emission being in the visible range. This emission occurs when an electron becomes excited to a state that has one or more excited states between it and the ground state (Fig. 5-9).

Luminescence Quanta in the violet part of the visible, ultraviolet, or X-ray spectra provide excitation energies to an excited energy state. Excited electrons then drop back to a lower excited state, emitting radiation corresponding to that energy transition before dropping to the ground state with another quantized emission. One of these changes produces visible photons. Alternatively, two successive long-wavelength absorptions may lead to an excited state producing short-wavelength luminescence. Luminescence is a narrow band of radiation emitted from a single electronic state rather than a mixture as in white light.

Luminescence that occurs immediately (in less than 10^{-9} sec) is fluorescence. Fluorescent minerals emit visible photons only so long as activating energy continues. The mineral fluorite $[CaF_2]$ fluoresces when some of the Ca is replaced by rare-earth elements (Fig. 5-9).

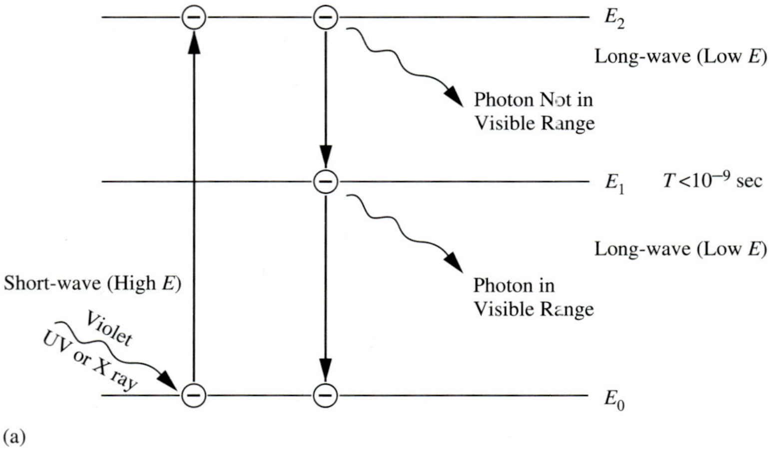

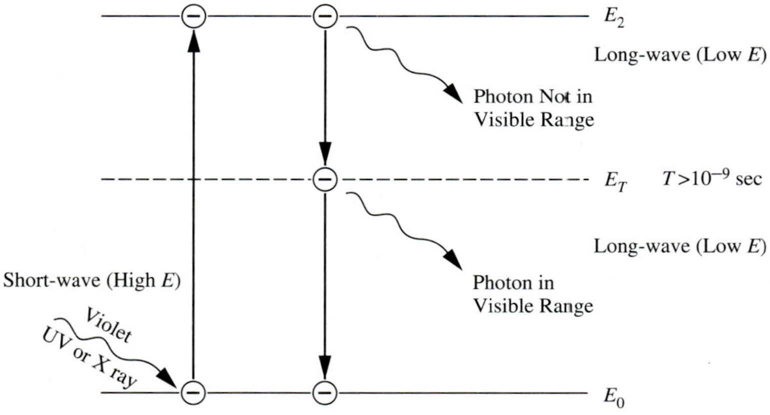

FIGURE 5-9 Luminescence in minerals. (a) Fluorescence. A photon in the violet, ultraviolet, or X-ray range of the electromagnetic spectrum excites an outer electron to a high-energy state. This electron then falls from its high excited state to a lower-energy excited state before falling to its ground state in less than 10^{-9} sec. Visible fluorescence occurs when one of these energy gaps lies in the visible range. (b) Phosphorescence. An electron is raised to an excited state as in fluorescence, but falls into a trapped state where it remains for more than 10^{-9} sec before falling to its ground state. Thus, phosphorescence continues after an energy source is cut off.

In some crystal structures an excited electron becomes trapped, for instance, in a defect or in a forbidden zone. An energy barrier between a trapped state and ground state for electrons can be small enough that thermal energy from ambient heat is sufficient to excite trapped electrons over it. Decay then proceeds at a finite rate, causing phosphorescence (decay time greater than 10^{-9} sec). Phosphorescence thus continues after cessation of activating energy. Sphalerite [ZnS] phosphoresces.

If a specimen must be heated to cause light emission, it is thermoluminescent. Some metamict zircons [$ZrSiO_4$] emit a flash of light when heated in the dark. Minerals that emit light as a result of rubbing, grinding, or crushing are triboluminescent. Cathodoluminescence is light emission resulting from electron bombardment of a mineral sample, and electroluminescence is nonincandescent light emission caused by an electric field or current.

Mineral species requiring impurities or structural defects for luminescence are allochromatic, in which case only some specimens or samples from particular mineral districts luminesce. Phosphor dopants, sometimes called luminescence activators, commonly have incomplete *d* or *f* electron orbitals the same as chromophores in absorption spectra. Thus, minerals with essential transition-metal or rare-earth elements may have idiochromatic luminescence, a useful property for prospecting for these minerals. Additionally, radicals with bonding best described by molecular-orbital formalism may also act as phosphors. Idiochromatic luminescence of scheelite [$CaWO_4$] results from charge transfer within its WO_4^{2-} tetrahedron.

Phosphors, like chromophores, are sensitive in varying degrees to their structural environment. Exciting an electron into a normally unoccupied orbital increases the effective radius of an ion. Thus, wavelength of photon emission is controlled by a crystal structure in an excited state rather than the ground state, as are most other mineral properties. Although luminescent colors of Cr^{3+} and Mn^{4+} are weakly influenced by their host structures, Mn^{2+} leads to fluorescence, which is green in tetrahedral coordination but red in octahedral coordination. Corundum doped with Cr is ruby red in white light and emits red when activated with ultraviolet light. Since *f* orbitals lie within inner electron shells, rare-earth phosphors tend to be insensitive to the structure of their host in that they interact only weakly with ligands.

Photon emission need not occur at the same site in a crystal structure as absorption. Efficiency of luminescence may be enhanced when sensitizers, which are energy absorbers, transfer their energy through a structure to activators, which are energy emitters. On the other hand, luminescence may be poisoned by other impurities, such as Ni^{2+} or Fe^{2+}, which have radiationless transitions to ground state by converting the energy into heat in the structure.

X-ray Fluorescence Fluorescence is not limited to the visible region of the electromagnetic spectrum, since energy beyond the visible range may be released by orbital electrons. A common method of nondestructive photochemical analysis uses fluorescence in the X-ray part of the electromagnetic spectrum. If an atom is bombarded with a high-energy X-ray beam, some incident quanta have sufficient energy to eject a K- or L-shell electron from it. An atom in this excited state has an inner electron missing. This atom returns to a lower energy state when an outer electron falls into this vacancy, thereby emitting a quantum of energy in the X-ray part of the spectrum. Since an energy gap between orbitals is unique, the exact energy and wavelength of this emitted quantum identifies which chemical element had its atoms excited.

When a K electron is ejected from its orbital, an atom is raised to a K excitation state (Fig. 5-10). When an outer electron falls into this K-orbital vacancy, K emission occurs. An electron from an L orbital causes $K\alpha$ radiation, and an M electron causes $K\beta$ emission. These emissions result in L and M excitation states, which are also useful for element identification in the common X-ray fluorescence spectrometer (XRF technique) (Fig. 5-11).

Fluorescence occurs in all parts of the electromagnetic spectrum. However, X rays longer than 1 nm (10 Å) and ultraviolet light shorter than 50 nm (500 Å) are absorbed very strongly by air. Many materials transparent to visible light are opaque to ultraviolet light and to large parts of the far-infrared spectrum. Problems of instrumentation thus limit usefulness of fluorescence in spectral ranges other than parts of infrared, visible, and short X-ray spectra. Furthermore, much long-wavelength fluorescence is allochromatic and, therefore, not useful for spectrochemical analysis.

Emission Spectrography For emission spectrographic analysis, an electric arc or laser beam vaporizes atoms of a mineral. These atoms are thermally excited, and each atom emits its characteristic radiation. Emission energies, which represent transitions between orbitals, are unique for each chemical element (Fig. 5-11). Emission intensity, to a first approximation, is proportional to the amount of an element present causing emission. Analysis of energies of emission in the visible range can provide the individual elements present and their amounts in a mineral specimen. For electron probe microanalysis (EMX), magnetic lenses focus an electron beam to a diameter of about 1 μm, thereby permitting spectral analysis of a very small crystal or very small parts of crystals having variable composition.

Absorption and Emission Spectroscopy Atomic absorption (AA) spectroscopy utilizes these same electronic transitions in a slightly different way. Light of a particular energy passes through a flame containing

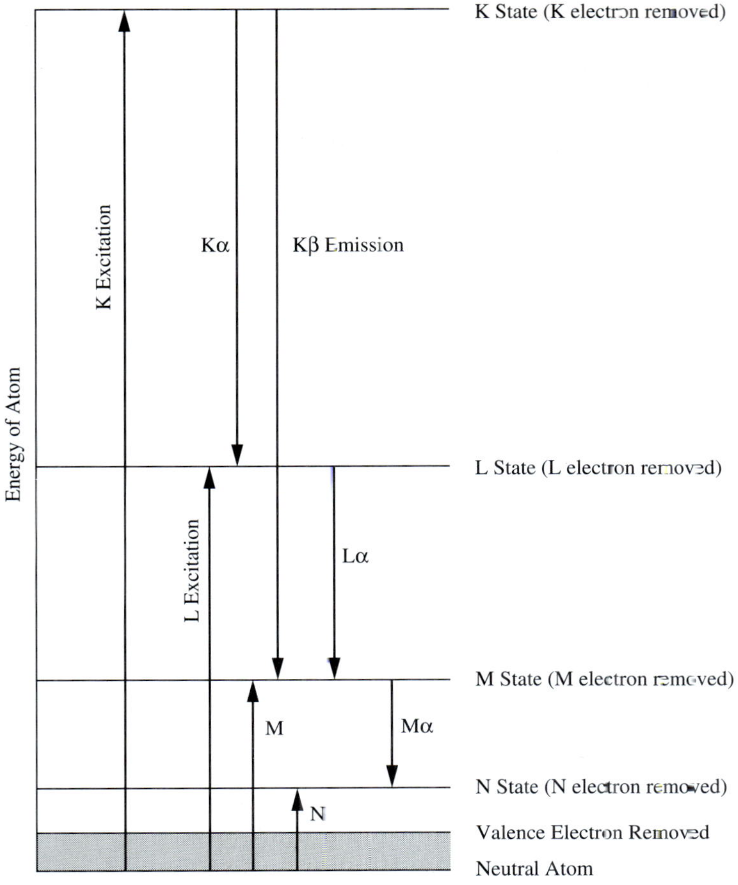

FIGURE 5-10 Atomic energy levels. The energy of an atom is least when all electrons are in their ground states. A small amount of energy accrues to an atom when a valence electron is removed; progressively more energy accrues as N, M, L, or K electrons are removed. Kα energy emission occurs when an L electron falls into a vacant K orbital; Kβ emission when an M electron fills a K vacancy. L and M emissions occur when L and M vacancies are filled from overlying shells.

the vapor of a dissolved mineral sprayed into the flame. An element with a transition that corresponds to the wavelength of this light beam absorbs photons from it. Amount of light absorption is, again to a first approximation, proportional to the amount of an element present in this flame. Each chemical element requires a different monochromatic light source.

Quantized structural vibrations have excitation energies in the near-infrared part of the electromagnetic spectrum (Fig. 5-2). Infrared absorption and reflection spectroscopy have long been used to characterize and

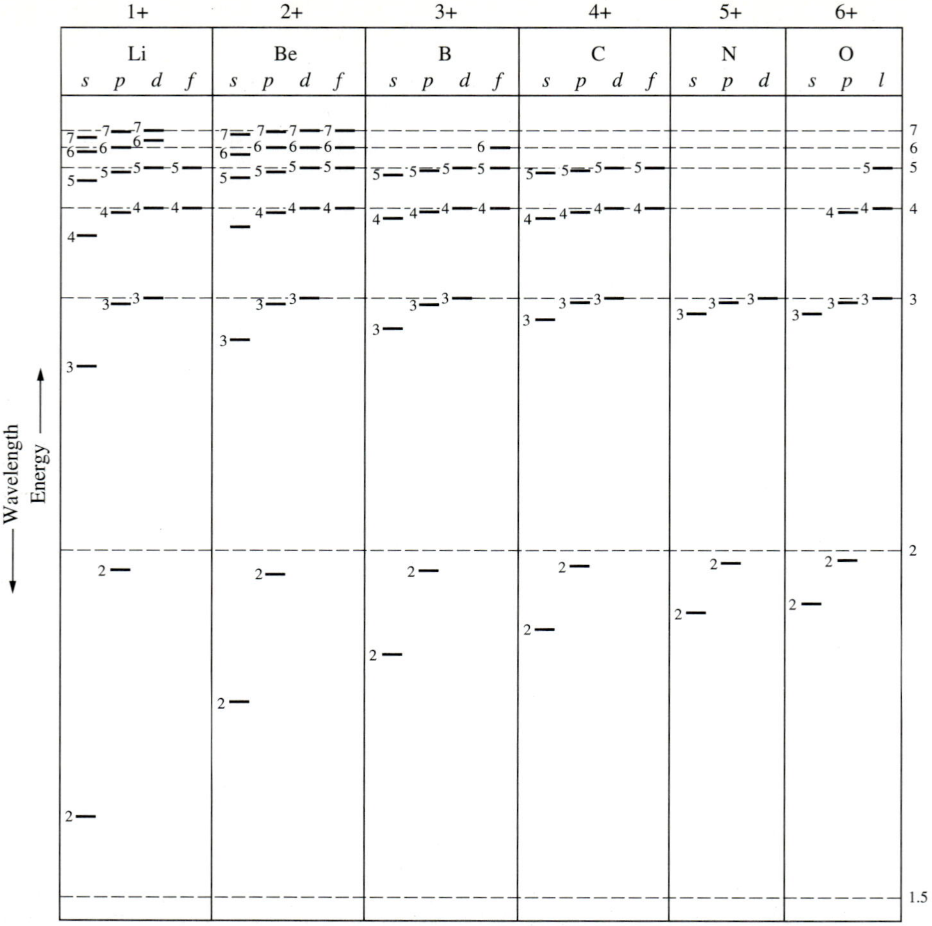

FIGURE 5-11 Energy levels of Li and Li-like ions. Relative energies of electron orbitals change with atomic number. Letters *s*, *p*, *d*, and *f* refer to azimuthal quantum number ℓ (Sec. 1-1), and numbers 1–7 are the principal quantum numbers *n* (Table 1-1). Transfer of electrons between orbitals, represented by horizontal bars, is quantized. Differences between orbital energies determine which quanta are absorbed and emitted; each element has a unique spectrum of absorption and emission energies. (After G. Herzberg, *Atomic Spectra and Atomic Structure*, 2nd ed. New York: Dover, 1944.)

identify organic molecules. In mineralogy, infrared spectra are interpreted in terms of structural location and orientation of OH^-, H_2O, H_3O^+, and CO_2 in hydrous and hydrated minerals, structural influence of hydrogen bonds, and degree of ionization of chemical bonds.

When a beam of light impinges on a transparent crystal, some of it ($\sim 10^{-5}$) scatters as a result of elastic collision between incident photons and electron clouds of ions, resulting in Rayleigh scattering. Some photons ($\sim 10^{-8}$), generally from a laser source, deform electron clouds, thus causing atomic nuclei to shift position in response to this displaced electron cloud. When this displacement corresponds to a normal mode of vibration, energy is absorbed from a light beam by this vibration, thereby decreasing its energy and increasing its wavelength by a small but finite amount when reemitted as Stokes-Raman shift scattering. Nuclei already in their excited states when their electron cloud deforms, add energy to a light beam and decrease its wavelength, in the anti-Stokes-Raman shift. Raman spectra yield details about individual ionic sites such as coordination numbers of individual ions and, in general, supplement X-ray diffraction data about minerals.

Although many of these spectra were unknown in 1913 when Niels Bohr proposed his atomic model, others were, including spectral discharge of H_2 excited by electric discharge, which was reported by J. J. Balmer in 1885. These spectra are all quantized and led Bohr to his atomic model, a modification of which is developed in Chap. 1. Energy emission and absorption in discrete packets (quanta) provide evidence that supports this atomic model. But they also permit mineralogists, petrologists, and geochemists to analyze more fully geologically interesting materials.

5-4 INTERACTION OF WAVES AND MINERALS

Light transmitted and refracted by crystalline matter requires description based on a wave theory of electromagnetic radiation. Such waves are mathematical devices that permit description and prediction of light interacting weakly with crystal structures. Transmission and reflection of light involve such a great flood of photons that treatment of light as a wave phenomenon is perfectly adequate to describe its behavior under these conditions. Analogously, a geologist may describe a beach form without reference to its individual sand grains.

Electromagnetic radiation, of which visible light is a small part, is characterized by electric (**E**) and magnetic (**H**) vectors that oscillate sinusoidally at right angles to each other and to the direction of propagation (Fig. 5-12). Inasmuch as **H** is always found at right angles to **E** and to the direction of propagation, only **E** needs to be given; specification of **H** adds no new information about a light wave, and its direction and phase may be assumed.

Light Interference Ordinary light sources, such as the sun or an incandescent wire, produce light with **E**'s randomly distributed about the propagation direction (Fig. 5-12b). Plane polarized light has an electric field restricted to one plane. Microscopic studies of optical properties of minerals are generally carried out with plane polarized light, and only that form will be considered further. A second, simplifying, restriction

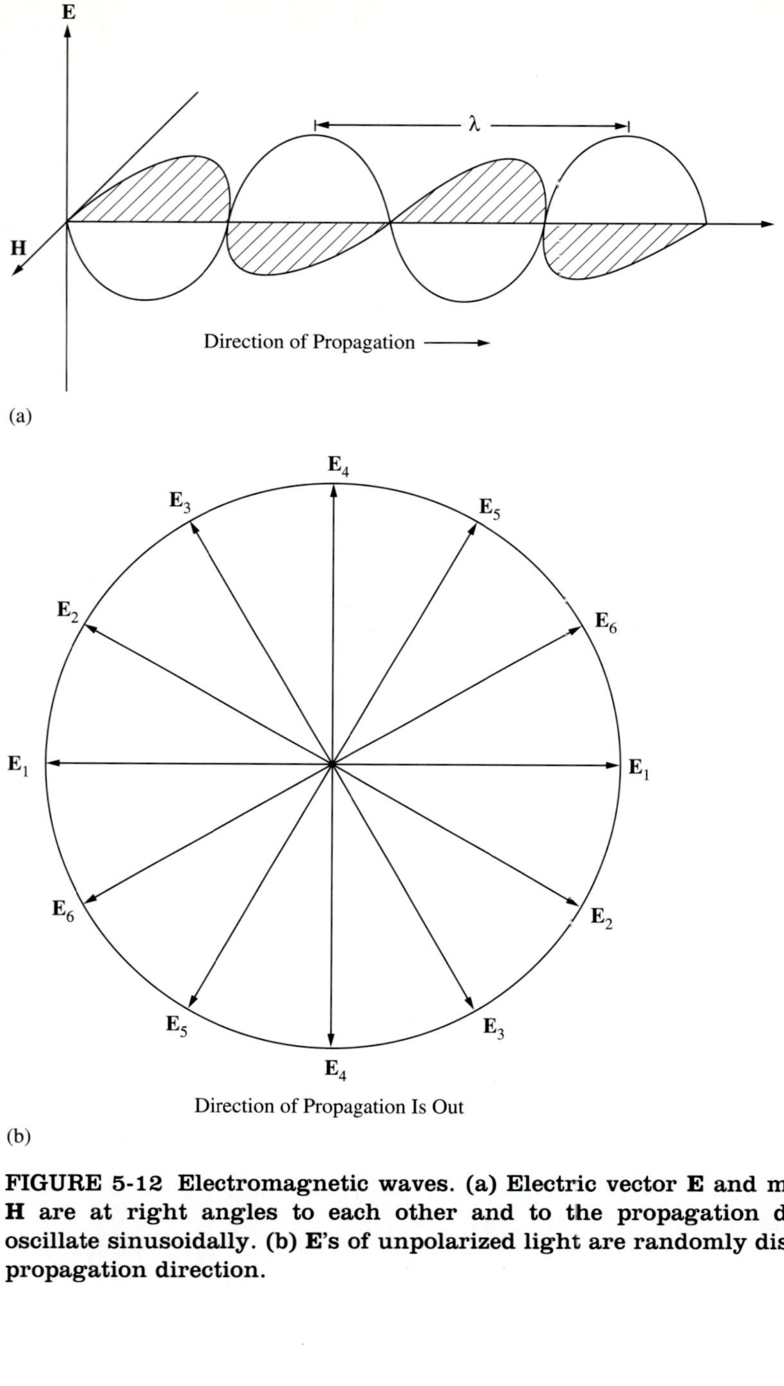

FIGURE 5-12 Electromagnetic waves. (a) Electric vector E and magnetic vector H are at right angles to each other and to the propagation direction. Both oscillate sinusoidally. (b) E's of unpolarized light are randomly distributed about propagation direction.

used here is that light is monochromatic; white light is a mixture of wavelengths between 400 and 700 nm (4000 and 7000 Å). Third, illustrations assume that light is fully in phase; however, except for lasers, it is not. These restrictions are simplifications that in no way affect the general validity of conclusions about light.

If **E**'s of two waves of plane polarized light are superimposed, these waves interfere with each other (Fig. 5-13). If two waves are in phase they reinforce each other by constructive interference; if out of phase by one-half wavelength, they cancel each other by destructive interference (Fig. 5-13a,b). Two waves out of phase by an arbitrary amount produce by interference a third wave of different phase and amplitude (Fig. 5-13c).

Light Refraction In a vacuum, light has a velocity of 3.0×10^{10} cm sec^{-1}. Light velocity is less than this value for all transparent materials. (Air is a transparent material, but the velocity of light in air differs so little from its velocity in vacuum that the difference may be ignored for most purposes.) To appreciate this diminished velocity, consider that each ion in a crystal structure consists of a nucleus surrounded by electrons in the form of an electron cloud (Fig. 1-1). The electric field of a light wave perturbs this electron cloud by causing it to oscillate about its nucleus (Fig. 5-14). This nucleus remains effectively immobile because it contains more than 99.9997% of an ion's mass.

An oscillating electric field, such as an electron cloud vibrating about its nucleus, generates its own electromagnetic radiation. Radiation generated by this electron cloud lags behind—is out of phase with—the primary electromagnetic radiation because of the small, but finite, inertia of an electron cloud. Therefore, this secondary radiation interferes with its primary radiation, resulting in a combined wave lagging behind a parallel reference wave traveling in a vacuum (Fig. 5-13).

Slowing of light in a crystal structure may be illustrated in two dimensions by a plane of atoms (Fig. 5-14). A light wave arrives at the first row of atoms where part of its energy oscillates electron clouds in that row. Its amplitude decreases, but wavelength remains the same between the first and second rows of atoms. Each electron cloud in the first row, however, sends out radiation of its own with the same wavelength but a different phase. (Since each electron cloud in each row radiates light as a point source, only those waves traveling in the direction of the original wave are not destroyed by interference.)

This secondary wave from the first row has the same wavelength as its primary but is out of phase with it and, therefore, interferes with it The net result is that this light wave is retarded and arrives late at the second row, compared with a reference wave. This retarded wave then acts as a primary wave on the second row, with this process repeated from row to row. Light in crystalline matter, although much longer in

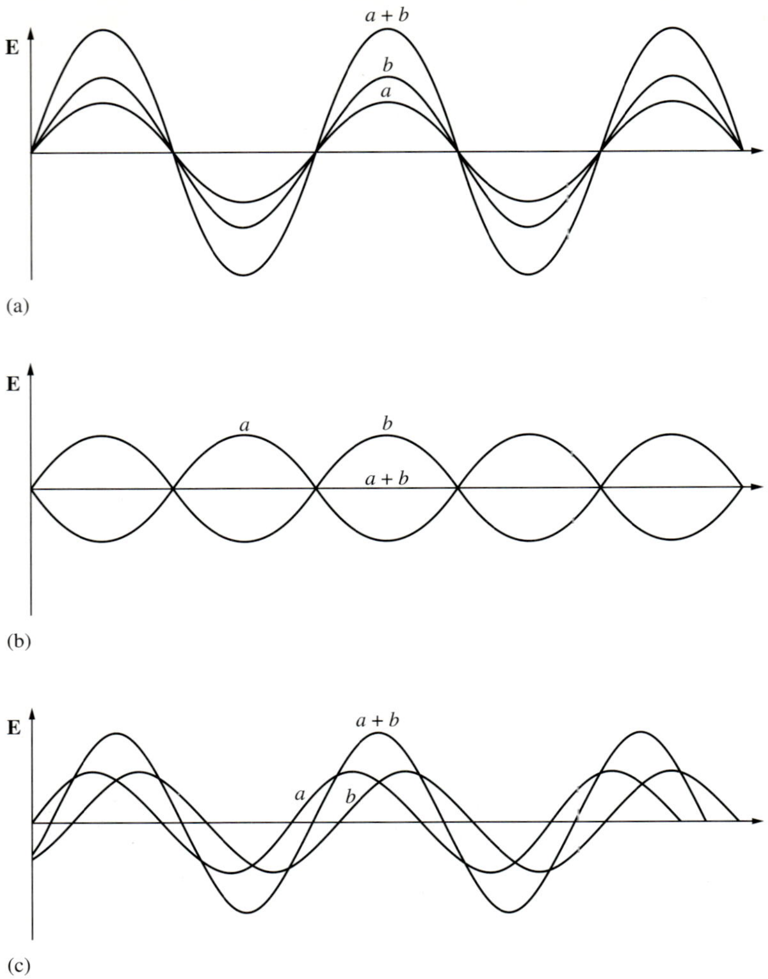

FIGURE 5-13 Wave interference. (a) Constructive interference. Wave *a* interferes constructively with wave *b* so that resultant wave $a + b$ has an amplitude equal to the sum of the interfering waves. (b) Wave *a* interferes destructively with wave *b*, so that resultant wave $a + b$ has no amplitude and, therefore, does not exist. (c) Wave *a* partially interferes with wave *b* such that a new wave $a + b$ of different amplitude and phase results.

wavelength than the size of electron clouds about atoms, is retarded in an analogous fashion. (Note that atoms do not have to have periodicity for light retardation since all matter slows light passing through it.)

Refractive Indices A stick of wood, stuck half in water at an angle, appears bent just at the water-air interface as a direct result of the

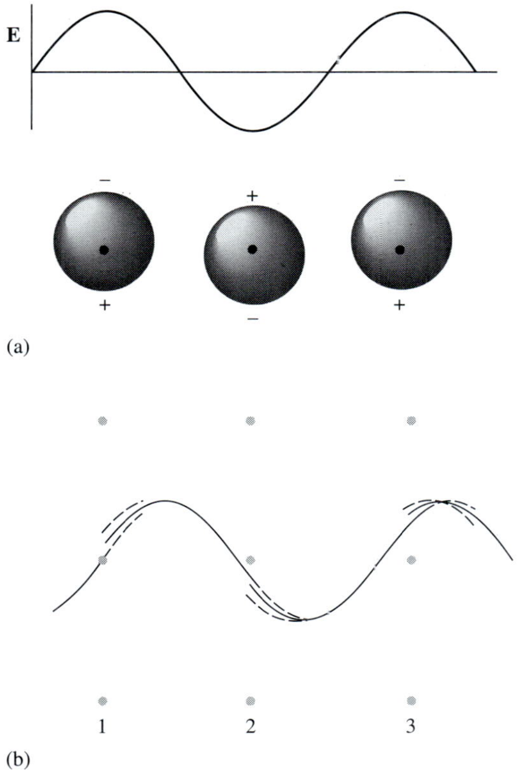

FIGURE 5-14 Retardation of light in crystals. (a) E of a light wave interacts with electrons of an ion, causing them to oscillate. Because of electron mass, this response lags behind the original wave. Electron cloud oscillation sets off secondary radiation, which lags behind the primary wave and interferes with it. (b) Light waves arriving at ion row 1 vibrate those electrons. Secondary waves interfere with primary waves so that resulting waves lag behind a reference wave. This resultant wave arrives late at row 2, where the process repeats with even greater retardation as a new resultant wave arrives late at row 3.

diminished velocity of light as it travels through the water, a denser, transparent medium. The ratio of the velocity of light in a vacuum (c) to the velocity of light in a transparent medium (v) is a number larger than unity, known as the index of refraction or refractive index (RI; plural, indices). Actual velocities of light in a mineral are not generally determined directly, but measurements of refractive indices are relatively simple operations. The larger a refractive index, the slower the velocity of light and the more a light wave is bent on passing obliquely into a transparent medium (Prog. 5-1). Consider a column of marchers obliquely approaching a roadway with instructions to march at half step on this roadway but

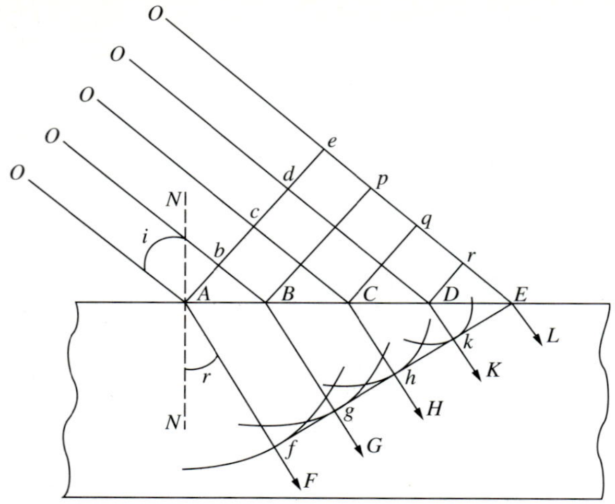

FIGURE 5-15 Snell's law. Light, upon entering a transparent medium, is refracted. The angle of incidence (*i*) is related to the angle of refraction (*r*) by the refractive index $n = (\sin i)/(\sin r)$.

full step on either side. This column will bend to cross the roadway only to resume a parallel direction on its opposite side. Such a roadway would have a refractive index of 2. Refractive index (n) is related to the angle of incidence (i) and the angle of refraction (r) by Snell's law: $n = (\sin i)/(\sin r)$ (see Fig. 5-15).

Since transparent minerals have a distinctive index or indices, measurement of refractive indices is a powerful tool in mineral identification. Except for faceted gemstones, angles of incidence and refraction are not commonly measured directly, because of irregularities in shapes of mineral fragments. When a mineral grain is immersed in a liquid of identical refractive index, however, its surface disappears because light is not refracted in passing across this mineral liquid boundary. A chunk of clear ice (mean $n = 1.31$) nearly disappears when immersed in water ($n = 1.33$).

Once an immersion liquid is found with a refractive index to match that of a mineral grain, the liquid's refractive index is determined by introducing it between two parallel glass plates and measuring its angle of refraction with a refractometer. The calculated index of the liquid thus corresponds to that of the matching grain. In practice, however, immersion liquids with known refractive indices may be purchased commercially and matched against mineral grains under a microscope.

When an incident light wave is normal to a surface of different refractive index, it proceeds with diminished velocity but without refraction. From Snell's law, if i and $\sin i$ approach zero, then $\sin r$ and r also

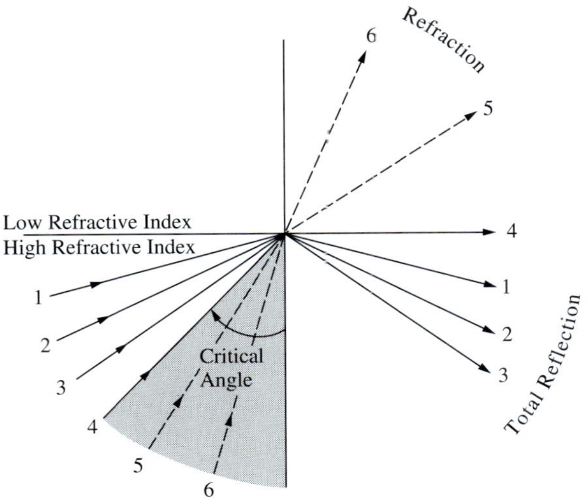

FIGURE 5-16 Critical angle of reflection. Some light traveling from material of high refractive index to material of low refractive index reflects totally at an interface between these two materials. Ray 4 strikes the interface at the critical angle, where it refracts parallel to this interface. Rays 5 and 6 strike this interface at less than the critical angle, where they refract into the low-index material. Rays 1–3 strike this interface at greater than the critical angle, where they reflect totally.

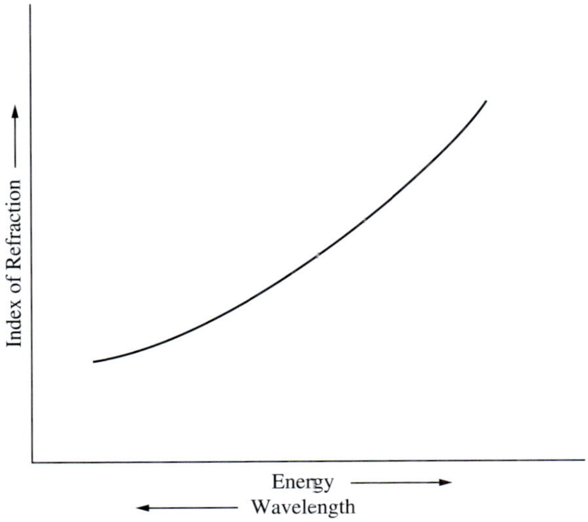

FIGURE 5-17 Light dispersion. Refractive index varies with light wavelength. In most materials this index increases with increasing energy and decreasing wavelength of light.

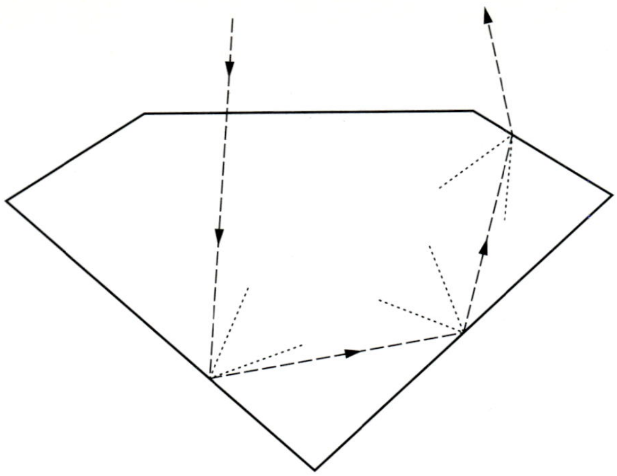

FIGURE 5-18 Diamond cut. Light (dashed line) entering a top facet of a cut diamond reflects totally from lower facets because their angle of incidence is greater than the critical angle (dotted lines at 24.5° from the facet normal), but reflect out of this gem at an upper facet giving "fire" to a properly cut stone.

approach zero since n has a finite value. As i approaches 90°, sin i approaches 1 and Snell's law reduces to $n = 1/(\sin r)$ or $\sin r = 1/n$. This value of $1/n$ defines a critical angle. At this critical angle a light wave parallel to a surface can be refracted into it at an angle, the sine of which is $1/n$, with no greater angle geometrically possible (Fig. 5-16). Light traveling in a reverse direction at an angle greater than this critical angle is reflected totally (Prog. 5-1). Did you ever swim under water and look up at its surface? At angles greater than 48.5° from the vertical (the critical angle for the water-air interface), the water surface has a metallic luster originating from total light reflection. To cover light paths in opposite directions, assign incidence to the higher-velocity medium and refraction to the lower (Prog. 5-1).

For white light, refractive index varies with wavelength; therefore, angle of reflection and critical angle also vary (Fig. 5-17). Newton displayed the spectrum of visible light by use of a glass prism. This dispersion or dispersive refraction of light accounts for fire in a well-cut diamond (Fig. 5-18). Facets of a diamond are cut so that the visible spectrum is spread out by dispersion and reflected totally by two back facets, to emerge in an optimum manner from an upper facet as fire. All minerals disperse light, but few more than diamond, making fake diamonds fairly easy to detect until recent years.

Mineral Luster Luster is related to the way in which light reflects from a surface of a mineral. Under the formalism of the band model, if the band gap of a mineral was smaller than the energy of red light, all light was absorbed and reflected. This quality of reflection is partially related to refractive index. To a first approximation, the greater the index, the brighter is the luster. Minerals with refractive indices greater than 3 generally display metallic luster, those between 2.6 and 3 a submetallic luster (compare Sec. 5-3). Adamantine luster, that typical of diamond, shows on minerals with refractive indices between 1.9 and 2.6. Approximately three fourths of nonmetallic minerals have refractive indices between 1.3 and 1.9 and give a vitreous luster, that of glass. (Crystal decanters and stemware are made of glass given a high refractive index by addition of Pb to their melts.)

Other qualities of luster recognized by mineralogists result from special mechanical or chemical properties of mineral surfaces. For example, halite, which is vitreous when freshly cleaved, develops a greasy luster caused by a surface hydration layer with different refractive index. Very fine grained and porous minerals, such as clays, scatter light completely to display a dull or earthy luster. Minerals with pearly luster, such as talc, mica, and some varieties of calcite and gypsum, owe their luster to the presence of many successive internal reflecting layers.

Microscope Resolution Wave characteristics of light limit resolving powers of optical microscopes for study of very small particles. When a wave grazes an edge of an obstacle or passes through a small aperture, it diffracts around edges and undergoes interference (Fig. 5-19). A limit of resolution (L) is the nearest distance two points may approach and still be resolved as two. This limit depends on light wavelength (λ), refractive index (n) of the light-transmitting medium, and the angular aperture (2α) of a microscope objective according to the equation

$$L = (\lambda/2n) \sin \alpha.$$

Numerical aperture (N.A.) is related to angular aperture by the equation

$$\text{N.A.} = n \sin \alpha.$$

A practical limit of N.A. to 1.4 limits resolution for yellow light ($\lambda = 580$ nm) to about 250 nm (2500 Å). This limit of resolution is many times the size of most clay and asbestiform mineral particles

One way to escape this limit of resolution is to use wavelengths shorter than visible light in a magnification system. In place of glass lenses of an optical microscope, an electron beam in an electron microscope is focused by electromagnetic lenses. Although electrons accelerated by 100 kV have an associated wavelength of approximately 0.004 nm (0.04 Å), design limitations prevent resolutions in an electron microscope to approximately 1 nm (10 Å). Hence, morphology of clay and asbestiform minerals too small to be resolved optically may be studied conveniently by electron microscopy.

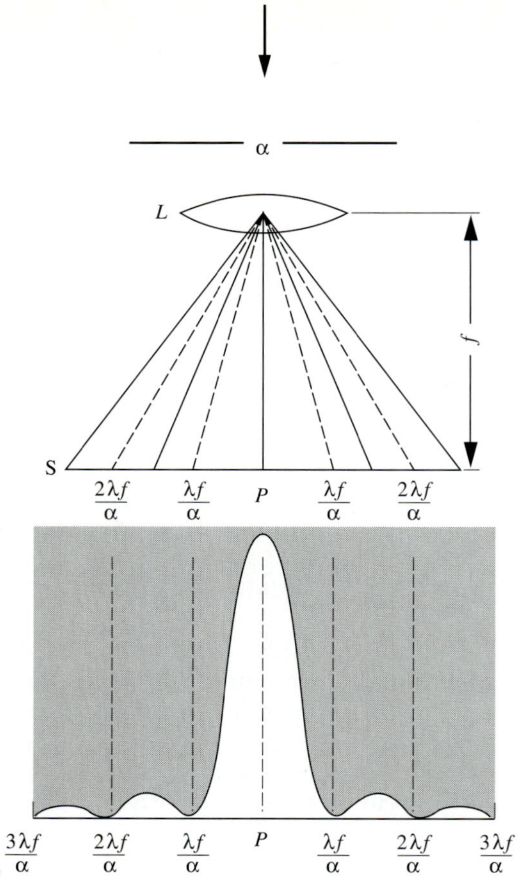

FIGURE 5-19 Optical diffraction.

5-5 LIGHT WAVES IN ANISOTROPIC MINERALS

That light velocity may vary with crystallographic direction has not been mentioned previously. Indeed, it is independent of direction in gasses, most liquids and unstrained glasses, and in minerals with isometric symmetry, which are isotropic. All other crystalline materials are anisotropic in that light velocity varies with crystallographic direction in all transparent minerals with tetragonal, trigonal, hexagonal, orthorhombic, monoclinic, or triclinic symmetry.

Distribution of ions and chemical bonds in a crystal structure determine light velocity passing through. In isometric crystals these distributions are the same in all three crystallographic directions. This is not the case in anisotropic crystals (compare Chaps. 2 and 3). Structural environments in tetragonal, hexagonal, and trigonal crystals may be quite

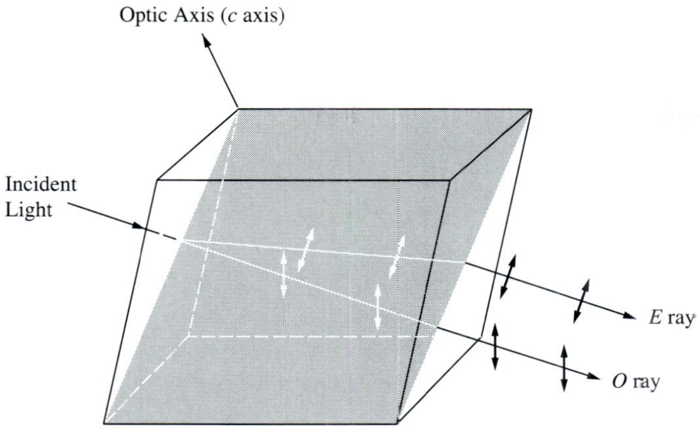

FIGURE 5-20 Double refraction in calcite. Light incident upon a cleavage fragment of calcite splits into two rays having their E's (electric vectors) at mutual right angles (arrows). These two rays diverge while passing through a crystal and reconverge as parallel rays upon emergence.

different in the **c** direction than in the **a** directions. In orthorhombic, monoclinic, and triclinic crystals, structural environments differ along all three crystallographic axes.

Double Refraction When light enters any anisotropic mineral at some general angle to its structure, it separates into two plane polarized light rays that have their **E** directions at mutual right angles; it is doubly refracted. Since velocity of a light ray depends on direction of its **E**, these two rays travel at different velocities in different directions. This effect of double refraction is best seen through a cleavage rhomb of clear calcite (Fig. 5-20). Here double refraction is great enough to cause double images to be seen even through very small fragments. The great difference in velocities of these two rays shows up in different apparent depths of these two images, since apparent thickness is inversely related to light velocity. Put on a pair of Polaroid sunglasses and rotate this cleavage fragment. First one image, then the other is filtered out by these polarizing sunglasses, demonstrating that each light ray is polarized. All anisotropic minerals refract doubly, but few have greater double refraction than members of the calcite group with their aligned planar CO_3^{2-} groups. Most minerals have considerably less.

Light velocity through any transparent medium depends on an interaction between the **E** of a light ray and electron cloud of ions in the medium. Spatial relationships between **E** and refractive index are displayed conveniently with an indicatrix, a geometric construction proposed by Fletcher in 1891 (Prog. 5-2). This indicatrix is constructed such that its

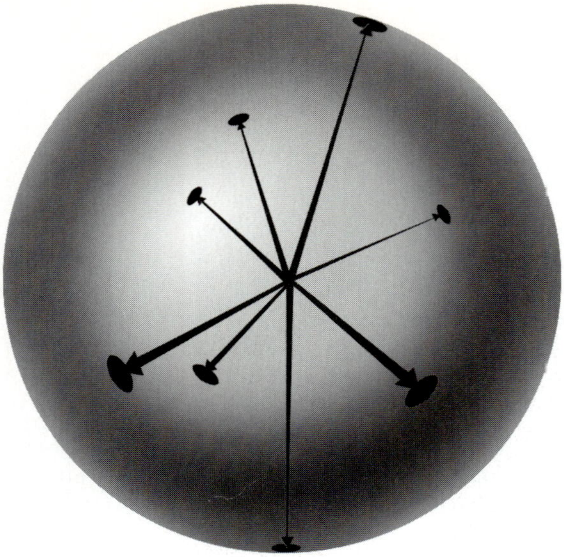

FIGURE 5-21 Isotropic indicatrix. An isotropic indicatrix is the surface of a sphere, the radius of which is proportional to the refractive index having its E parallel to that radius. Refractive index is independent of direction in isotropic materials.

radius is proportional to refractive index *n* in any **E** direction. Since refractive index *n* is the same regardless of crystallographic direction in isotropic crystals, an isotropic indicatrix is a trivial spherical surface (Fig. 5-21).

Anisotropic minerals refract doubly with two light rays with different **E** in different directions at different velocities (Fig. 5-22). Anisotropic indicatrices are a variety of ellipsoidal surfaces. Optical properties of tetragonal, hexagonal, and trigonal minerals relate to indicatrices that are spheroids of revolution that are optically uniaxial. Orthorhombic, monoclinic, and triclinic optical properties relate to indicatrices that are triaxial ellipsoids with optically biaxial characteristics.

Uniaxial Minerals When an anisotropic mineral refracts doubly, two mutually orthogonal **E**'s are permitted (allowed vibration directions) and their behavior is encapsulated by a uniaxial indicatrix (Fig. 5-23, Prog. 5-2). At right angles to certain special ray directions, optic axes, all **E**'s are permitted, just as they are in isotropic substances. In uniaxial minerals, double refraction produces two rays called ordinary (o ray) and extraordinary (e ray). Ordinary rays have permitted **E** at right angles both to ray direction and to **c** crystallographic axis, which in this case is

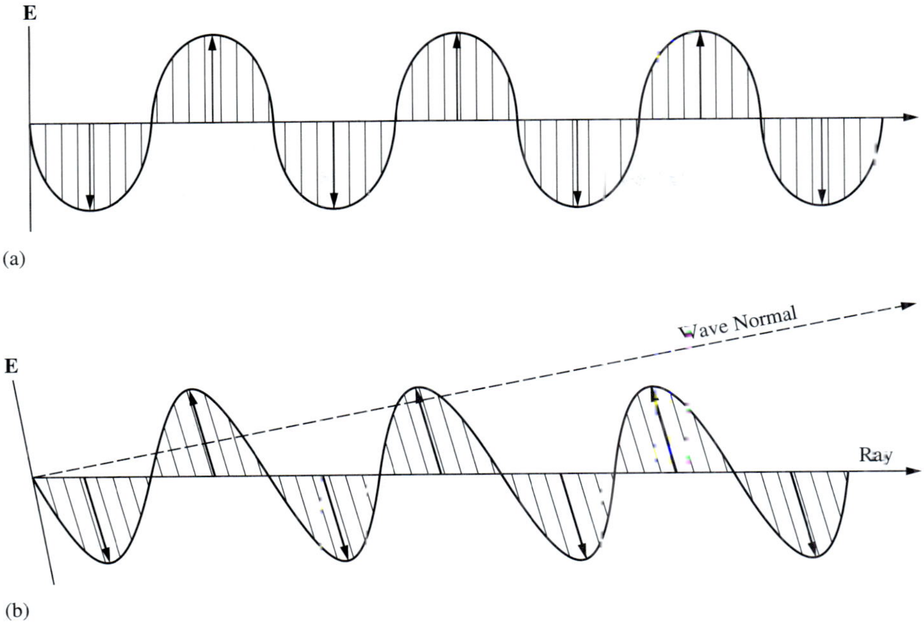

FIGURE 5-22 Ordinary and extraordinary wave and ray directions. (a) An ordinary ray has its E at right angles to its ray direction; wave and ray direction are the same. (b) An extraordinary ray has its E not at right angles to its ray direction; ray and wave directions are not parallel.

an optic axis. Upon entering or leaving a crystal, o rays follow the ordinary laws of refraction (Snell's law). The o rays have their **E**'s in the **a** crystallographic plane.

Extraordinary rays have their **E**'s at right angles to the **E**'s of ordinary rays and to the direction of light wave propagation. These directions define a plane that includes the **c** axis, but with **E** generally not parallel to **c**. When a light ray impinges on electron clouds that are asymmetrically constrained as they are at any general angle to a crystallographic axis, these electron clouds do not oscillate precisely parallel to **E**. Their secondary radiation is not only out of phase with the original ray, but generates an **E** that is not parallel as well (Fig. 5-21b). The direction at right angles to **E** in the plane containing both **E** and a light ray is a wave normal. Since in this case wave normals are not parallel to ray directions, these rays do not follow the ordinary laws of refraction and are thus extraordinary.

These relationships are assembled schematically in a uniaxial indicatrix and sections through this indicatrix (Fig. 5-22). Ordinary refractive indices are labeled ω, and extraordinary refractive indices are labeled ϵ'. The maximum or minimum refractive index, the one with its **E** parallel

(a) (b)

FIGURE 5-23 Uniaxial indicatrices. These indicatrices are surfaces of ellipsoids of revolution, every radius being proportional in length to the refractive index of a light wave having its E parallel to that radius. (a) Uniaxial positive indicatrix. (b) Uniaxial negative indicatrix.

to the **c** axis, is ϵ. Optic signs of uniaxial minerals are positive if $\epsilon > \omega$ or negative if $\epsilon < \omega$. The index ϵ' may take on any value between ϵ and ω, depending on crystallographic direction of a light ray. Uniaxial indicatrices are ellipsoids of revolution, prolate if positive and oblate if negative (Fig. 5-23).

Two directions are of special importance in uniaxial indicatrices. First, all rays traveling in the **c** axis direction have their **E**'s in the **a** axial plane, which has identical electron-cloud distributions in each **a** direction. Since rays with **E**'s in this plane all have the same refractive index ω, this section through an indicatrix is circular. Since all **E**'s are permitted in a circular section, a ray traveling parallel to **c** behaves as though it were isotropic with refractive index ω. In uniaxial minerals the optic axis, which is defined as the direction normal to a circular section, is the **c** crystallographic axis.

A second special case is a light ray traveling at right angles to an optic axis (in this case parallel to the **a** plane). This ray is split into two rays, one with its **E** parallel to **c** with refractive index ϵ and the other in the circular section with index ω. Since the **E** of the extraordinary ray is parallel to the optic axis (**c**) and at right angles to the ray direction, the wave normal is parallel to the ray direction so that both rays follow ordinary laws of refraction in this special set of directions.

Consider a planar section through an indicatrix that contains both wave normals, both ray directions, the **E** of the extraordinary ray, and the **c** crystallographic axis (Fig. 5-24). The **E** of the ordinary ray is normal to this section. For uniaxial positive indicatrices, the semimajor axis of this section is the optic axis, which is proportional to ϵ, and the semiminor

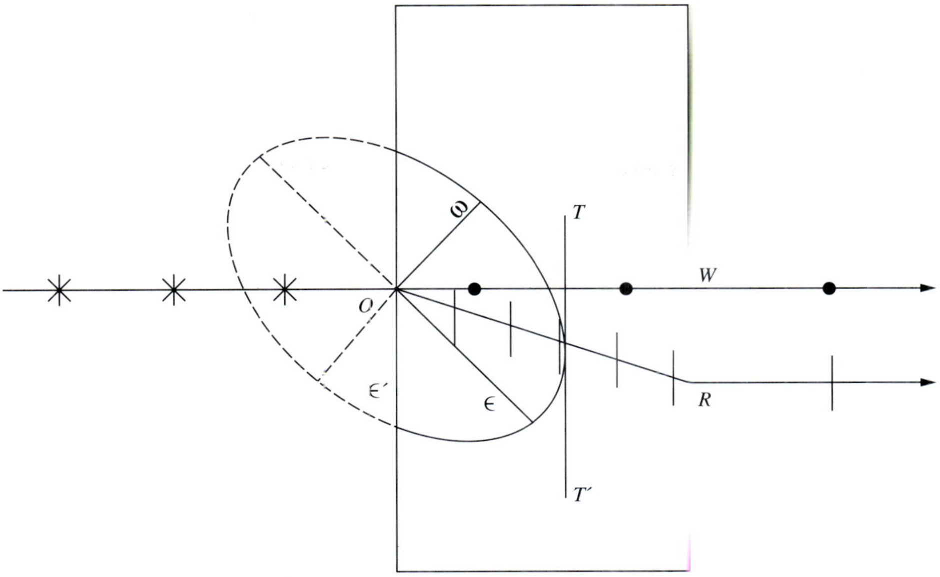

FIGURE 5-24 Light transmission through uniaxial crystals. Unpolarized light ray resolves into two rays polarized with **E**'s normal to one another. *OW* = wave direction and ordinary ray direction. *OR* = extraordinary ray direction. Vertical bars represent **E**'s in the plane of the page; dots represent **E**'s normal to the plane of the page.

axis is proportional to ω. The wave normal for both rays is *OW*, which is also the ordinary-ray direction. The **E** of the ordinary ray is normal to this section, but proportional to ω, which is the radius of the circular section. The **E** of the extraordinary ray is normal to *OW* and proportional to ε′.

Optical properties of minerals may be deduced by imagining an appropriate section of an indicatrix to be located wherever convenient within a mineral grain. A case in which a mineral slice is generally oriented with respect to optic directions illustrates this procedure (Fig. 5-23). This indicatrix is located such that a ray of light normal to a grain surface impinges its center. Upon entering this mineral grain, unpolarized light breaks into two polarized rays with the **E** of the extraordinary ray parallel to this section of the indicatrix and the **E** of the ordinary ray normal to it. The ordinary ray propagates through the grain at reduced velocity but without change in direction. The extraordinary ray also propagates through this grain at reduced velocity, but in the direction *OR*, which is where the wavefront is tangent to the indicatrix at *TT*′. This extraordinary ray continues until it emerges from the far side of this slice, where its ray direction resumes a path normal to its wavefront.

Biaxial Minerals As with uniaxial minerals, refractive indices in biaxial minerals vary with the **E** of a light ray from a maximum value γ to a minimum value α at right angles to one another. The refractive index at right angles to the $\alpha\gamma$ plane is β. These three axial directions are commonly labeled X, Y, and Z with relative values $X < Y < Z$. For **E**'s that do not coincide with these principal axes X, Y, and Z, refractive indices are intermediate between γ and β (γ') or between β and α (α').

For orthorhombic minerals, crystallographic symmetry requires that each principal axis correspond to a crystallographic axis, although in no particular order. In monoclinic minerals, one principal axis corresponds to the unique diad or mirror plane. No necessary symmetrical relationship relates principal optic directions with crystallographic directions in triclinic minerals.

A biaxial indicatrix is a triaxial ellipsoid with principal axes X, Y, and Z (Fig. 5-25, Prog. 5-2). Since β has a value between those of γ and α, each quadrant in an XZ section through this indicatrix must have a radius equal to β. Furthermore, each octant of this indicatrix must contain a whole family of radii equal to β. This family of equal radii defines two circular sections, their normals being the two optic axes of a biaxial indicatrix. The Y direction is thus the intersection of these two circular sections, which places the two optic axes in the XZ plane. The angle between optic axes is $2V$. When $2V_z$ is acute, a mineral is biaxial positive, and when $2V_x$ is acute, the mineral is biaxial negative. In other words, either $Z\,(+)$ or $X\,(-)$ is in the acute bisectrix (BxA). When $2V$ is 90°, the optic sign is indeterminant, and when $2V$ is 0° an indicatrix appears uniaxial. Different dispersions in the different optic directions, however, can change the shape of the indicatrix with change in wavelength.

Other than the two circular sections, all sections through a triaxial ellipsoid are ellipses. The principal sections XZ, XY, and YZ have semimajor and semiminor axes equal to γ and α, β and α, and γ and β, respectively. All general sections through a biaxial indicatrix are ellipses with semimajor axes γ' and semiminor axes α'.

A light ray traveling normal to a circular section has all **E**'s permitted and, therefore, behaves as though a biaxial crystal were isotropic in that direction. A light ray traveling normal to one of the principal sections breaks into two polarized rays with orthogonal **E**'s and refractive indices proportional to the semimajor and the semiminor axes of these sections, α, β, and γ. These are all ordinary rays with ray directions parallel to wave normals because tangents of a biaxial indicatrix in the directions X, Y, and Z are parallel to these principal sections.

A light ray for which an indicatrix is randomly oriented is broken into two extraordinary rays with orthogonal **E**'s. These two extraordinary

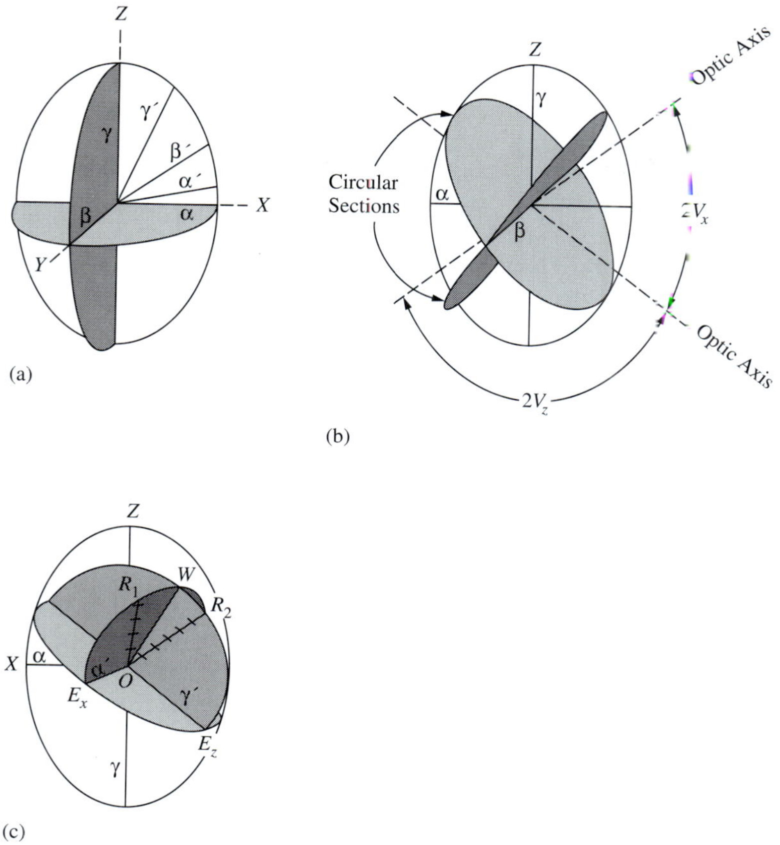

FIGURE 5-25 Biaxial indicatrices. (a) Biaxial indicatrix with principal planes and refractive indices shown. (b) Circular sections through a biaxial indicatrix with optic axes at right angles to them. (c) Wave (*OW*) and ray (*OR*$_1$ and *OR*$_2$) directions for light passing through a biaxial indicatrix in a general direction.

rays have a common wavefront that is an elliptical section with semiaxes proportional to α' and γ' (Fig. 5-25). In practical optical work with minerals, these general sections through a mineral grain and its associated indicatrix yield little useful information and are avoided by rotating a grain to a principal or circular section or by seeking other grains that have a useful orientation.

In summary, electromagnetic wave theory accounts for light behavior as it propagates through transparent minerals. When light waves pass through transparent materials, their **E**'s interact with orbital electrons. This interaction merely slows light in isotropic materials, whereas in anisotropic minerals it polarizes light and may cause it to change direction as well. A Fletcher indicatrix provides a graphic device for visualizing results of these interactions.

Kinds and distributions of electron clouds in a crystal structure determine how electromagnetic waves behave as light propagates through it. Heavy ions have more electrons, thus more inertia, causing large velocity changes as seen in large refractive indices. Polarizable ions slow light waves more than ions with low polarizability because polarizable electron clouds are more mobile. Denser polymorphs have more electron clouds per unit volume than lighter polymorphs and, hence, have higher refractive indices.

Birefringence, the difference between velocities and refractive indices of the two light rays in anisotropic minerals, results from structural differences in different crystallographic directions. Quartz, with little difference in electron clouds between **c** and **a** crystallographic directions, has low birefringence. Calcite group minerals, with their stacks of trigonal planar CO_3^{2-} groups, have large birefringence. These optical effects are powerful tools in mineral characterization and identification with a polarized light microscope.

Although the name of the inventor of the microscope is lost to history, Galileo Galilei reported in 1614 using an optical tube to see "flies which look as big as lambs." In 1625, naturalist John Faber named this type of optical tube a microscope after the model of the already named telescope (*tele,* distant; *scope,* seeing; *micro,* minute). By the time Robert Hooke published his description of microscopes and their uses in 1665, compound lenses replaced simple ones, thereby reducing lengths of microscope tubes from greater than 1 m to something resembling modern microscopes.

Although microscopes were widely used in biological studies, most geologists ignored them for two centuries. Even after William Nicol of Edinburgh published, in 1829, his description of construction of a two-piece calcite prism that transmitted only plane polarized light and, in 1831, his prescriptions for preparing mineral thin sections for microscopic study using his nicol prisms, geologists scorned these instruments. After all, who would use a microscope to study mountains?

A student at Edinburgh, Henry Clifton Sorby, published voluminously on microscopic studies of minerals and rocks after Nicol's death in 1851. These studies using nicol prisms were picked up by K. H. F. Rosenbusch in Germany and A. Michel-Lèvy in France and became the modern science of optical mineralogy and petrography.

5-6 DIFFRACTION

X-ray diffraction provided the first direct evidence for atoms periodically arrayed in crystals (Sec. 1-4). Now X-ray diffraction is absolutely essential to characterize a new mineral species and is extremely useful in identifying minerals routinely. It is the tool of choice in determining crystal structures.

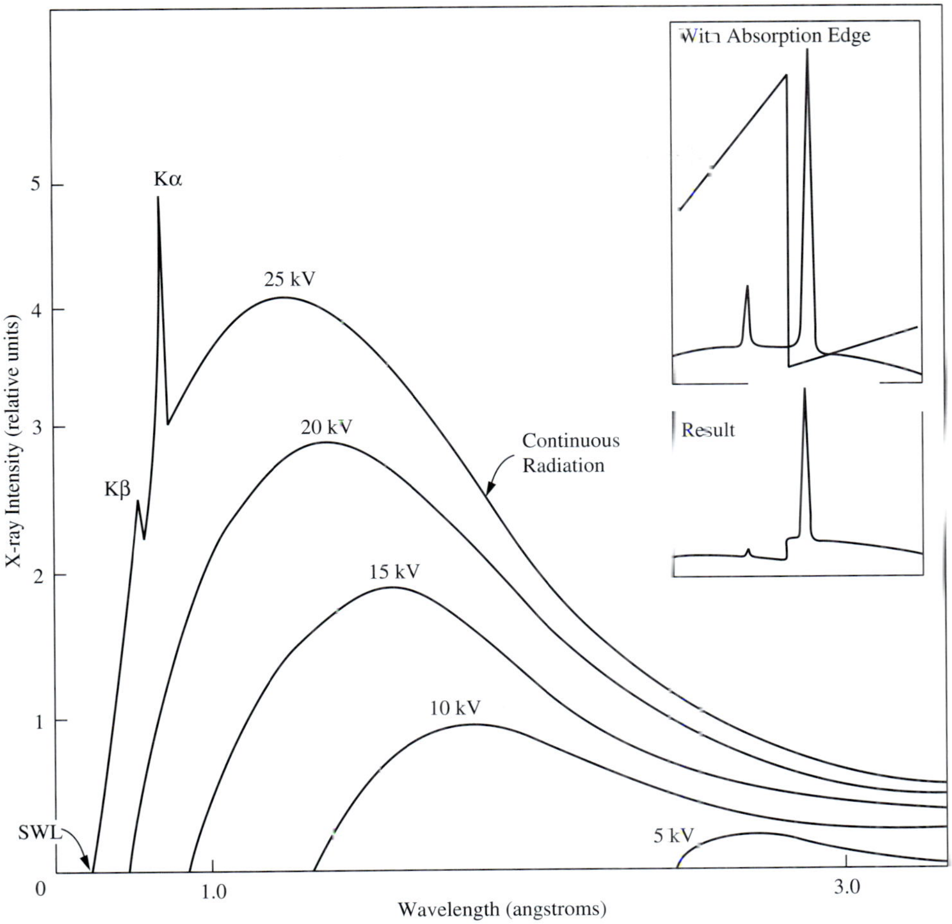

FIGURE 5-26 X-ray spectra. The X-ray spectrum for molybdenum is shown for various voltages. When applied voltage is greater than 25 kV, K electrons are expelled from this target metal so that it emits characteristic radiation superimposed on its continuous radiation. (After B. D. Cullity, *Elements of X-ray Diffraction*. Reading, MA: Addison-Wesley, 1956).

X rays are electromagnetic radiation with wavelengths between 50 nm and 0.5 pm (500 and 0.005 Å) (Fig. 5-1). Although commonly placed between ultraviolet light and gamma rays, X rays overlap both. This overlap results from practical, not theoretical, distinctions among different types of radiation. According to convention, ultraviolet light comes from valence electron transitions, X rays from inner orbital transitions, and gamma rays from atomic nuclei. Radiation of a wavelength in one of these zones of overlap coming from a black box cannot be uniquely assigned a name based on wavelength alone.

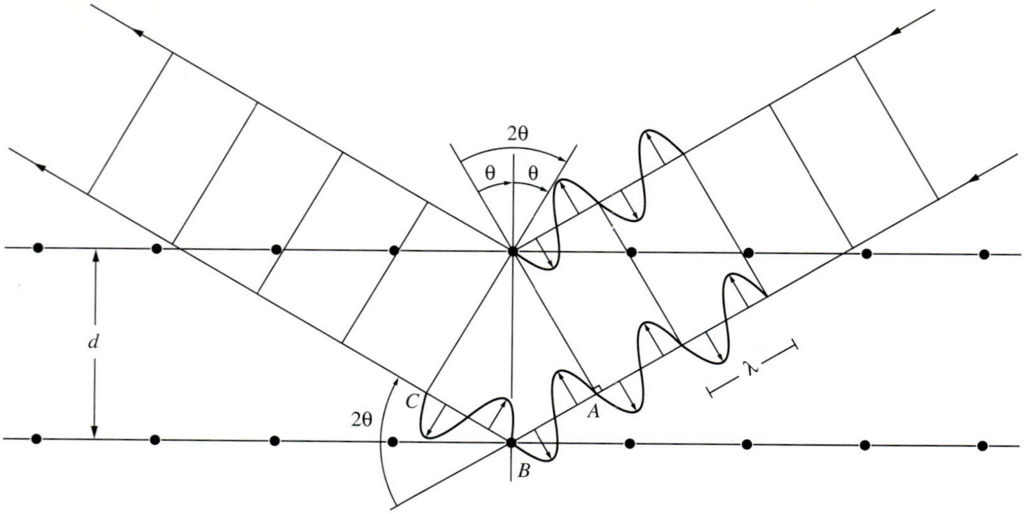

FIGURE 5-27 Conditions for X-ray diffraction. Diffraction occurs only when the path-length difference *BC* + *CD* is an integral multiple of the wavelength λ of incident radiation. Wavelength λ, interplanar spacing *d*, and the angle of diffraction are related by the Bragg equation $n\lambda = 2d \sin \theta$.

X-ray Sources Electrons accelerated by a strong (30–50 kV) electric field gradient have considerable kinetic energy. When these high-velocity electrons strike an anode, they decelerate, with their kinetic energy being converted to heat (>99%) and to radiation in the X-ray range of the electromagnetic spectrum. When the kinetic energy of an electron converts entirely to an X-ray quantum, this quantum has the highest possible energy possible for a given voltage and the shortest wavelength. Thus, each electric field gradient determines its own short-wavelength limit (SWL) of radiation. Partial conversion of kinetic energy yields radiation of lower energy and longer wavelength; a mixture of wavelengths is designated white radiation, the kind used in medical and dental analyses. (Friedrich and Knipping performed the first X-ray diffraction with white radiation. Most modern X-ray diffraction studies utilize monochromatic radiation.)

As an electric field gradient that accelerates electrons is increased, its SWL decreases. When the SWL decreases to a point where kinetic electrons can expel K electrons from a metal anode, the anode begins to emit its own characteristic radiation (Sec. 5-4). Characteristic monochromatic radiation from an anode metal is used for analysis of crystal structures (Fig. 5-26). After filtering to remove unwanted white radiation and other energies also present, a beam of X rays is aimed at a piece of crystalline material. X-ray quanta are scattered by atoms in this crystal much like photons of visible light are scattered by dust motes, with one important difference. Atoms in a crystal are arrayed periodically.

X-ray Scattering Each atomic particle in a crystal structure may scatter incident X-ray quanta. (Now this argument requires a switch to wave theory.) Although scattering may be random in direction, radiation occurs only in those directions where interference is constructive (Fig. 5-27). Destructive interference eliminates radiation in all other directions. Bragg's law, $n\lambda = 2d \sin \theta$, summarizes conditions for constructive interference and X-ray diffraction. When path differences between monochromatic X rays scattered from successive layers in a crystal structure are integral multiples of this wavelength of radiation constructive interference causes diffraction. Whether diffraction occurs depends on X-ray wavelength, d spacing between atomic layers, and angle 2θ between X-ray source and detector (Fig. 5-26, Prog. 5-3).

Diffraction may be visualized as coming from structural planes, planes with rational Miller indices. *Reflecting plane* refers to these planes, as though X rays reflected from them. Reflecting is an unfortunate term erroneously suggesting a process akin to light reflection. A diffracted beam from a crystal results from atomic planes scattering quanta from well below a mineral surface, whereas optical reflection comes from a surface layer only. X-ray diffraction occurs only at Bragg angles, whereas optical reflection occurs at all angles. Furthermore, a good optical mirror has an efficiency of nearly 100%, whereas only a small percentage of an incident X-ray beam is diffracted. Usage of the term *reflecting plane* for diffraction unfortunately is well established; however, the use of one word to cover two ideas does not reduce those two ideas to one.

X-ray Structures Bragg angles of diffraction may be measured experimentally with a goniometer and any device that detects X rays. Each crystal structure has associated with it one of 14 Bravais space lattices (Sec. 3-5), and each lattice point has associated with it an asymmetric unit (Sec. 3-7). Thus, periodic arrays of layers of atomic particles represent three-dimensional structures. Each layer is separated by a distance d, which depends on lattice parameters (Table 3-3) and the Miller indices of these layers (Fig. 3-12). Measured Bragg angles of diffraction and known wavelength of characteristic target radiation are used to calculate d spacings of any crystal structure (Fig. 5-4). A sufficient number of d spacings permit unique determination of a crystal structure. All structures illustrated in Chap. 2 were determined in just such a manner. Furthermore, d spacings of a mineral of unknown identity can be matched against published d spacings to identify a mineral specimen in question (Table 5-5) and, ionic sizes may be estimated from measured d spacings (Table 1-3).

TABLE 5-5 X-ray Diffraction Data for Gypsum (2θ Values for Cu Kα Radiation, λ = 154 pm (1.54 Å))

$hk\ell$	2θ (deg)	d (pm)	I/I_0
020	11.6	761	45
021	20.7	428	90
041	29.0	307	30
200, 221	31.1	287	100
112	32.1	279	20
150, 220	33.4	268	50
202	36.1	249	20
242	43.3	209	14
311, 152	43.7	207	20

$hk\ell$ = Bragg indices of diffraction; 2θ = Bragg angle; d = spacing between $hk\ell$ layers; I/I_0 = intensity relative to strongest intensity.

Order of a diffracted beam is the number n in the Bragg equation. Path difference is one wavelength for $n = 1$, two wavelengths for $n = 2$, and so forth. A second-order diffraction is geometrically identical to having an additional diffraction plane midway between first-order diffraction planes. Although this extra layer may not exist in a real crystal structure, its visualization may be convenient. When this conceptual tool is used, diffraction order n is incorporated into d spacing values (Table 5-4). Thus, second-order diffraction from {100} planes comes from hypothetical planes called {200}, third-order diffraction for {111} planes from hypothetical {333} planes, and so forth. These diffraction planes, whether real or hypothetical, have Bragg indices 100, 200, 111, 333, and so forth (note, there are no closures about Bragg indices, Table 3-2).

Reciprocal Space A convenient graphic representation of orders of diffraction, of diffraction spacing, of Bragg angles, and of whether a specific diffraction order can occur may be constructed from reciprocals of lattice parameters. In reciprocal space, crystallographic directions **a***, **b***, and **c*** are parallel to face normals of a unit cell, but spacing of reciprocal lattice points is the reciprocal of their distances in direct space (Prog. 5-4). Thus, reciprocal 100 is at $1/d_{100}$ and reciprocal 200 is at $1/d_{200}$ ($= 2/d_{100}$) in the **a*** direction from an arbitrarily selected origin at 0,0,0 in a reciprocal lattice (Fig. 5-28). Each point in a reciprocal lattice represents a specific interplanar distance in direct space.

Within a reciprocal lattice, construct a sphere (circle in Fig. 5-28) with a radius that is the reciprocal of the characteristic radiation ($1/\lambda$) of a target metal. This sphere in reciprocal space is located so that a point on its surface lies at the origin 0,0,0. Rotate this sphere about the origin, and its surface will contact each reciprocal lattice point within $2/\lambda$ of the

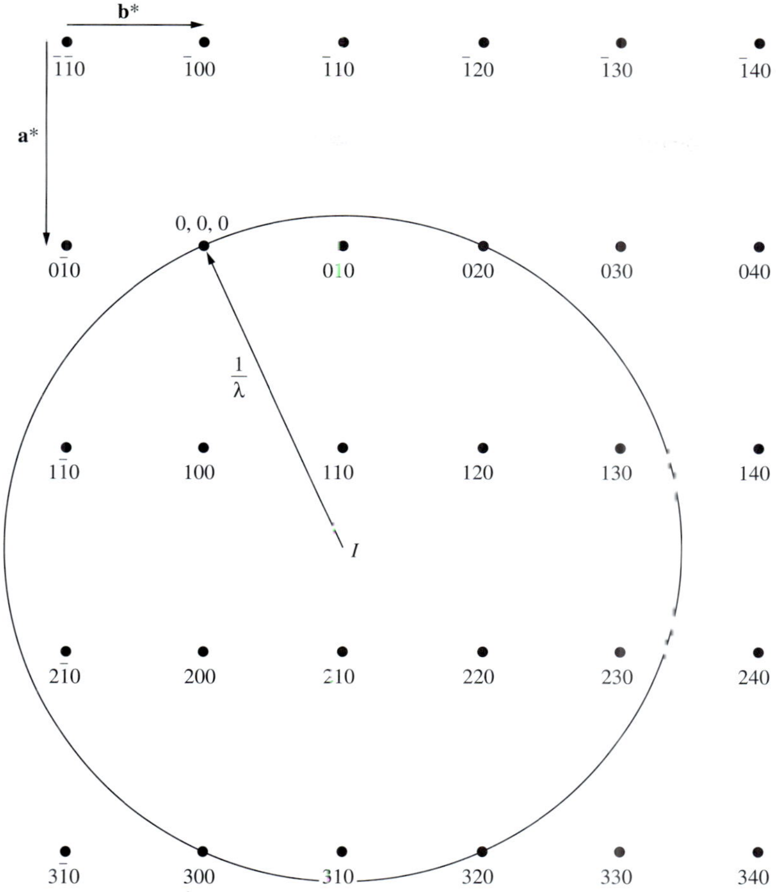

FIGURE 5-28 Reciprocal space. Lattice points in reciprocal space represent diffraction planes in direct space. The surface of a sphere (circle in a two-dimensional net) with radius 1/λ (reciprocal wavelength) intersecting an arbitrary origin (0,0,0) graphically shows limitations inherent in the Bragg equation. Rotation of this sphere about an origin will cause its surface to intersect all reciprocal lattice points within 2/λ of the origin. Each intersection gives the angle at which diffraction occurs for each lattice plane. Here the circle intersects 020, 300, and 320.

origin. Each position of this sphere where it encounters a reciprocal lattice point represents an angle where diffraction occurs. If two points are on the surface of the sphere at any given angle, these two diffractions are angularly indistinguishable. Furthermore, no point further from the origin than $2/\lambda$ represents diffraction for that wavelength. This limit is inherent in the Bragg equation. The maximum value for θ is 90°; hence, the maximum value for d is $\lambda/2$.

Reciprocal space graphically represents geometric limitations inherent in the Bragg equation. Values for the sine of angles are always unity or less. Rearrangement of the Bragg equation shows that $n\lambda/2d$ must also equal unity or less. For first-order diffraction $n = 1$, λ must be less than $2d$. Since d spacings of crystals are mostly less than 300 pm (3 Å), radiation must be less than 600 pm (6 Å) in wavelength to be useful for X-ray diffraction. Further rearrangement of the Bragg equation shows that n cannot be greater than $2d/\lambda$. For d spacing on the order of 30 pm and λ equal to 154 pm (1.54 Å) for commonly used CuKα radiation, $n <$ 4 and no higher orders of diffraction can occur. This limitation may be avoided by employing target metals with characteristic radiation of shorter wavelength.

As noted in our discussion of electron microscopy (Sec. 5-4), electrons accelerated by 100 kV have an associated wavelength of approximately 4 pm (0.04 Å). Hence, electron diffraction is an analytical technique employed in studies of crystalline materials. Since an electron beam can be focused electromagnetically, structures of fine-grained clay mineral particles and thin asbestiform fibers may be analyzed by this technique.

FURTHER READINGS

Bloss, F. D., *An Introduction to the Methods of Optical Crystallography.* New York: Holt, Rinehart and Winston, 1961.

Burns, R. G., *Mineralogical Applications of Crystal Field Theory.* New York: Cambridge University Press, 1970.

Cullity, B. D., *Elements of X-ray Diffraction.* Reading, MA: Addison-Wesley, 1956.

Frye, K., *Encyclopedia of Mineralogy.* New York: Van Nostrand Reinhold, 1981.

Hartshorne, N. H., and A. Stuart, *Practical Optical Crystallography.* London: Edward Arnold, 1964.

Herzberg, G., *Atomic Spectra and Atomic Structure,* 2nd ed. New York: Dover, 1944.

Kieffer, S. W., and A. Navrotsky, *Microscopic to Macroscopic.* Washington, DC: Mineralogical Society of America, 1985.

Nassau, K., *The Physics and Chemistry of Color.* New York: Wiley, 1983.

Peckett, A., R. Phillips, and N. F. M. Henry, *The Colors of Opaque Minerals.* London: Open University Press, 1989.

Phillips, W. R., *Mineral Optics.* San Francisco: Freeman, 1971.

Phillips, W. R., and D. T. Griffin, *Optical Mineralogy.* San Francisco: Freeman, 1981.

Shelley, D., *Optical Mineralogy,* 2nd ed. New York: Elsevier, 1985.

Wahlstrom, E. E., *Optical Crystallography,* 5th ed. New York: Wiley 1979.

Zussman, J. (ed.), *Physical Methods in Determinative Mineralogy,* 2nd ed. New York: Academic Press, 1977.

6

THE PHASE RULE AND PHASE DIAGRAMS

A popular, although undoubtedly futile, pastime is to debate about who has made the single greatest achievement in a particular field of endeavor. Neither science in general, nor mineral science in particular, is free from such interesting comparisons. Be that as it may, contributions by Josiah Willard Gibbs to scientific thought have probably had as much impact on modern science and technology as those of any other individual. He, in one elegant publication, shaped the 20th-century course of experimental mineralogy and that of metallurgy, ceramic science, physical chemistry, and materials science in general, as well. Much of what can be said today about igneous and metamorphic petrology and about the earth's interior derives from his theoretical contributions.

Gibbs' influential paper, "On the Equilibrium of Heterogeneous Substances," appeared in two parts, in 1876 and 1878, in the *Transactions of the Connecticut Academy*. There it languished for many years, not so much because of the relative provinciality of this journal in the European world of science, but more because its mathematical rigor was beyond the training of most chemists and mineralogists of that era. Wilhelm Ostwald (1891) translated this paper into German, and Henry Le Chatelier (1899) translated it into French. Both scientists gave as their reason for undertaking these translations the importance of the theoretical questions posed by Gibbs' paper that were not experimentally demonstrated yet. Many scientists have elaborated on this work, including H. W. Bakhuis Roozeboom and F. A. H. Schreinemakers, but Gibbs' original work remains the ultimate arbiter in questions of the science of materials.

Gibbs' phase rule is so rigorous and completely general in its statements about matter under equilibrium conditions that, in spite of years of dedicated search by the world's top materials scientists, no exceptions to it have been found. Indeed, today apparent exception to it prompts research scientists to search for something wrong in their experiments, commonly a failure to obtain equilibrium conditions. Whenever a rock turns up with more phases in it than allowed by Gibbs' phase rule, geologists automatically record that this rock contains a disequilibrium assemblage of mineral phases.

6-1 PHASES, COMPONENTS, AND INTENSIVE VARIABLES

Gibbs' phase rule is a relationship among phases, components, intensive variables, and degrees of freedom of a system.

Phases A phase is a homogeneous, physically distinct, and mechanically separable part of a system. A phase may be solid, liquid, or vapor. A mineral species is an example of a crystalline phase, and each mineral species in an equilibrium assemblage, or system is a separate phase. Grain boundaries between minerals of the same species are not generally taken into account, because theoretical treatment given to a mineral species is the same whether a mineral is a single crystal or a mosaic of many crystals. Minerals are homogeneous at equilibrium, by definition and they are physically distinct. They are mechanically separable based on their differing physical properties.

A liquid or a gas is a phase. Only one gas occurs in a system at equilibrium, because part of a definition of a gas is that it is miscible with all other gases. A system may have one or more liquid phases, since some liquids mix and others do not. Oil and water do not mix; they form a two-phase system. Alcohol and water mix in all proportions and, therefore, form a single phase. (That alcohol and gasoline do not mix is a legal and moral statement, not a physical one.)

Components Choose components of a system from its constituents as the smallest number necessary to represent conveniently all phases in a system. A component is not necessarily equivalent to a chemical element, a chemical compound, or a constituent. Any system may be broken down in terms of constituent parts, which need not be chemical compounds or even chemical elements. For example, electrons may be treated as constituents in a system of iron oxides. Components are only those constituents the concentrations of which can undergo independent variation in different phases of a system. Select those that work best.

This selection will be dictated by observations and experiments; it may change with different conditions of pressure and temperature. For instance, a crystal or cleavage fragment of calcite is a one-component system consisting of $CaCO_3$. Squeezed to the stability field boundary where calcite and aragonite coexist as stable phases, it is still a system of one component, $CaCO_3$, in two phases, aragonite and calcite. Heated to its dissociation to CaO and CO_2, however, it becomes a two-component system because the relative amounts of CaO and CO_2 can now be varied independently, which cannot be done when $CaCO_3$ is in calcite or aragonite form.

Unary System Consider a flask of boiling water. This flask contains liquid water, one phase, and water vapor, a second phase. If this flask is sealed and its heat source removed, the same two phases remain. As this flask cools, proportions of the phases will change and the pressure inside the flask will change, but the number of phases remains two. Within this flask there is a one-component system, since H_2O represents the composition of each phase. This system cannot be treated as consisting of two components, H and O, because pure water and pure steam always have these constituents in a ratio of 2:1, which cannot be varied independently of one another. If this flask of water chills sufficiently, ice crystallizes. The number of components remains at one, while the number of phases goes from two to three. Further removal of heat from this flask results in an increased proportion of ice at the expense of the other two phases, but pressure and temperature remain constant so long as three phases of a single component, H_2O, coexist at equilibrium. These three phases define an observed triple point (t.p.) for water.

Binary Systems Consider olivine, a crystal solution with a composition intermediate between forsterite [Mg_2SiO_4] and fayalite [Fe_2SiO_4]. A single phase, olivine, can be represented by proportions of the two end members of this crystal solution series. These end members, Mg_2SiO_4 and Fe_2SiO_4, are the two components of this system. If a crystal of olivine is heated until it begins to melt, two phases, one crystalline and the other a melt, coexist. These two phases have different chemical compositions, but each composition is represented in terms of two components of this system by a linear combination of Mg_2SiO_4 and Fe_2SiO_4.

When heated, calcite dissociates into lime and carbon dioxide according to the chemical reaction

$$CaCO_3 \rightleftharpoons CaO + CO_2.$$

Three phases coexist at equilibrium when this dissociation is partly complete. These three phases do not have the same chemical composition, but their compositions are not independently variable. Thus, this dissociation equation represents a system of three phases consisting of three chemical compounds and three constituents, but the system is represented by two components. If CaO and CO_2 are chosen as components, a third constituent $CaCO_3$ may be defined as

$$CaCO_3 = CaO + CO_2.$$

Similarly, if $CaCO_3$ and CaO are chosen as constituents, a third constituent is defined by

$$CO_2 = CaCO_3 - CaO.$$

Negative quantities of components may be used to define constituents of a phase in a system if it is convenient to do so. Such a selection is arbitrary, but arbitrary means that nothing within a system requires specifying which two constituents are components; it does not mean abandoning the rules of this system.

Intensive Variables Other variables necessary for describing a system include mass, volume, density, refractive index, temperature, pressure, electric field, magnetic field, entropy, free energy, and chemical potential. These variables are differentiated according to whether they are divisible among parts of a system. Clearly, if a system is divided, mass and volume are apportioned to different parts of this system; they are extensive variables. Intensive properties are not divisible. Splitting a system does not alter temperatures of its separate parts, nor pressure and chemical potentials. Analysis of mineral associations using the phase rule treats the number of different phases that can coexist and, therefore, concerns intensive variables only.

Pressure is force per unit area with units of pascals, Pa (newtons meters^{-2}, N m^{-2}). (Another unit of pressure in common mineralogical usage is 1 bar = 10^5 Pa, which is about 1 atmosphere.) Actual pressure measurements are usually indirect. Measurements include use of elastic constants, which relate force to displacement of a particular metal and use of materials with known relationships of pressure to electric resistance. Pressure-registering instruments utilizing these materials are calibrated to deadweight testing devices and to defined phase transformations (Table 6-1).

Temperature is defined relatively in terms of heat flow. Heat flows from a hotter body (one of higher temperature) to a cooler body (one of lower temperature). Temperature scales are calibrated arbitrarily to phase changes just as the Mohs hardness scale is calibrated for one mineral scratching another. Most temperature measurements are in terms of other properties of a system. In the thermodynamics of an ideal gas, temperature, pressure, and volume are related by the formula $PV = nRT$ (Sec. 1-8). Thus, pressure or volume is arbitrarily held constant and temperature

TABLE 6-1 Practical Pressure Scale

Transition	P (kPa)	T (°C)
Mercury, m.p.	756.9	0
Bismuth, I-II	2550	25
Thallium, I-II	3670	25
Barium, I-II	5500	25
Bismuth, III-V	7700	25

can be measured with a gas thermometer in terms of the remaining variable. In other words, if pressure is held constant, temperature is proportional to volume. Electrical conductivity of many substances depends on temperature, so electrical resistance of a heated wire can be used to calculate its temperature. Thermocouples operate because two different metals have measurable voltages that change with temperature. Optical pyrometers relate temperature to emission wavelength in the visible range. Other wavelengths, such as infrared, also depend on the temperature of a body of matter.

In precise modern work, certain phase transformations occur at fixed temperatures, and these transformations can be measured with high precision (Table 6-2). These transformations define a temperature scale and are used to calibrate those measuring instruments used in modern research. Temperature values between these reference points are established by interpolation based on one of the principles given in the preceding paragraph. (Above the melting point of Au^0 no internationally accepted scale exists; seek a specific statement about the temperature scale calibrations used above this temperature.)

Chemical Potentials Systems considered in this chapter are assumed to be at equilibrium. Equilibrium conditions exist when pressure, temperature, and chemical potential are uniform throughout a system. Uniform pressure and temperature are easy ideas to comprehend. As stated in Sec. 1-8, under equilibrium conditions, systems have no tendency to change. Since $\Delta G = 0$, the chemical potential, μ, of each constituent must be the same in all phases.

Consider again the three systems discussed under phases and components for the purpose of illustrating what is meant by chemical potential and equilibrium. In the example of boiling water in a sealed container, the chemical potential of water in the vapor phase is equal to that in the liquid phase. At equilibrium, exactly the same number of water molecules evaporate as condense, giving the system a dynamic balance. At the triple point, the chemical potential of H_2O is the same in the solid, liquid, and vapor phases. Amount of heat in this system can alter volumes or relative proportions of phases present, but these are extensive variables.

TABLE 6-2 Practical Temperature Scale*

Transition	°C
Oxygen, b.p.	−182.67
Water, m.p.	0.00
Water, t.p.	0.01
Gallium, m.p.	30.0
Water, b.p.	100.00
Indium, m.p.	156.635
Tin, m.p.	232
Zinc, m.p.	419.505
Sulfur, b.p.	444.6
Silver, m.p.	960.8
Gold, m.p.	1063.0
Palladium, m.p.	1552
Platinum, m.p.	1769

*Pressure is 101.3 kPa (1 standard atmosphere) except for the triple point of water.

Olivine in equilibrium with its melt has a composition different from its melt, but the fayalite component of the liquid solution has the same chemical potential as the fayalite component of the crystal solution; the forsterite component also has the same chemical potential in both phases. Partitioning of the two components between the two phases may be different, but the chemical potentials are the same when this system is in equilibrium.

At equilibrium in the system CaO—CO_2 where $CaCO_3$ is stable in the presence of CaO and CO_2, CO_2 has the same chemical potential in gas and in calcite. The CaO has the same chemical potential in lime and in calcite. In summary, one condition of equilibrium is that no gradients of temperature, pressure, or chemical potential exist in a system. As a consequence, no equilibrium system has any tendency to change as long as intensive conditions of equilibrium do not change.

Heterogeneous Equilibrium There are two distinct kinds of equilibrium, homogeneous and heterogeneous. Homogeneous equilibrium, with which you became familiar in analyzing liquids in your chemistry laboratory exercises for unknown solutes, refers to equilibrium within a single phase, commonly water or some other solvent. Heterogeneous equilibrium refers to a multiphase system in which the chemical potential of each constituent is the same in every phase. Mineral associations are treated in terms of heterogeneous equilibrium because more than one crystalline phase may coexist.

Equilibrium systems are commonly labeled by the number of components they contain. Thus, H_2O is a one-component system, whereas $CaO—CO_2$ and $Mg_2SiO_4—Fe_2SiO_4$ are two-component systems. These are also called unary and binary systems. Systems of 3, 4, . . . , n components exist.

6-2 GIBBS' PHASE RULE

The phase rule is an absolutely rigorous and completely general statement about the numbers of different phases that may coexist under conditions of heterogeneous equilibrium. A question of whether real mineral assemblages form under equilibrium conditions is a practical one discussed in Chap. 7. This rule was worked out in a purely formal and mathematical way by J. Willard Gibbs.

Variance Any system is completely defined if all its state properties are known (Sec. 1-8). Since chemical and physical properties are related by known laws, knowledge of one permits calculation of others in accordance with these laws. Put in another way, in the system H_2O, water vapor exists alone over a wide range temperature and pressure (Fig. 1-18). But stipulating temperature and pressure gives unique values for other intensive variables such as density and refractive index. Similarly, this system containing liquid and vapor phases is indeterminant as to their intensive physical and chemical properties. In this case, however, stipulating either pressure or temperature fixes the other as long as both phases are present. At a triple point in this system, however, where ice, water, and vapor coexist, simple stipulation that all three phases are present in equilibrium fixes for all time temperature, pressure, and chemical potential of components of this system. All other intensive properties of each phase are also fixed.

In the system H_2O, when one phase is present, two intensive variables must be arbitrarily stipulated to define this system. Such a system has two degrees of freedom; it is divariant. When two phases are present, only one intensive variable is arbitrary and this system has one degree of freedom; it is univariant. At a triple point there are no degrees of freedom, and this unary system H_2O is invariant. In general, degree of freedom, or variance, of a system is the number of intensive variables that can be varied independently and arbitrarily without causing a phase change. The phase rule is a completely general statement that relates variance of a system to numbers of components and numbers of phases.

First Principles Consider a system of C different components existing in P different phases. How many degrees of freedom F does this system have? The full composition of each phase P in a system of C components is defined by stipulating $C - 1$ of its components; since the whole system is the sum of its component parts, the last component can be arrived at by difference. Since each phase is uniquely defined by $C - 1$ composition variables and the intensive variables of pressure and temperature, there are $C + 1$ independent variables for each phase P. With P phases in a system, this gives us a total of $PC + P$ independent system variables.

There have to be as many equations of state relating these variables as there are variables in order to define uniquely the state of a system. (This number is a simple algebraic requirement that n independent equations are needed to solve uniquely for n unknowns. For n unknowns and $n - 1$ equations, one unknown must be assigned an arbitrary value for a unique solution of these equations.) If there are fewer equations of state than variables, a system has variance or degrees of freedom and values for some intensive properties must be stipulated in order to define the state of a system uniquely. Under conditions of equilibrium, the pressure, the temperature, and the chemical potential of each component are the same in all phases. Therefore, by selecting one phase containing all components of a system as a standard phase, chemical potentials of all phases can be related to those of a standard phase by equations of state. For a system of P phases there exist $P - 1$ equations for each component. Since there are C components plus pressure and temperature, there are $(C + 2)(P - 1)$ equations in all.

Since variance or degrees of freedom F of a system is the difference between the number of independent variables and the number of equations,

$$F = [PC + P] - [CP + 2P - C - 2] = C - P + 2,$$

which is Gibbs' phase rule.

Now we can analyze the system H_2O in terms of this phase rule (Fig. 1-18). If only one phase—be it ice, water, or vapor—exists in this unary system, P and C both equal 1 and the phase rule gives $F = 1 - 1 + 2 = 2$. Pressure and temperature can be independently varied without bringing about a phase change. If any two phases are present, the phase rule predicts $F = 1 - 2 + 2 = 1$. This system is then univariant, and stipulation of either pressure or temperature uniquely defines the state of this system. When three phases are present in a unary system (a triple point), $F = 1 - 3 + 2 = 0$, and this system is invariant.

By way of summary, note that derivation of Gibbs' phase rule is completely general and without reference to any chemical or mineralogic reality. This generality is what makes it such a powerful tool in studying mineral assemblages. Most mineral assemblages, however, formed over a limited range of temperatures and pressures and, thus, are divariant. If $F = 2$, as in many geologic processes, then $P = C$. This empirical relationship, first enunciated by V. M. Goldschmidt, is the Mineralogical Phase Rule, sometimes called the Goldschmidt Phase Rule, a useful relationship applicable to many igneous and metamorphic rocks.

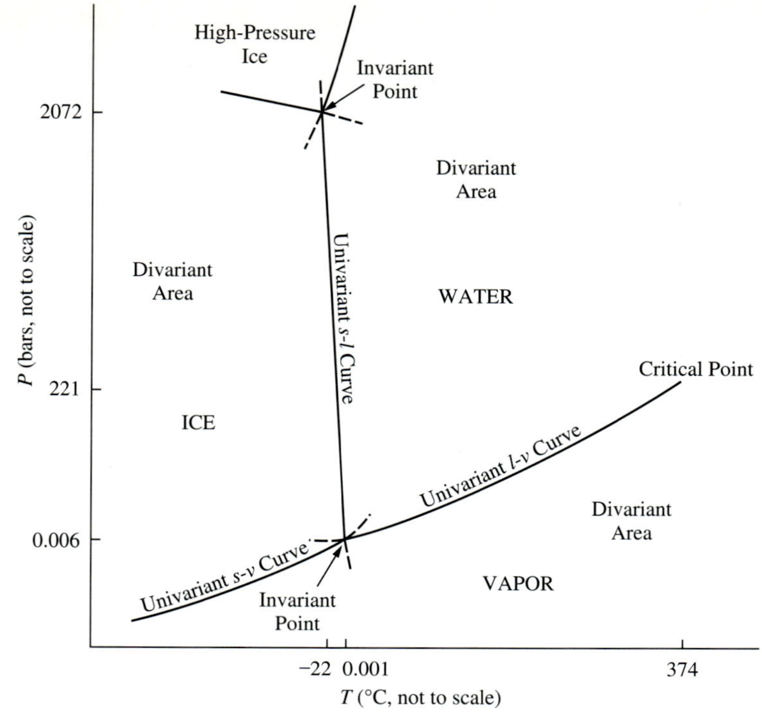

FIGURE 6-1 Partial phase diagram for water. Four phases are shown. Where only one phase appears, both pressure and temperature may be varied independently and arbitrarily without changing the number of phases present. Where two phases coexist along a univariant curve, either pressure or temperature, but not both, may be varied without changing the number of phases present. At triple points where three phases coexist, neither pressure, temperature, nor any other intensive variable may be changed without causing one phase to disappear. Metastable extensions of univariant curves are dashed.

Phase Space Phase diagrams represent simple chemical and mineralogic systems graphically (Fig. 6-1). Common practice plots temperature as a horizontal axis increasing to the right and pressure as a vertical axis increasing to the top of a phase diagram. Many geologists, attempting to represent phase relationships more realistically, plot pressure increasing toward the bottom of a phase diagram in simulation of pressure increasing with depth into the earth. Confusing as it may seem at the outset, you must learn to deal with both conventions simply because both conventions are used.

At equilibrium, conditions of divariance are represented by areas on a phase diagram, univariance by lines, and invariance by points. Two triple points are shown for the system H_2O, one involving ice, water, and vapor, the other ice, high-pressure ice, and water. The univariant curve representing ice-vapor equilibria extends from a triple point to absolute-zero temperature and zero pressure. The univariant curve representing ice-water connects two triple points. (Other phases of ice, not shown on Fig. 6-1, are separated by univariant curves connecting triple points.) The univariant curve representing liquid-vapor extends to a critical end point, where distinction between liquid and vapor ceases to exist. (Refer to water as a fluid beyond its critical end point.)

Metastability Each univariant curve has a metastable extension beyond an invariant point. Metastability occurs because some additional energy is required to nucleate a new phase (Sec. 7-1). Gibbs' phase rule applies to metastability and, in the absence of nucleation energy to start a new stable phase, metastable phases exist. When a univariant curve terminates at an invariant point, its metastable extension extends into the divariant stability region of the phase not present on that univariant curve. This metastable extension represents a two-phase assemblage that is in a higher energy state than the area of the one-phase field represented.

The stable phase of carbon at the earth's surface is graphite, but diamonds persist because high activation energy is required to nucleate the stable phase, graphite (Sec. 7-1). Diamonds presumably nucleated and grew within their stability field in the earth's deep continental crustal keel. Alternatively, a phase may not have a stability, but may nucleate and grow metastably, for instance ice IV (Fig. 1-17). This condition may occur if such a metastable phase has a higher nucleation probability than a competing stable phase (Sec. 7-1). Empirically, whether an existing phase is stable or unstable may be difficult to determine. Even when a phase change occurs spontaneously, any resulting phase may or may not be a stable phase in a system. Thus, during chemical weathering of a mineral not stable at the earth's surface (e.g., olivine), initial weathering products (e.g., a smectite + geothite) need not represent phases that are stable there (e.g., kaolinite + hematite).

6-3 BINARY SYSTEMS WITH NO COMPOUNDS

A binary system is one with two components ($C = 2$), only one of which may be varied independently since the two necessarily add up to 100%. By Gibbs' phase rule, invariance ($F = 0$) occurs when four phases ($P = 4$) coexist, univariance ($F = 1$) when three phases ($P = 3$) coexist, divariance ($F = 2$) when two phases ($P = 2$) coexist, and trivariance ($F = 3$) when only one phase ($P = 1$) exists. Complete graphic representation of binary systems requires three orthogonal coordinates in three-dimensional pressure-temperature-composition space (PTX space). In such a PTX plot, trivariance exists as a volume within which one composition and two intensive variables, commonly pressure and temperature, may be changed arbitrarily without causing a phase change.

To portray binary systems graphically on paper, we set one variable, commonly (but not necessarily) pressure, at a fixed value. The result is an isobaric, polythermal, two-component phase diagram. A system may be represented fully by a series of such diagrams at different fixed pressures. For each such diagram, the phase rule reduces to $F = C - P + 1$ by restriction.

Crystalline Immiscibility Two components may be immiscible in a crystalline state (no crystal solution between them); they may be partially miscible; or complete crystal solution can exist between them. An isobaric section of a binary system with complete crystalline immiscibility between component *A* and component *B* may be represented with pure *A* on the left and pure *B* on the right with temperature increasing upward (Fig. 6-2). Different admixtures of these two end members are shown as percentages along an arbitrary base line. The melt point for pure *A* is represented by *Ta*, for pure *B* by *Tb*. Mixtures of *A* and *B* commonly melt at lower temperatures than either pure substance because of mutual solution effects.

A liquid with composition 75*A* 25*B* (75% *A* and 25% *B*) may be cooled reversibly without phase change until it reaches a liquidus curve between *liquid* area and *solid A plus liquid* area at a temperature between *Ta* and *Te* (eutectic temperature, Fig. 6-2; Prog. 6-1). At this point, crystals of pure *A* appear in this liquid, thereby shifting liquid composition away from *A* and toward lower temperatures along this liquidus curve. Continued reversible temperature decrease causes further crystallization of pure *A*, while liquid composition migrates along this liquidus curve toward a eutectic point, the lowest temperature at which a liquid can exist between *A* and *B* in this system. When the temperature of this system has dropped to *Te*, liquid composition in equilibrium with crystals of *A* has shifted to the eutectic composition, in this case 60*A* 40*B*. This system *A*—*B* has two components; at its eutectic point three phases (*A*, *B*, and eutectic liquid) coexist stably; and this system is arbitrarily isobaric. Therefore, $F = C(2) - P(3) + 1 = 0$; this system is isobarically invariant. Further removal of heat from this system causes simultaneous equilibrium crystallization of *A* and of *B* without further change in temperature until all eutectic liquid crystallizes.

The texture of a resulting mix of crystals might have large crystals of *A* that grew from melts along the liquidus curve, surrounded by a matte of smaller crystals of *A* and *B*, which crystallized at the eutectic temperature (Fig. 6-2b). Composition of this matte is the eutectic composition 60*A* 40*B*, but composition of large crystals plus matte is that of the starting composition, 75*A* 25*B*.

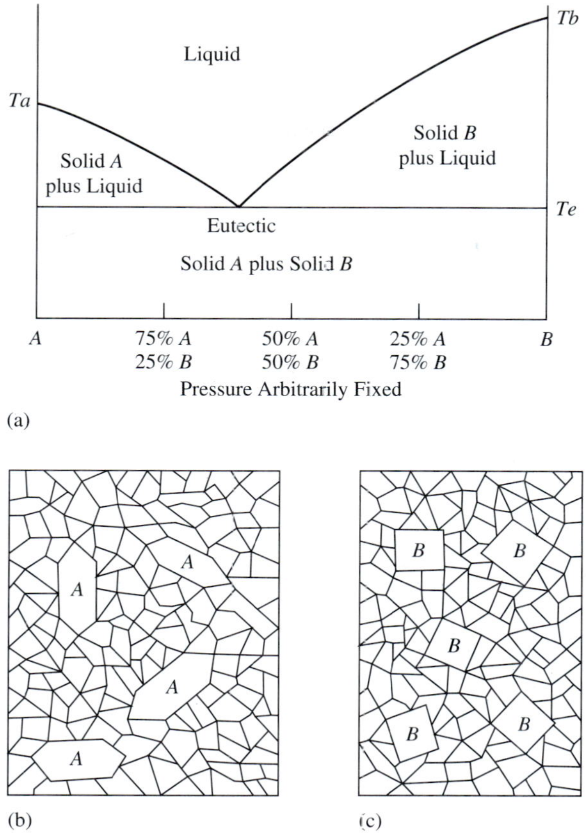

FIGURE 6-2 Two-component system *A*—*B* with a eutectic point. (Letters refer to hypothetical components and compositions that arbitrarily have just the properties necessary to produce the phase diagram shown.) A eutectic composition gives the lowest temperature at which liquids exist in a system. (a) Isobaric temperature-composition phase diagram for two-component system *A*—*B* with complete liquid miscibility and no crystal miscibility. (b) Texture of crystals crystallized from a composition on the *A*-rich side of the eutectic composition; crystals of *A* in a groundmass of small crystals of *A* and *B* in eutectic proportions. (c) Texture of crystals crystallized from a composition on the *B*-rich side of eutectic composition; crystals of *B* in a groundmass of small crystals of *A* and *B* in eutectic proportions.

A liquid with composition 25*A* 75*B* may be cooled without phase change until it reaches a liquidus curve at some temperature between *Tb* and *Te*. When this liquidus curve is reached on cooling, crystals of pure *B* come into equilibrium with this melt composition. Further cooling increases the amount of *B* crystals and drives liquid composition toward its eutectic composition. Crystallization continues until the temperature drops to *Te*, where a melt of eutectic composition 60*A* 40*B* coexists in equilibrium with crystals of *A* and crystals of *B*. At this point, *A* and *B* crystallize simultaneously and isothermally until this entire system is crystallized.

A resulting texture might have large crystals of *B* encased in a groundmass of crystals of *A* and of *B* in eutectic proportions (Fig. 6-2c). Composition of this matte is the same whether initial liquids started out on its *A* side or its *B*, 60*A* 40*B*. Under equilibrium crystallization, bulk compositions of final crystal mixes are the same as the initial melt composition. Initial melt composition with respect to eutectic composition determines whether early crystals are *A* or *B*.

Equilibrium melting relationships in this system are geometric reversals of crystallization sequences. Any mixture of crystals of *A* and of *B* may be heated without phase change to the eutectic temperature for this system. At this temperature, melting of both solids occurs isothermally (and isobarically by restriction) until either all *A* crystals or all *B* crystals have been consumed in forming a liquid of eutectic composition. Depending on original composition of starting crystal mix with respect to this eutectic composition, the remaining crystals of *A* or of *B* are in equilibrium with melt just above *Te*. Further increase in temperature results in decrease in amount of remaining crystalline phase until the appropriate liquidus curve intersects the original composition of the initial crystalline system, at which point melting is complete.

PTX Space So far, this system *A*—*B* has been isobarically restricted. Change in pressure changes melt points of pure end-member components (*Ta* and *Tb*), eutectic melt temperature (*Te*), and eutectic composition (Fig. 6-3). None of these temperature changes with changing pressure need to be by the same amount or at the same rate. Each isobarically restricted invariant point lies on a univariant curve in PTX space. Each isobarically restricted univariant curve lies on a divariant surface in PTX space, and each divariant area crosses a trivariant volume. These melt curves may be projected from PTX space onto a PT plane on which composition is not graphically represented.

Binary systems like these, that is, with complete liquid miscibility and complete or nearly complete crystalline immiscibility, of geologic interest include albite-quartz, anorthite-quartz, albite-diopside, anorthite-diopside, anorthite-forsterite, and parts of orthoclase-quartz. Also of general interest is the system ethylene glycol–water (automobile coolant).

Complete Crystalline Miscibility A second type of binary system of geologic importance is one in which complete miscibility exists in liquid and crystalline phases (Fig. 6-4). As in previous cases, *Ta* and *Tb* are melt points of pure *A* and of pure *B*, respectively. Addition of small amounts of *A* into crystalline *B* brings about melt point depression. Because of

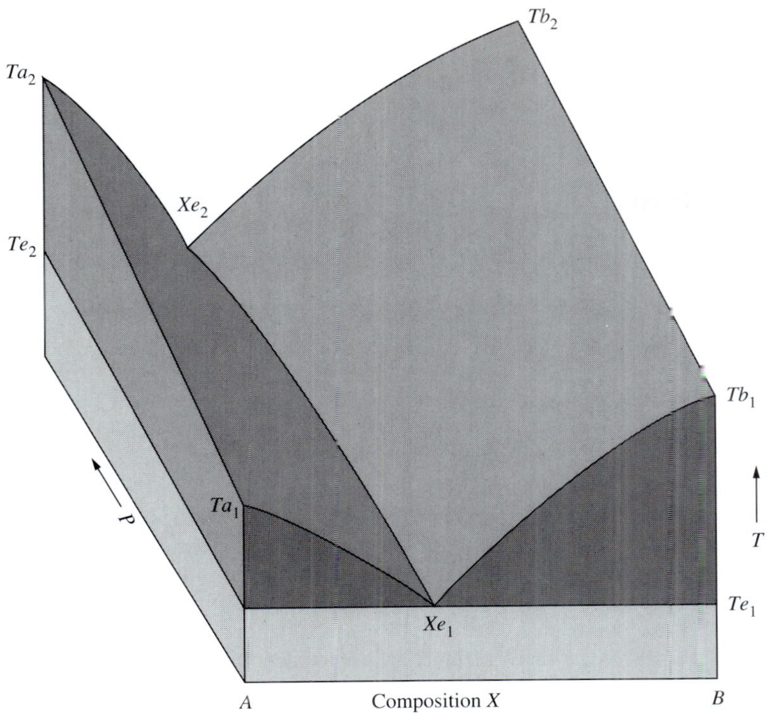

(a)

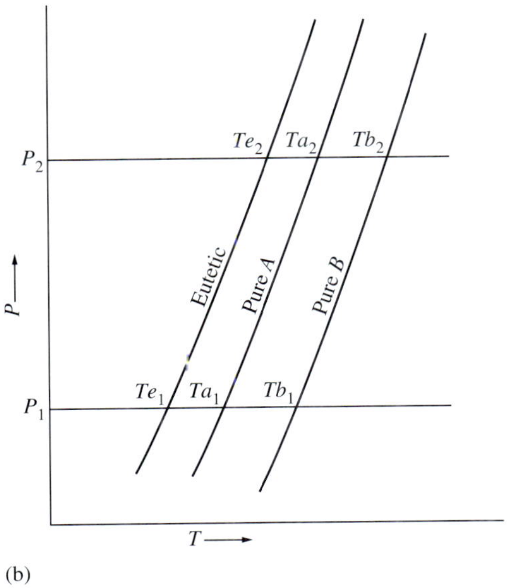

(b)

FIGURE 6-3 PTX phase prism of a two-component system. (a) Pressure-temperature-composition prism for a two-component system as in Fig. 6-2. Note that both eutectic temperature and composition change with changes in pressure. (b) Projection of melting curves onto the PT plane of the PTX prism.

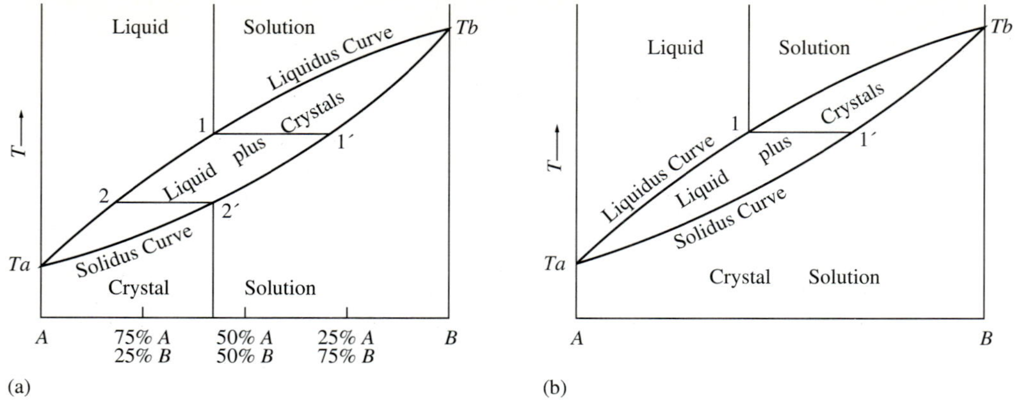

FIGURE 6-4 Binary isobaric system with complete miscibility of both liquid and crystalline phases. (a) A liquid of composition 60*A* 40*B* cools to the liquidus curve at point 1, where it is in equilibrium with crystals of composition at point 1′. As this system cools further, crystals react with melt so that liquid compositions follow the liquidus curve while crystal compositions follow the solidus curve. Liquid composition reaches point 2 in equilibrium with crystals of composition at point 2′, where equilibrium crystallization becomes complete. (b) A liquid of composition 60*A* 40*B* at point 1 is in equilibrium with crystals of composition at point 1′. If crystals separate from reaction with melt as they form, liquid compositions migrate down the liquidus curve to *Ta*, giving a suite of disequilibrium crystals ranging in composition from point 1′ to pure *A*.

mutual solubility of crystalline *A* and crystalline *B*, however, addition of *B* to crystalline *A* does not bring about melt point reduction; it raises this melt point. In this system, a solidus curve lies below a liquidus curve to define an area of variable liquid and crystalline compositions in this system *A*—*B*.

Phase relationships during crystallization of a liquid intermediate in composition between *A* and *B* can be illustrated with liquid 60*A* 40*B* (Prog. 6-1). This liquid can be cooled without change in phase to the liquidus curve (point 1). At this liquidus curve, crystals of composition 25*A* 75*B* on a solidus curve (point 1′) come into equilibrium with liquid of composition 60*A* 40*B* on the liquidus curve in this system. Since equilibrium requires a system to be isothermal, tie lines connecting crystals in equilibrium with liquids must define horizontal tie lines in TX space. For all compositions and temperatures in this two-phase region between these solidus and liquidus curves, crystal compositions lie on the *B* side of liquid compositions. As system temperatures decrease, crystal compositions migrate along this solidus curve as liquid compositions migrate along their liquidus curve away from crystal compositions. As these composition shifts occur, amounts of liquid decrease while amounts of crystalline material increase. Under equilibrium conditions, the last liquid crystallizes (point 2) when crystal composition arrives at this system's original composition (point 2′, which is compositionally equal to point 1). At all temperatures below the solidus curve, *AB* crystal solution is the only phase present.

Equilibrium melting relationships follow a geometrically reverse path of equilibrium crystallization. But equilibrium processes require instant compositional adjustment to all temperature changes. If crystals or liquids fail to adjust their compositions because of slow diffusion rates or mechanical separation of crystals from melt, crystallization becomes fractional as a reacting system changes composition.

Fractionation By contrast with equilibrium crystallization, reactions may follow a fractionation path. Under conditions of complete fractionation, no reaction occurs between crystals and melt. In reality, a complete continuum exists between completely fractional crystallization histories and completely equilibrium sequences. Under conditions of complete fractional crystallization with no reaction between crystalline phases and its parent melt, melt composition migrates along the liquidus curve from a point of initial crystals 40*A* 60*B* to a last drop of melt of pure *A* composition (Fig. 6-4b). A resulting sequence of crystalline phases, not in mutual equilibrium, ranges in composition from 40*A* 60*B* to a last minute crystal of pure *A* composition.

Fractionation paths during melting are not reverse paths of fractional crystallization. Given an initial homogeneous crystalline material of composition 40*A* 60*B*, heating to the solidus curve yields an initial melt of 25*A* 75*B* (point 2). Removal of this and subsequent melt phases depletes the initial and subsequent crystalline phases in *A*, causing the composition of the crystalline phases to migrate along the solidus curve until a final crystal of pure *B* coexists with a final melt of almost pure *B*. Liquids from this fractional melting process would range from 25*A* 75*B* to pure *B* and would not be in mutual compositional nor in thermal equilibrium. The complete difference between melting and crystallization fractionation paths is especially important in more complex natural systems, such as magma chambers, because determining crystallization history of a rock tells us nothing about what its future history will be on remelting in a later geologic episode.

Addition of pressure as a variable changes the liquidus-solidus loop (Fig. 6-4) to an envelope of two surfaces, as all melt temperatures represented on it vary with pressure changes. Binary systems with complete miscibility of liquid and of crystalline components near the solidus include albite-anorthite (plagioclase) and forsterite-fayalite (olivine) crystal solution series.

Partial Crystalline Miscibility Between these two extremes of total crystalline miscibility and complete crystalline solution, various possibilities of partial crystalline solution and immiscibility may occur. A solvus curve represents this case of partial crystalline miscibility (Fig. 6-5; Prog. 6-1). A two-phase region lies under this solvus, with one-phase regions outside it. Within a solvus curve, isothermal (isobaric) compositional tie lines connect *B*-rich crystal solutions with *A*-rich crystal solutions. The top of a solvus may lie thermally below a liquidus-solidus loop (Fig. 6-5a) or may intersect it (Fig. 6-5b).

Liquidus-solidus loops with a minimum (instead of a eutectic point) result from a subsolidus solvus. Note that composition of the apex of a solvus need not coincide with minimum composition (Fig. 6-5a). Intersection of a liquidus-solidus loop with a solvus yields a eutectic point on a three-phase tie line. All gradations between complete crystalline immiscibility (where solidi are vertical in Fig. 6-2a) and complete crystalline miscibility (Fig. 6-4) may exist, including degrees of partial miscibility (Fig. 6-5). Changes in pressure may shift a system, for instance, from nonintersection of solvus and solidus to their intersection at a different pressure (Prog. 6-2).

Consider equilibrium crystallization of composition 40*A* 60*B* (point 1 in Fig. 6-5a). At temperature T_1, liquids of that composition are in equilibrium with crystals of composition 30*A* 70*B* (point 1′). Cooling causes increase in *B*-rich crystals, which react with this melt and shift melt compositions along a liquidus curve and crystal compositions along a solidus curve toward a minimum on this liquidus-solidus loop (Prog. 6-1). At temperature T_2, a last drop of liquid with composition 50*A* 50*B* coexists at equilibrium with crystals of initial composition 40*A* 60*B* (2–2′). Further cooling from T_2 to T_3 causes no phase change. At T_3, homogeneous crystals of composition 40*A* 60*B* intersect a solvus and come into equilibrium with a second crystal solution phase of composition 70*A* 30*B*. This second crystal solution phase then exsolves from the original crystalline phase with cooling below T_3. On further cooling, compositions of these two crystal solution phases migrate down each side of this solvus, *A*-rich crystals becoming richer in component *A* while *B*-rich crystals become richer in component *B*.

Fractional crystallization in a binary system with a minimum drives melt compositions to this minimum on its liquidus-solidus loop. Indeed, one difference between a minimum and a eutectic point is that crystallization in a system with a eutectic point always results in liquids of eutectic composition, whereas arrival at a minimum composition requires fractionation. A binary system of great geologic interest and involving minimum melting relationships is the high-pressure part of the system albite-orthoclase. (This system is not completely analogous since water is a component of melts in this system and orthoclase is not stable at temperatures high above the minimum temperature.)

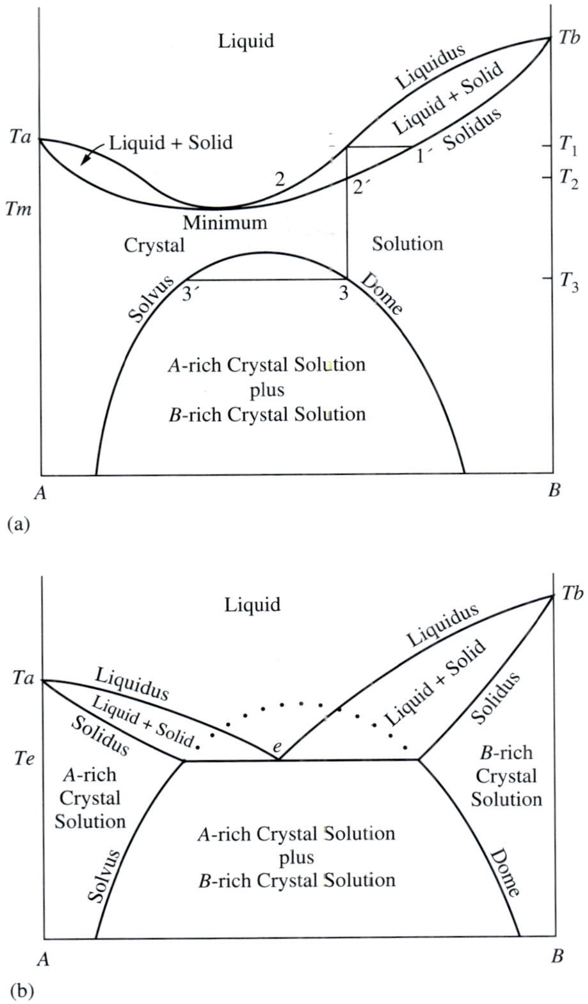

FIGURE 6-5 Binary isobaric systems with a solvus. (a) Binary system with a subsolidus solvus and a minimum in the liquidus-solidus loop. Equilibrium crystallization of a liquid at point 1 yields crystals of composition at point 1′. Subsequent cooling causes liquid compositions to migrate to point 2, while crystal compositions migrate to point 2′, where crystallization is complete at the original composition. Further cooling brings the homogeneous crystal solution to point 3 on the solvus. There *B*-rich crystals come into equilibrium with *A*-rich crystals of a composition at point 3′. Further cooling causes *A*-rich and *B*-rich crystals to become even purer along the flanks of this solvus. (b) Binary isobaric system with a solvus intersecting the liquidus-solidus loop. This system has a eutectic point on a three-phase tie line. Decreasing mutual crystalline solubility shifts both solidus and solvus toward pure end-member compositions (compare Fig. 6-2).

6-4 BINARY SYSTEMS WITH COMPOUNDS

A binary compound between A and B in composition may melt congruently (that is, melt to liquids of its exact composition, Fig. 6-6) or it may melt incongruently (that is, dissociate to a liquid and another crystalline phase, both of compositions different from this binary compound, Fig. 6-7). Congruent melting of a compound A_2B within system A—B merely divides it into two binary systems, A—A_2B and A_2B—B. Each of these subsystems may be treated independently, since no equilibrium or fractional crystallization or melting process can change any liquid composition from one side of A_2B to the other (Prog. 6-3). Systems of geologic interest containing congruently melting binary compounds include periclase-(forsterite)-(enstatite)-quartz and corundum-(kyanite, andalusite, sillimanite)-(mullite)-quartz. Although not compositionally colinear, the system nepheline-(albite)-quartz is similar.

Incongruent Melting An incongruently melting binary compound A_2B, when heated to its dissociation temperature (Tp in Fig. 6-7), melts to crystals of pure A and a melt of composition 50A 50B (Prog. 6-3). Further heating above temperature Tp causes crystals of A to dissolve progressively in this melt, shifting its composition away from B toward A_2B. The last crystals of A dissolve when melt composition arrives at original composition A_2B.

Consider a liquid of composition 80A 20B. Upon cooling to the liquidus curve, crystals of pure A drive melt compositions away from component

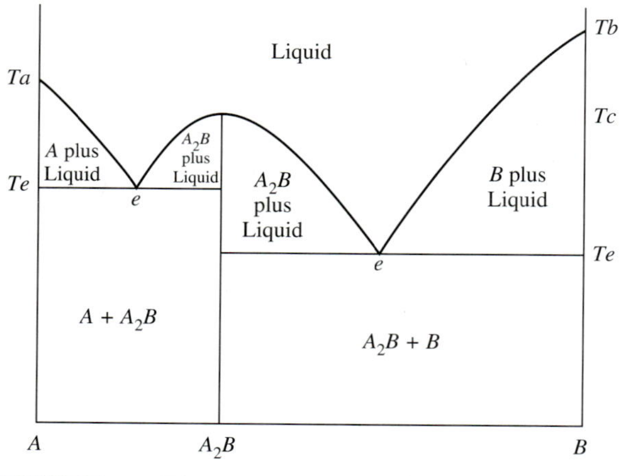

FIGURE 6-6 Binary isobaric system with a congruently melting binary compound. A congruently melting binary compound permits the system A—B to be treated as two separate systems, A—A_2B and A_2B—B, each with its own eutectic point.

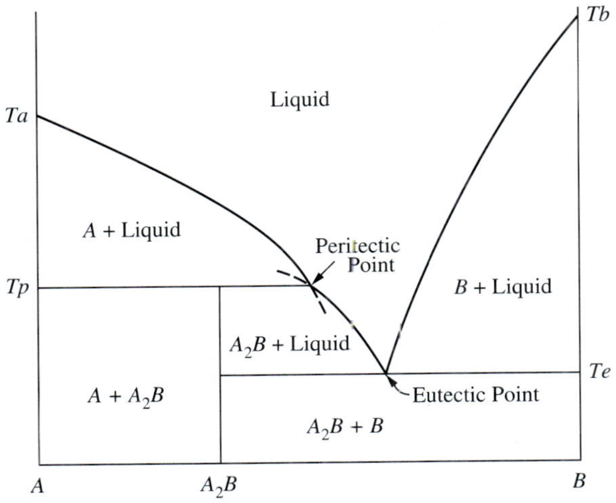

FIGURE 6-7 Binary isobaric system with an incongruently melting binary compound. This binary compound A_2B dissociates at a peritectic temperature to crystals of pure A and a liquid of peritectic composition Note that this liquid composition is not between two reacting crystal compositions. Liquids of A_2B composition first yield crystals of pure A on cooling to the liquidus curve. At the peritectic point this liquid reacts with crystals of A to yield crystals of A_2B under equilibrium crystallization conditions. Failure to react with crystals of A causes fractional crystallization, which in turn drives liquid compositions to the eutectic point.

A. This sequence continues until temperature falls to the peritectic temperature *Tp*. Here a three-phase tie line isothermally (and isobarically by restriction) connects crystals of *A*, crystals of A_2B, and liquid 50*A* 50*B* (Prog. 6-3). Under equilibrium conditions, crystals of *A* react with this liquid to form crystals of A_2B. Since the original composition 80*A* 20*B* is on the *A* side of A_2B, this reaction consumes the liquid without using up all *A* crystals, leaving a mixture of crystals of *A* and crystals of A_2B. Had the original composition been on the *B* side of A_2B, this peritectic reaction would have consumed *A* crystals before the peritectic liquid, so further crystallization of A_2B would have driven the liquid composition to a eutectic point on a three-phase tie line where A_2B crystals, *B* crystals, and eutectic liquid coexist.

During fractional crystallization of liquid of composition 80*A* 20*B*, crystals of *A* drive liquid compositions to the peritectic composition. Since under pure fractionation crystals do not react further with melts, subsequent crystallization of A_2B drives melt compositions to the eutectic point between A_2B and *B*. Fractional crystallization thus produces the disequilibrium crystal assemblage $A + A_2B + B$, because liquid compositions could migrate across the composition A_2B. Of geologic interest, orthoclase melts incongruently to leucite plus quartz. Carbonate minerals also melt incongruently to CO_2 and their metal oxides, which generally react with silicate minerals.

Other types of binary systems with somewhat different phase relationships are known, some of significant geologic interest. Those systems discussed in preceding pages are illustrative of some principles of reading phase diagrams. They also represent most binary systems involving common rock-forming minerals and suffice for discussions of mineral genesis (Chap. 7).

6-5 LIQUIDUS SURFACES IN TERNARY SYSTEMS

Although ternary compositions may be represented on two-dimensional paper, intensive variables such as pressure and temperature require either four dimensions for full representation of phase relationships or some kind of simplified sections or projections. The latter course usually is followed.

Ternary compositions are best represented on triangular graphs (Fig. 6-8). Each binary sideline is read in the same manner as binary compositions in binary systems. Each sideline is 0% of the component represented at the opposite corner. Ternary compositions are read as percentage of each component by distance of composition from the opposite sideline. Note that the sum of these three percentages must equal 100%.

Ternary Eutectic Point One method of representing melting and crystallization relationships on a ternary isobaric composition diagram superimposes isothermal contour lines of a liquidus surface (Fig. 6-8b). This practice yields a contour map of thermal hills and valleys to represent phase relationships (Prog. 6-4).

Boundary binary systems in a ternary system with no crystalline miscibility (Fig. 6-8b) must also have complete crystalline immiscibility (Fig. 6-2a). Each isothermal point on a binary liquidus line becomes one end of an isothermal contour line on a liquidus surface. Each binary eutectic point is the head of a cotectic line (thermal valley), these cotectic lines meeting at a ternary eutectic point, the lowest temperature on this liquidus surface.

Some relationships represented on a liquidus surface diagram may be illustrated with crystallization sequences of selected compositions. Consider composition 10*A* 50*B* 40*C* (point 1, Fig. 6-8b). On cooling to 925°C, this liquid composition intersects the liquidus surface in the primary field of component *B*, where *B* is the crystalline phase at the liquidus surface. Precipitation of crystals of *B* on cooling this system drives its liquid composition directly *away* from the component *B* corner of the triangular diagram (Prog. 6-4). Liquid composition migrates away from *B* until it intersects the cotectic line between the primary fields of *B*

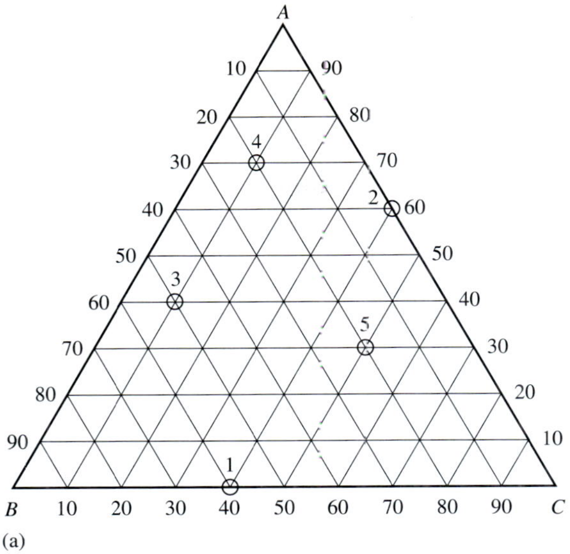

(a)

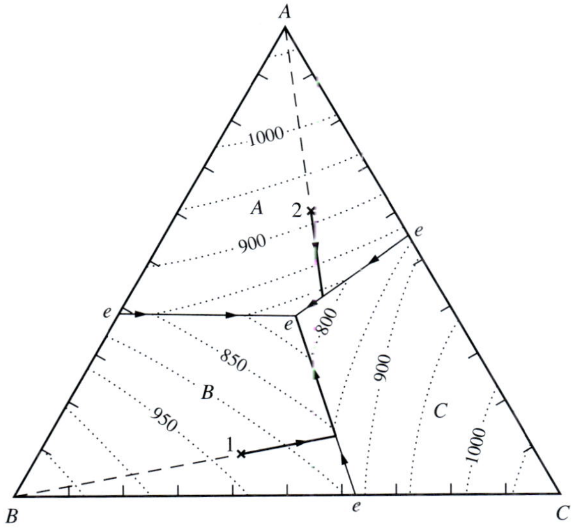

(b)

FIGURE 6-8 **Ternary graph and liquidus surface. (a) Ternary graph used for representing three-component systems. Compositions: (1) 0*A* 60*B* 40*C*, (2) 60*A* 0*B* 40*C*, (3) 40*A* 50*B* 10*C*, (4) 70*A* 20*B* 10*C*, (5) 30*A* 20*B* 50*C*. (b) Ternary isobaric liquidus surface with ternary eutectic point. Isothermal contour lines (dotted) represent this liquidus surface. Cotectic thermal valleys (solid lines) connect each binary eutectic point with the ternary eutectic point. Letters on this liquidus surface indicate primary crystallization fields for each crystalline phase. Upon cooling, liquids of composition 1 begin to crystallize *B* at about 930°C. Crystallization of *B* drives liquid compositions to a cotectic thermal valley between primary fields *B* and *C*. Simultaneous crystallization of *B* and *C* drive liquid compositions to a ternary eutectic composition at about 780°C. Simultaneous crystallization of *A*, *B*, and *C* proceeds isothermally (and isobarically) until all liquid is consumed.**

and *C* at composition 15*A* 35*B* 50*C* at 860°C between the binary eutectic point on the *B*—*C* sideline and the ternary eutectic point. From this point, crystals of *C* coprecipitate with crystals of *B* in a ratio such that liquid composition migrates away from the *B* and *C* component corners along this cotectic line to lower temperatures. Falling temperature drives liquid compositions to the ternary eutectic point 40*A* 30*B* 30*C* at 760°C, where *A*, *B*, and *C* crystallize simultaneously and isothermally until all liquid is gone.

Crystallization of a composition represented by point 2 (Fig. 6-8b) begins at 920°C in the primary field of component *A*. Crystallization of pure *A* drives liquid compositions directly away from composition *A*. Liquid composition reaches the cotectic between the primary fields of *A* and *C* at 780°C between the *A*—*C* binary eutectic point and the ternary eutectic point. Simultaneous crystallization of *A* and *C* drives liquid compositions down the cotectic to the ternary eutectic point where *A*, *B*, and *C* crystallize isothermally until all liquid is gone.

Fractional Melting Equilibrium melting is the geometric reverse path of equilibrium crystallization. Fractional melting in a ternary system with one ternary eutectic point produces results that are dramatically different. Consider fractional melting of composition 10*A* 50*B* 40*C* (point 1, Fig. 6-8b). Melting begins at the temperature of the ternary eutectic composition 40*A* 30*B* 30*C* at 760°C. If liquid is continuously removed from this system, melting proceeds isothermally while the system changes composition along a straight line directly *away* from that ternary eutectic composition. When the residual system's composition reaches the *B*—*C* join, all of component *A* has been removed in a melt phase of eutectic composition. Melting ceases completely until the temperature reaches the *B*—*C* binary eutectic temperature of 890°C. At this point, isothermal fractional melting resumes with separation of binary eutectic melt of composition 38*B* 62*C* driving the residual system away from that composition until all of component *C* is consumed. Melting ceases until temperature rises to the melt point of pure *B*, where it melts isothermally. Fractional melting in this system thus produces three distinct liquids—one having a ternary eutectic composition, a second having a binary eutectic composition, and a third of pure *B* composition—with no intermediates to these three liquids.

Most ternary systems of geologic interest are more complicated than this hypothetical system. Perhaps the simplest examples are silica-anorthite-wollastonite and spinel-forsterite-leucite.

Liquidus with One Cotectic Line If one boundary binary system of a ternary system exhibits complete crystalline miscibility, while the other two exhibit total crystalline immiscibility, a single cotectic line characterizes its liquidus surface (Fig. 6-9a; Prog. 6-4). Boundary binary systems *A*—*B* and *A*—*C* have eutectic points (Fig. 6-2a), and system *B*—*C* has a liquidus-solidus loop (Fig. 6-4). Crystallization of a liquid composition represented by point 1 begins at 1020°C with precipitation of crystals of pure *A* driving liquid composition directly away from *A* composition across this liquidus surface until it intersects the cotectic line between primary fields *A* and *BC* at 960°C. At this point crystals of *A* are joined by crystals of a *BC* crystal solution that is richer in component *C* than is the liquid in equilibrium with it. With falling temperature, liquid compositions follow the cotectic line as crystals of *A* and of *BC* accumulate until all liquid is consumed. During this crystallization along this cotectic line, however, *BC* crystals continuously react, with remaining melts becoming progressively *B* rich with falling temperature (Fig. 6-4). Composition of the final *BC* crystal solution from equilibrium crystallization can be determined by drawing a straight line from *A* through the initial bulk composition to the *B*—*C* binary sideline. This intersection marks the composition of the crystals of *BC* crystal solution.

A melt of composition 2 (Fig. 6-9a) begins to crystallize with falling temperature at 980°C with precipitation of *BC* crystal solution crystals having composition represented by point 3. Further cooling drives liquid compositions away from the *B*—*C* sideline. Because reaction between *BC* crystals and liquid causes these crystals to become increasingly *B* rich, the direction of liquid composition changes continuously in response to changes in composition of crystals separating out. While *BC* crystal composition migrates from points 3 to 4, liquid composition follows a curving path labeled equilibrium (Fig. 6-9a). When liquid composition reaches the cotectic line, crystals of *BC* and of *A* precipitate simultaneously, while liquid composition follows the cotectic valley to lower temperatures. Crystallization becomes complete when the composition of *BC* crystals arrives at point 5, which is colinear with the original composition (point 2) and the *A* apex of the triangle. The final liquid composition is on the cotectic line at around 900°C.

Fractional crystallization in this system yields somewhat different results. If *BC* solution crystals do not react with melts in this system, liquid compositions follow the path labeled fractional, since composition *C* is systematically removed from this system under fractionation. When liquid composition reaches the cotectic line during fractional crystallization, therefore, it is leaner in composition *C* than if crystals and liquid maintained equilibrium with each other. At the cotectic line, crystals of *A* and of *BC* drive the composition of the remaining liquid down this thermal valley all the way to the *A*—*B* binary eutectic point because removal of *C*-rich *BC* crystals depletes the system in *C*. Haplobasalts (simple synthetic simulated basalt) have a liquidus surface of this shape with the system diopside-albite-anorthite.

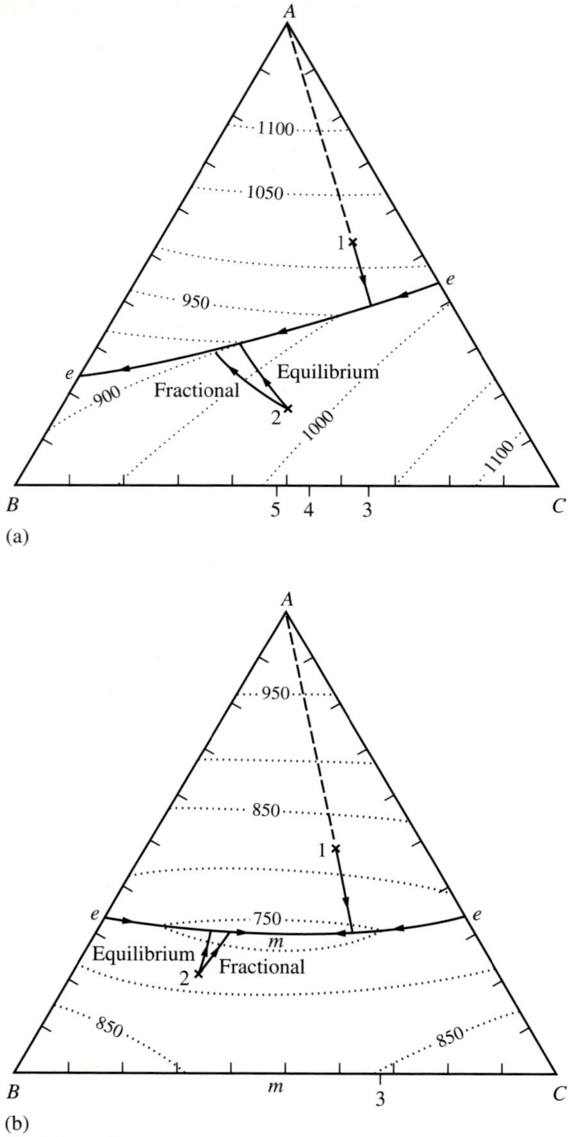

FIGURE 6-9 Ternary isobaric liquidus surfaces without ternary eutectic points. (a) Ternary isobaric liquidus surface with a monotonously falling cotectic thermal valley between binary eutectic points. (b) Ternary isobaric liquidus surface with a cotectic thermal valley with a minimum. Arrows in thermal valleys indicate directions of falling temperatures.

Liquidus Surface with Minimum Another ternary system with a single cotectic line has a ternary minimum on it (Fig. 6-9b). In this system, two boundary binary systems (*A*—*B* and *A*—*C*) show total crystal immiscibility while the third (*B*—*C*, Fig. 6-5a; Prog. 6-4) has a minimum in its liquidus-solidus loop above a solvus. Liquids with composition 1 begin to crystallize pure *A* upon cooling to 830°C. Crystallization of *A* drives liquid compositions away from *A* composition until a liquid arrives at the cotectic line between the primary fields of *A* and of *BC*. At this point, *C*-rich *BC* crystals coprecipitate with crystals of *A* driving liquid compositions thermally down the cotectic valley away from the *A*—*C* sideline. Reaction between liquid and *BC* crystals causes them to change composition until their composition becomes colinear with the *A* apex (point 3) and the initial composition (point 1), at which point all liquid is consumed. Fractional crystallization of composition 1 permits the last liquid to arrive at the minimum composition of this system.

A liquid with a composition represented at point 2 begins to crystallize a *BC* solution crystal of composition 90*B* 10*C*. Cooling and equilibrium reaction causes crystals to change composition to 75*B* 25*C*, while liquid composition changes composition on the curve labeled equilibrium to the cotectic line. Coprecipitation of *A* and of *BC* solution crystals continues until liquid is consumed when *BC* crystals have composition 70*B* 30*C*. The final liquid composition does not quite reach the ternary minimum point under equilibrium crystallization.

In a case of complete fractional crystallization, liquid composition follows the curve labeled fractional across the liquidus surface until it reaches the cotectic line where liquid is in equilibrium with *BC* crystals having composition 65*B* 35*C*. Continued fractional crystallization drives liquid composition clear to the ternary thermal minimum point where crystallization is complete. The system albite-orthoclase-quartz when saturated with water (a haplogranite) has a liquidus surface of similar configuration.

6-6 TERNARY SYSTEMS WITH COMPOUNDS

Both binary and ternary compounds generally complicate geologically realistic ternary systems. Effect of these compounds depend mostly on whether they melt congruently or incongruently. If a binary compound A_2B melts congruently in a system *A*—*B*—*C*, it may be divided into subsystems A_2B—*B*—*C* and *A*—A_2B—*C*, each of which may be treated independently (Prog. 6-4). Two congruently melting compounds give three subsystems to be treated independently, and so forth. A congruently melting ternary compound *ABC* (Fig. 6-10a) permits division of system

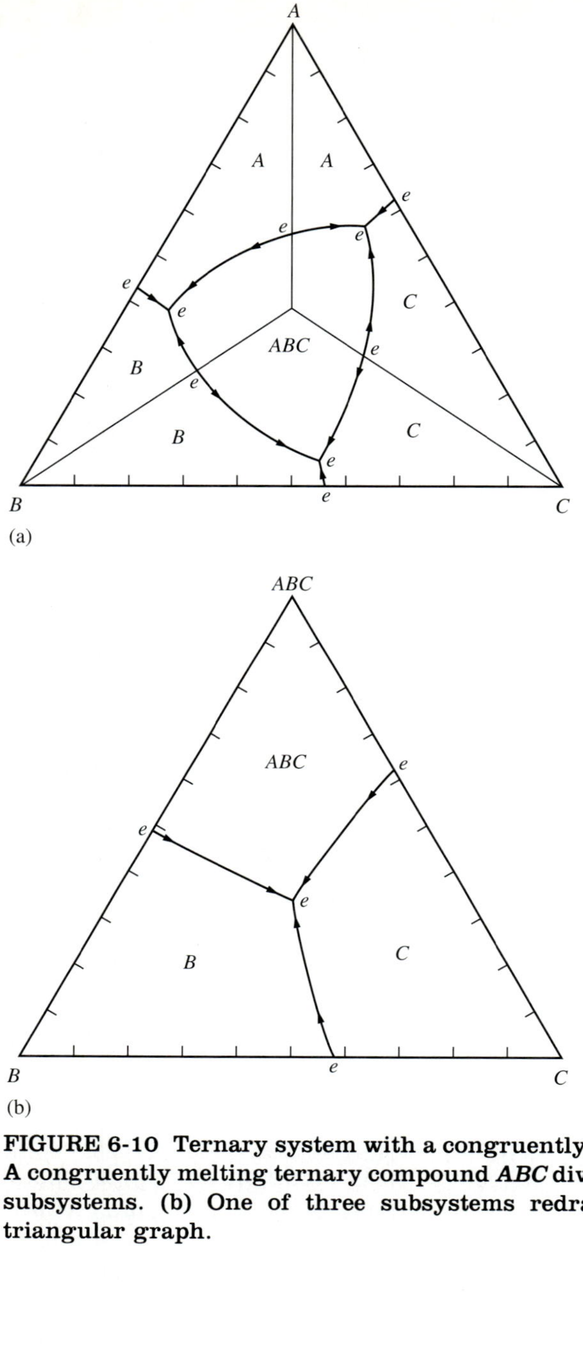

FIGURE 6-10 Ternary system with a congruently melting ternary compound. (a) A congruently melting ternary compound *ABC* divides a system into three ternary subsystems. (b) One of three subsystems redrawn to a standard equilateral triangular graph.

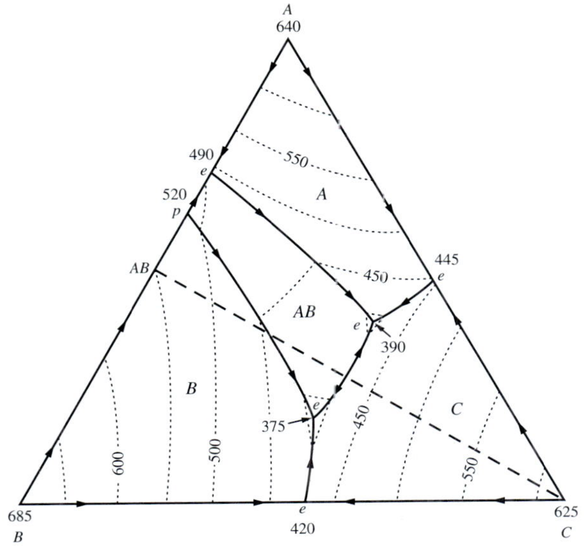

FIGURE 6-11 Ternary isobaric system with an incongruently melting binary compound. Compound *AB* melts to *B* plus liquid *p*, thus permitting melt compositions to cross the *AB*—*C* join and preventing subdivision of the system *A*—*B*—*C*.

A—*B*—*C* into three ternary subsystems, *A*—*ABC*—*B*, *A*—*ABC*—*C*, and *B*—*ABC*—*C* (Prog. 6-4). Liquidus surface relationships of each of these subsystems may be replotted as a separate system (Fig. 6-10b).

Incongruent Binary Compound Graphical representation and interpretation of phase relationships become somewhat complicated if one or more compounds in a system melt incongruently. A system with an incongruently melting binary compound cannot be subdivided into two subsystems to be treated separately because fractional crystallization may drive liquid compositions from one subsystem to the other (Fig. 6-11). Each binary eutectic point heads a cotectic thermal valley that descends thermally to a ternary eutectic point. Two ternary eutectic points are connected by a cotectic thermal valley that has a maximum where it crosses the *AB*—*C* join. The binary peritectic point heads a cotectic thermal inflection that becomes a thermal valley as it descends thermally across the *AB*—*C* join (Prog. 6-4).

Crystallization of liquid compositions in primary fields *A*, *AB*, and *C* do not involve peritectic reactions (see Fig. 6-8b). In these parts of the system equilibrium and fractional crystallization sequences arrive at the same eutectic liquid compositions, which composition is governed by which side of the *AB*—*C* joint starting compositions began to crystallize.

Initial liquid compositions on the *AB*—*C* join in primary fields *AB* and *C* have unique crystallization histories constrained by the fact that no excess component *A* or *B* can drive residual liquid compositions off this join to a ternary eutectic point. Consider a liquid composition on this join in primary field *AB*. Crystallization of *AB* drives this liquid composition away from that component until it arrives at the thermal maximum on the cotectic boundary. There crystallization of *AB* and of *C* proceeds isothermally (and isobarically) until the last liquid disappears, leaving a crystalline assemblage of *AB* + *C*. A similar sequence transpires for liquids on this join in primary field *C*.

Liquid compositions on the *A* side of the *AB*—*C* join in primary field *B* undergo peritectic reactions. Equilibrium crystallization of a liquid within this compositional area begins with crystallization of *B*, which drives liquid compositions directly away from *B* composition. Upon arrival at the peritectic inflection, crystals of *B* react with liquid to form *AB* crystals while *B* crystals resorb. This reaction drives liquid compositions along the peritectic thermal inflection on the liquidus surface until all *B* crystals are resorbed at a composition colinear with initial liquid composition and *AB*. Once *B* crystals resorb, crystallization of *AB* drives liquid compositions across its primary field to one of the cotectic thermal valleys where crystallization of *A* or *C* drives liquids to the 390°C ternary eutectic for final crystallization of *A* + *AB* + *C*.

Liquid compositions on the *B* side of the *AB*—*C* join and to the *AB* side of a point where the peritectic curve crosses the *AB*—*C* join also undergo peritectic reactions. Crystallization of pure *B* drives liquid compositions away from composition *B* until they arrive at the peritectic inflection in the liquidus surface. There *B* crystals react with the liquid to crystallize *AB*. This reaction forces liquid compositions along the peritectic boundary until it turns into a cotectic thermal valley at the *AB*—*C* join. Since *B* crystals remain in the system, further crystallization of *AB* drives the liquid to the 375°C ternary eutectic point where *AB*, *B*, and *C* crystallize in eutectic proportions.

Under conditions of fractional crystallization, liquids do not react with *B* crystals at the cotectic inflection, so crystallization of *AB* drives liquid compositions across the primary field of *AB* to the cotectic thermal valley between primary fields *AB* and *A*. Further crystallization drives liquids to the 390°C eutectic point for final crystallization. Thus, in primary field *B* on the *B* side of the *AB*—*C* join and on the *AB* side of the intersection between this join and the peritectic curve, final liquids may arrive at either eutectic composition, depending on whether crystallization is fractional or equilibrium. Hence, a ternary system with an incongruently melting binary compound cannot be divided into independent subsystems.

Note some generalizations about ternary liquidus surfaces and their interpretation. First, a primary phase field bounded by cotectic or peritectic curves determines which phase crystallizes first on cooling a liquid to a

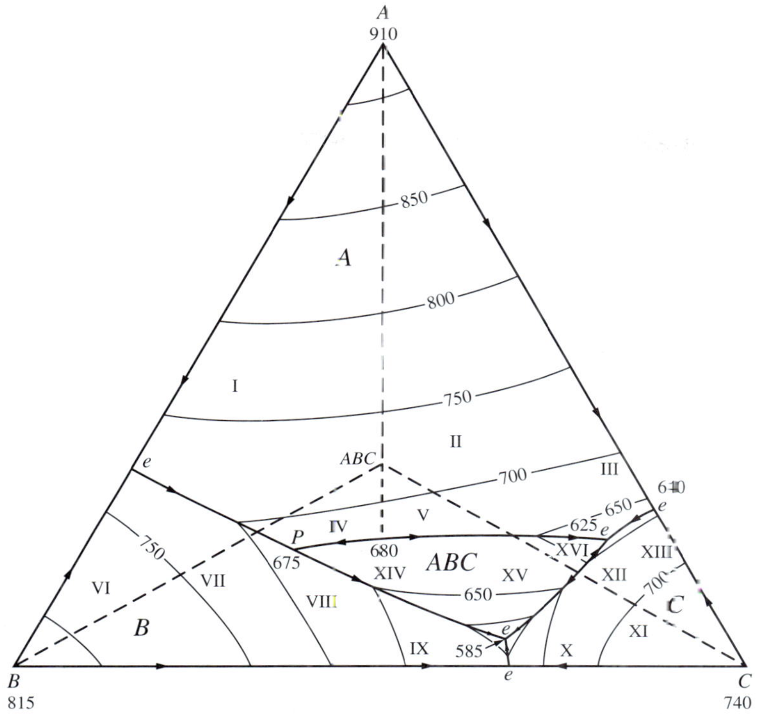

FIGURE 6-12 Ternary isobaric system with an incongruently melting ternary compound. Arrows on cotectic thermal valleys and surface inflections indicate falling temperatures. Compound *ABC* melts to *A* plus the liquid composition represented by a maximum on the peritectic inflection curve. Crystallization sequence for numbered representative compositions are given in Table 6-3.

liquidus surface. Second, subsequent crystallization drives liquid compositions directly *away* from a point representing crystal composition. Third, liquid temperature never rises during a crystallization sequence. Fourth, there are no abrupt changes in liquid composition—it changes incrementally during crystallization. Fifth, regardless of which composition crystallizes first in equilibrium with a melt, a final assemblage consists of the phases defined by the joins between compositions. In other words, a final crystal assemblage has the same composition as the starting liquid after equilibrium crystallization. Sixth, equilibrium melting sequences are a geometric reverse of equilibrium crystallization sequences. Finally, fractional melting sequences are not a geometric reversal of fractional crystallization sequences, and fractional melting produces abrupt changes in melt compositions.

Incongruent Ternary Compound An incongruently melting ternary compound may drastically modify the shape of a ternary liquidus surface,

TABLE 6-3 Equilibrium Crystallization Sequences for Compositions in Fig. 6-12

Comp	Temp (°C)	Phases
I	>760	L
	760–720	*A* + L
	720–675	*A* + *B* + L
	675	*A* + *B* + *ABC* + L
	<675	*A* + *B* + *ABC*
II	>725	L
	725–670	*A* + L
	670–625	*A* + *ABC* + L
	625	*A* + *ABC* + *C* + L
	<625	*A* + *ABC* + *C*
III	>680	L
	680–635	*A* + L
	635–625	*A* + *C* + L
	625	*A* + *C* + *ABC* + L
	<625	*A* + *C* + *ABC*
IV*	>725	L
	725–677	*A* + L
	677–675	*A* + *ABC* + L
	675	*A* + *ABC* + *B* + L
	675–585	*B* + *ABC* + L
	585	*B* + *ABC* + *C* + L
	<585	*B* + *ABC* + *C*
V*	>690	L
	690–678	*A* + L
	678	*A* + *ABC* + L
	678–600	*ABC* + L
	600–585	*ABC* + *B* + L
	585	*ABC* + *B* + *C* + L
	<585	*ABC* + *B* + *C*
VI	>780	L
	780–720	*B* + L
	720–675	*B* + *A* + L
	675	*B* + *A* + *ABC* + L
	<675	*B* + *A* + *ABC*
VII*	>740	L
	740–690	*B* + L
	690–675	*B* + *A* + L
	675	*B* + *A* + *ABC* + L
	675–585	*B* + *ABC* + L
	585	*B* + *ABC* + *C* + L
	<585	*B* + *ABC* + *C*
VIII	>690	L
	690–655	*B* + L
	655–585	*B* + *ABC* + L
	585	*B* + *ABC* + *C* + L
	<585	*B* + *ABC* + *C*

TABLE 6-3 continued

Comp	Temp (°C)	Phases
IX	>645	L
	645–600	*B* + L
	600–585	*B* + *C* + L
	585	*B* + *C* + *ABC* + L
X	>620	L
	620–590	*C* + L
	590–585	*C* + *B* + L
	585	*C* + *B* + *ABC* + L
	<585	*C* + *B* + *ABC*
XI	>710	L
	710–630	*C* + L
	630–585	*C* + *ABC* + L
	585	*C* + *ABC* + *B* + L
	<585	*C* + *ABC* + *B*
XII	>680	L
	680–650	*C* + L
	650–625	*C* + *ABC* + L
	625	*C* + *ABC* + *A* + L
	<625	*C* + *ABC* + *A*
XIII	>680	L
	680–635	*C* + L
	635–625	*C* + *A* + L
	625	*C* + *A* + *ABC* + L
	<625	*C* + *A* + *ABC*
XIV	>670	L
	670–645	*ABC* + L
	645–585	*ABC* + *B* + L
	585	*ABC* + *B* + *C* + L
	<585	*ABC* + *B* + *C*
XV	>660	L
	660–600	*ABC* + L
	600–585	*ABC* + *C* + L
	585	*ABC* + *C* + *B* + L
	<585	*ABC* + *C* + *B*
XVI	>655	L
	655–645	*ABC* + L
	645–625	*ABC* + *C* + L
	625	*ABC* + *C* + *A* + L
	<625	*ABC* + *C* + *A*
*ABC**	>720	L
	720–680	*A* + L
	680	*A* + *ABC* + L
	<680	*ABC*
A-*ABC*	>(720–910)**	L
	(720–910)–680	*A* + L
	680	*A* + *ABC* + L
	<680	*A* + *ABC*

*Equilibrium crystallization sequences in which an early crystal phase is subsequently resorbed by reaction with the liquid (L).
**Exact temperature of beginning of crystallization depends on the initial ratio of *A* to *ABC*.

depending on exact location of the primary field of the ternary compound (Fig. 6-12 is but one possibility). Although only one possible configuration is illustrated, principles of crystallization are invariably the same (Prog. 6-4). All three sides of the system illustrated (Fig. 6-12) are binary systems with complete crystalline immiscibility (Fig. 6-2a). Each binary eutectic point heads a cotectic thermal valley leading thermally downward to one of two ternary eutectic points in the system. Because the primary field of crystallization of ternary compound *ABC* does not include composition *ABC*, there is a ternary peritectic point. The cotectic boundary between the primary field of *A* and that of *ABC* is a peritectic inflection that becomes a thermal valley as it leads to a ternary eutectic point. This peritectic curve has a maximum where it becomes colinear with the join *A*—*ABC*. (See Table 6-3 for selected crystallization sequences.)

Examples of mineralogically interesting ternary systems with incongruently melting binary phases include carnegieite-kalsilite-silica, with orthoclase melting incongruently, and anorthite-forsterite-silica, with pyroxene melting incongruently. The system periclase-corundum-silica has two incongruently melting binary compounds, mullite and clinoenstatite, and one incongruently melting ternary compound, cordierite.

6-7 TERNARY ISOTHERMAL ISOBARIC SECTIONS

Although isothermal contours on a ternary isobaric liquidus surface portray melting and crystallization sequences rather clearly, they do not show solvus domes and other subsolidus relationships. One method of representing all relationships in ternary systems utilizes isobaric, isothermal sections through a pressure-temperature-composition hyperprism. All phase relationships in ternary systems may be revealed graphically with a series of different isobaric, isothermal sections at different pressures and temperatures (Prog. 6-5).

Although invariance in ternary systems requires coexistence of five phases ($0 = 3 - 5 + 2$), invariance occurs at a unique pressure and temperature that generally does not appear when pressure and temperature are arbitrarily selected. A different kind of plot is required to show invariance adequately. Furthermore, invariance commonly involves a vapor phase that has been systematically ignored for the sake of simplicity. Univariance requires coexistence of four phases (for instance, a ternary eutectic liquid and three crystalline phases), but it, too, is restrictive and does not appear at arbitrarily selected pressures and temperatures. Thus, three-, two-, and one-phase regions typically appear on these diagrams when temperature and pressure are arbitrarily chosen.

Complete Crystalline Immiscibility Consider a ternary system with total crystalline immiscibility and no compounds (Fig. 6-8b). Through this isobaric temperature-composition prism, select an isothermal surface that intersects its liquidus surface at a temperature above its ternary eutectic temperature but below its binary eutectic temperatures (Fig. 6-13a). The central area of this surface represents a liquid one-phase region (*a*–*b*–*c*) bounded by an isotherm on its liquidus surface. All compositions that plot outside the central area are subliquidus.

Three three-phase subliquidus areas are *A* + *B* + liquid *c*, *A* + *C* + liquid *b*, and *B* + *C* + liquid *a*. The three phases represented at each corner of the three-phase triangles all coexist within these triangles, their relative proportions given by their positions (each three-phase area could be replotted on Fig. 6-8a). Each three-phase area is bounded by two-phase areas: *B* + liquid *a*–*c*, *A* + liquid *b*–*c*, *C* + liquid *a*–*b*, *A* + *B*, *B* + *C*, and *A* + *C*. The first three two-phase regions have a single crystalline phase coexisting with a liquid of variable composition, and the last three are boundary binary systems to this ternary system.

Note that on a ternary isothermal, isobaric section of this sort (Fig. 6-13a), adjacent areas differ only by one in number of phases present. One-phase areas are bounded by two-phase areas. Two-phase areas are bounded by one-phase and three-phase areas. The liquid area shrinks toward a point, and the two-phase regions shrink toward lines as successive isothermal sections through this prism approach its ternary eutectic temperature. A section taken at this eutectic temperature has an invariant point representing four phases: crystalline *A*, *B*, and *C* and the eutectic liquid. Sections at all lower temperatures are single three-phase areas for crystalline *A*, *B*, and *C* in any proportion.

Limited Crystalline Miscibility Many components of geologic interest have variable composition with limited miscibility of crystalline phases (Fig. 6-5; Prog. 6-5). Miscibility, limited or complete, is indicated by hatch marks along binary joins and by crystal solution areas around components (Fig. 6-13b). One result of this miscibility is that binary join lines become areas, and two-phase area have liquid and crystalline compositional variability. Where two crystal solutions are in equilibrium with a liquid, however, all three compositions are unique for a given pressure and temperature.

The liquid area reduces to a point at the eutectic isotherm where compositions of each crystalline phase is unique Below that isotherm, the central area represents a single three-phase area bordered by two-phase areas. Although each component shows crystalline solution toward both other components, there is a unique component composition for any equilibrium assemblage in this system. Within each two-phase region, each component composition is uniquely related to the other component composition by a tie line. Only in one-phase areas of crystal solution is phase composition independently variable.

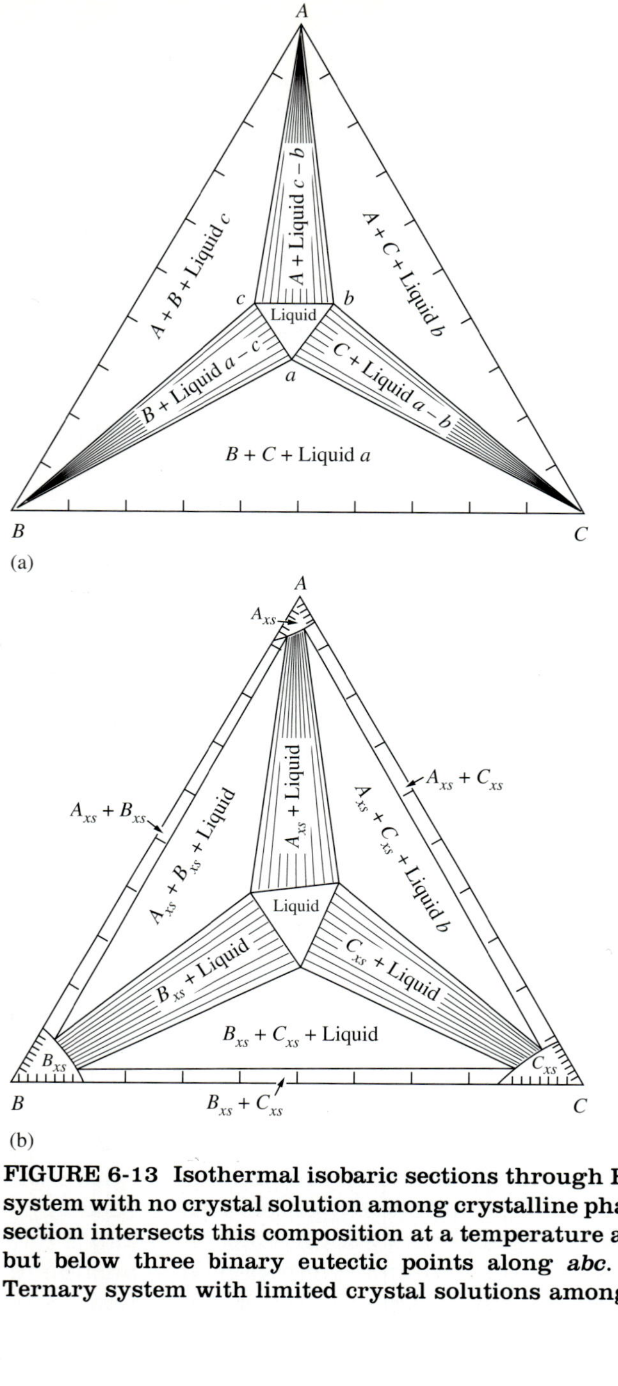

FIGURE 6-13 Isothermal isobaric sections through PTX hyperprism. (a) Ternary system with no crystal solution among crystalline phases. This isothermal isobaric section intersects this composition at a temperature above a ternary eutectic point but below three binary eutectic points along *abc*. Compare Figure 6-10b. (b) Ternary system with limited crystal solutions among crystalline phases.

6-8 QUATERNARY SYSTEMS

Quaternary systems in which one component is a vapor phase under pressure and temperature conditions of interest are commonly treated as pseudoternary systems by projecting quaternary compositions onto the vapor-free base of a composition tetrahedron. Compositions of vapor-free phases are, of course, plotted directly. Components having a vapor constituent as an essential part of their composition are projected geometrically by extending a line from the vapor apex of a tetrahedron through the component to a point where it intersects the opposite face. This projected phase may be a vapor-saturated liquid phase or a crystalline phase. Examples of the latter include micas and amphiboles in a system where H_2O is a vapor component and calcite and dolomite where CO_2 is a vapor component.

Projections Although such projections are common practice for representation of quaternary systems, you must remember the stipulated presence of this vapor phase. Phase relationships in a vapor-free system may be quite different from projected phase relationships in a system with a vapor phase, however similar the two diagrams may appear. For example, compare phase relationships for SiO_2 (Fig. 1-17) with a projection of the system SiO_2—H_2O (Fig. 4-1). Furthermore, in considering applications of phase relationships in real mineralogic situations, composition of a vapor phase must be taken into account. Vapor composition will not be that of a pure vapor end member and proportions of anhydrous constituents dissolved in it generally will not be the same as those proportions in other phases with which it is in equilibrium. For example, distribution coefficients between vapor and liquid are rarely unity.

Quaternary System with a Vapor Phase Consider a quaternary system in which one component is a vapor phase such as water or CO_2 (Fig. 6-14; Prog. 6-6). The vapor-free base of a composition tetrahedron may be treated as a pseudoternary system *A*—*B*—*C* with a liquidus surface contoured in isotherms. But if that vapor *V* component dissolves in this melt, its composition is projected from *V* composition to the vapor-free base *A*—*B*—*C*. Furthermore, in cases of binary compounds involving a vapor phase, such as carbonates or hydrates, those compositions are also seen in projection.

The vapor-free ternary system *A*—*B*—*C* reveals complete liquid miscibility and crystalline immiscibility (compare Fig. 6-8b) with binary eutectic points each heading a cotectic thermal valley leading to a ternary eutectic point. Each ternary face (*ABV*, *BCV*, *ACV*) of this composition tetrahedron is geometrically identical to *A*—*B*—*C*, but with its ternary eutectic point involving crystalline *V* (for instance, ice or dry ice) vanishingly close to pure *V*.

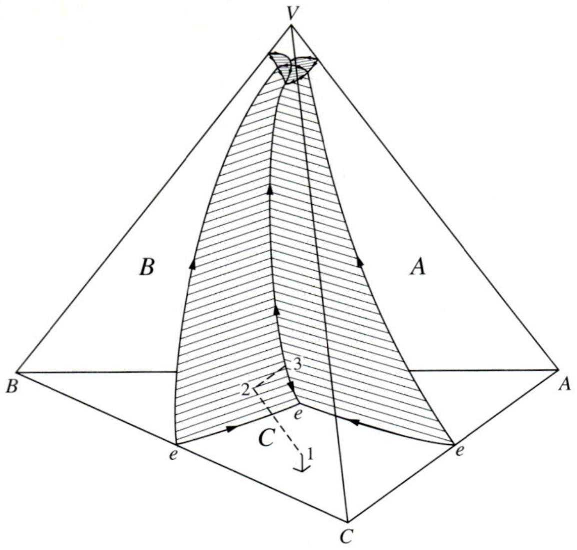

FIGURE 6-14 Schematic polybaric polythermal equilibrium phase diagram for a quaternary system *A*—*B*—*C*—*V* in which the *V* component represents a vapor phase present in melts, generally in small amounts. A composition labeled 1 begins to crystallize *C* when cooled to the liquidus temperature for that composition. Crystallization of pure *C* drives liquid compositions directly away from *C* composition until they encounter the primary volume boundary at point 2. Beginning at point 2, *B* and *C* crystallize simultaneously, driving the liquid composition away from the *B*—*C* join until it encounters the four-phase cotectic line entering the composition tetrahedron from the eutectic point on the vapor-free base. There crystals of *A* join *B* and *C*, and the liquid composition migrates along the four-phase cotectic line to a quaternary eutectic point, where crystals of *A*, *B*, and *C* coexist with crystals of *V*, nearly pure *V* vapor, and nearly pure *V* liquid.

Each ternary eutectic point heads a univariant curve leading to a quaternary eutectic point that is vanishingly close to the *V* apex of the composition tetrahedron. For invariance with four components, Gibbs' phase rule ($F = C - P + 2$, $0 = 4 - P + 2$, $P = 6$) requires the presence of six phases, crystals of *A*, *B*, *C*, and *V* plus liquid and vapor, conditions not particularly relevant to terrestrial petrology.

Volumes represent primary fields of crystallization in a quaternary system. Consider a *C*-rich melt with a small percentage of dissolved *V*. On cooling to its liquidus temperature, crystals of *C* drive liquid compositions directly away from the *C* apex of this tetrahedron until the liquid composition arrives at a cotectic plane either with *A* or with *B*. Further crystallization of *C* either with *A* or with *B* drives the liquid composition toward a univariant line rising from the ternary, vapor-free eutectic point on the base of the composition tetrahedron.

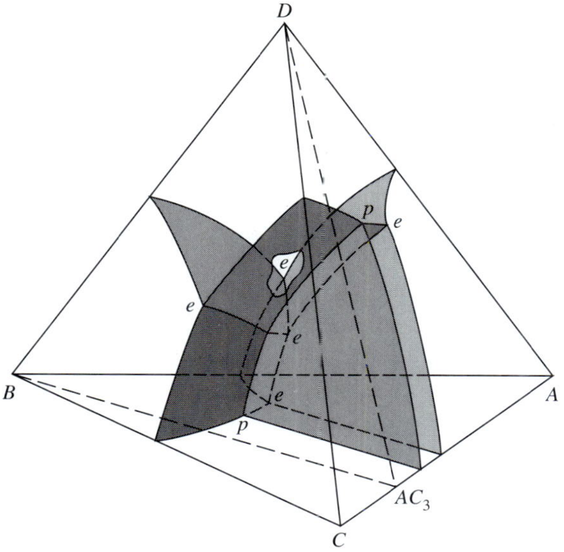

FIGURE 6-15 Schematic isobaric phase diagram for a quaternary system *A—B—C—D* with an incongruently melting binary compound AC_3. Two faces of the composition tetrahedron have ternary eutectic points, *A—B—D* and *B—C—D*. Because of incongruently melting AC_3, two faces have ternary peritectic and eutectic points, *A—B—C* and *A—B—D*. Each ternary peritectic point heads a four-phase cotectic curve, all of which meet at a five-phase invariant point where liquid coexists with crystals of *B*, *C*, AC_3, and *D*. Another four-phase cotectic curve falls thermally from this point to another five-phase invariant point where liquid coexists with *A*, AC_3, *B*, and *D*.

All crystallization of *A*, *B*, and *C* enriches the remaining liquid in *V*. Depending on the components involved and the total pressure on a real system, a vapor phase saturated with all other components may separate from an *ABC*-rich melt. Since a separate vapor phase generally is much less dense than the liquid that exsolved it, this vapor phase will tend to rise and escape from the rest of this system. Furthermore, since the *A*:*B*:*C* ratio of a vapor is generally not the same ratio as in a coexisting liquid, vapor escape leads to a composition change in this system. Veins associated with igneous rocks may result from such vapor escape.

A quaternary system in which one of the components is a vapor in small percentage amounts may be conveniently represented as a pseudoternary system with compositions projected from the vapor apex onto the vapor-free base with the vapor component subsumed into system pressure, P_V. In systems where cotectic lines and planes curve in a composition tetrahedron (Fig. 6-14), this projected position of these cotectic lines and planes depends on the vapor content of any liquid, and this content varies with P_V. The haplogranite system albite-orthoclase-quartz-water is treated in this fashion, as are siliceous dolomitic marbles in the quinary system CaO—MgO—SiO_2—CO_2—H_2O.

Quaternary System Without a Vapor A quaternary system where compositions of interest are central to its composition tetrahedron is less amenable to meaningful projections than one where interesting compositions lie close to one face. Consider a quaternary system (Fig. 6-15) in which two ternary boundary systems have a ternary eutectic point (A—B—D and B—C—D, compare Fig. 6-8b) and two have an incongruently melting binary compound (A—B—C and A—C—D, compare Fig. 6-9b). Primary crystallization volume for compound AC_3 does not include the plane AC_3—B—D.

During equilibrium crystallization of compositions in the primary crystallization volume of C on the C side of the plane AC_3—B—D, removal of crystals of C from a melt drives melt compositions to the peritectic plane between the volumes of C and AC_3. Under equilibrium crystallization, liquid compositions are confined to that plane up to its intersection with the primary volumes of B or D. Under fractional crystallization when crystals of D do not react with a melt, melt compositions can then migrate across the primary crystallization volume of AC_3. The basalt system olivine-clinopyroxene-plagioclase-quartz is treated in this fashion.

FURTHER READINGS

Denbigh, K., *The Principles of Chemical Equilibria*. London: Cambridge University Press, 1985.

Ehlers, E. G., *The Interpretation of Geological Phase Diagrams*. New York: Freeman, 1972.

Ernst, W. G., *Petrologic Phase Equilibria*. New York: Freeman, 1976.

Findlay, A., A. N. Campbell, and N. O. Smith, *The Phase Rule and Its Applications*, 9th ed. New York: Dover, 1951.

Gibbs, J. W., *Scientific Papers*, Vol. 1. New York: Dover, 1961.

Levin, E. M., C. R. Robbins, and H. F. McMurdie, *Phase Diagrams for Ceramists*. Columbus, OH: The American Ceramic Society, 1964.

Masing, G., *Ternary Systems*. New York: Dover, 1960.

Ricci, J. E., *The Phase Rule and Heterogeneous Equilibrium*. New York: Van Nostrand Reinhold, 1951.

Schreinemakers, F. A. H., *Equilibria in Ternary Systems: In-, Mono-, and Di-variant Equilibria*. University Park: The Pennsylvania State University, 1965.

7

MINERAL GENESIS

Any individual who has contemplated an apparently endless array of minerals in a museum or at a minerals show may have an erroneous notion that mixtures of minerals that one may expect to encounter in nature may be even greater. In fact, variety in any given mineral assemblage—be it in common rock or in a mining district—is quite restricted in comparison with all possible combinations of chemical elements present.

This narrow restriction in numbers of different minerals and mineral assemblages found in most rocks of the earth's crust derives from two sources: distribution of elements in the earth's and other planetary crusts, and reactions that occur between minerals under conditions of heterogeneous equilibrium (Chap. 6). A mineral does not merely exist. Its very existence implies an origin and a subsequent history that may be inferred from a mineral itself, from its composition and compositional variations, from its environs, and from other minerals with which it is intimately associated.

A glance at any modern periodic chart of the chemical elements reveals the existence of more than 100 different elements. Of these, only 94 appear in the earth's crust. All isotopes of the transuranium elements (other than Pu) have half-lives so short that any that might have been present during early stages of crustal evolution have completely decayed since then. Half-lives of U, Th, and Pu are sufficiently long that a measurable portion of primordial U, Th, and Pu is still present to form minerals. Other elements between Bi and U occur only as their daughter products commonly found in association with them. The most recent addition to the list of naturally occurring elements is Tc (number 43), now known to be formed by neutrino bombardment of Mo in molybdenite [MoS_2].

TABLE 7-1 Major Components of Earth's Crust (weight percent)

Oxide	Continental	Subcontinental	Oceanic	Total
SiO_2	60.22	59.35	48.44	57.60
Al_2O_3	15.18	15.07	15.85	15.30
Fe_2O_3	2.48	2.55	2.67	2.53
FeO	3.77	3.82	6.11	4.27
MgO	3.05	3.14	6.89	3.88
CaO	5.51	5.97	12.15	6.99
Na_2O	2.99	2.90	2.57	2.88
K_2O	2.86	2.79	0.46	2.34
H_2O^+	1.37	1.43	1.31	1.37
CO_2	1.20	1.57	1.87	1.40
Total	98.63	98.59	98.32	98.56

Data from A. B. Ronov and A. A. Yaroshevsky, "Earth's crust geochemistry," in R. W. Fairbridge (ed.), *The Encyclopedia of Geochemistry and Environmental Sciences*. New York: Van Nostrand Reinhold, 1972.

Crustal Abundances Relative familiarity with the chemical elements used in industry and technology in no way indicates their relative crustal abundances. Only 12 elements account for 99% by weight of the earth's continental crust (Table 7-1). Nine out of 10 ions in this crust are either O^{2-}, Si^{4+}, or Al^{3+}, and O^{2-} makes up 94% of its volume. Furthermore, many unfamiliar elements are far more abundant than technologically and historically familiar ones (Fig. 7-1). Rubidium is more abundant than Ag or Zn, Ce is more abundant than Ne, and Li is more abundant than Hg. Gold, perhaps the first element worked by ancient peoples, ranks in abundance behind such electronic age elements as Ga, Ge, Cd, Hf, and all stable rare-earth elements.

Some elements are dispersed and only rarely concentrated as essential components of mineral species. Ions of these elements are similar enough in size and charge to common ions that they substitute in common minerals without appreciable change in properties. Prime examples of dispersed elements include Ga in Al minerals, Ge in Si minerals, and Hf in Zr minerals, although hafnon [$(Hf,Zr)SiO_4$] has been reported. Chemical elements are familiar if they crystallize in their own, easily recognized minerals, for example Au, Pb, and Cu. Thus, simplicity of mineral assemblages results partly from paucity of elements truly abundant in the earth's crust and partly because some elements rarely or never concentrate as essential constituents of minerals. Minerals in ordinary granite contain measurable amounts of Ga, Ge, and Ba, even though these elements do not occur in chemical formulas for minerals making up granite.

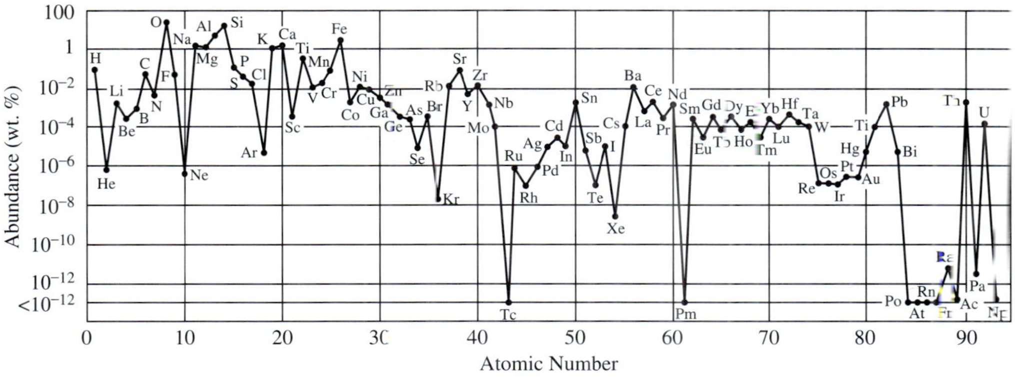

FIGURE 7-1 Continental crustal abundances of the chemical elements. Only eight elements appear in the continental crust in abundances greater than 1%. Note that many space-age elements occur in greater abundances than well-known elements, such as Ag and Au. (After B. Mason, *Principles of Geochemistry*. New York: Wiley, 1966, p. 47.)

7-1 CRYSTAL GROWTH

A rock is anything making up a structural (mappable) unit of a planetary crust or mantle. Most rocks are composed of mineral grains (coal and obsidian excepted). These minerals did not always exist; they had to have a beginning sometime and somewhere. And from that beginning, or nucleation, they had to grow to their present size, ranging anywhere from submicroscopic to tens of meters in greatest dimension.

Nucleation Crystal growth begins with a nucleus. This nucleation may take place in a medium that is solid (either crystalline or glassy), liquid, or vapor (crystal growth in outer space may be considered to have occurred in a very rarified gas). Nucleation and crystal growth can, but do not always, occur when a parent or host material passes into a stability field of a crystalline phase as a result of changes in pressure, temperature, composition, or some combination of changes. It may also occur along a metastable extension for a phase (Sec. 6-2).

Nucleation generally does not occur immediately when these changes bring a parent medium to the edge of a stability field for a crystalline phase; nucleation and growth require some degree of supersaturation and take time. A stability field boundary marks a location in PTX space where phases from opposite sides of this boundary are equally stable. Thus, at a field boundary represented by the reaction

$$\text{jadeite} + \text{quartz} \rightleftharpoons \text{albite},$$
$$NaAlSi_2O_6 + SiO_2 \rightleftharpoons NaAlSi_3O_8,$$

all three phases are equally stable and at equilibrium may coexist together. In reality, however, the assemblage jadeite + quartz does not produce albite upon arrival at this field boundary; supersaturation by passage beyond it into the stability field of albite precedes nucleation. An assemblage of minerals is supersaturated within its stability field if the phase (in this example, albite) is absent or in such amounts that free energies of its components in the medium (in this example, jadeite and quartz) are greater than free energies of its components in a stable crystalline phase. Supercooling or undercooling is more specific if a stability field is entered by falling temperature. Quenching refers to rapid penetration into or passage through a stability field due to sudden changes in pressure, temperature, or both. Quenching may also result from sudden escape of a volatile phase, such as an aqueous fluid formerly in equilibrium with condensed phases by raising their liquidus and solidus temperatures.

Nucleation may be homogeneous or heterogeneous. Homogeneous nucleation occurs when random motions of constituent atoms, ions, or molecules form an ordered nucleus that may grow to a critical size to permit further crystal growth. Nucleation is highly improbable, especially at low degrees of supersaturation, that is, near a stability field boundary. With increasing penetration into a stability field during cooling, nucleation rates increase exponentially at first then decrease again when further supercooling decreases thermal activity of a system. Volcanic glass exists because thermal quench of a magma was too rapid to permit formation of nuclei and growth of crystals. Volcanic rock tends to be fine grained because many nuclei formed during quench of its precursor magma (as lava). Some extremely coarse-grained plutonic igneous rocks, such as anorthosites, result from remaining for long periods of time close to liquidus temperatures causing few nuclei and, therefore, only a few crystals that are consequently able to grow to a very large size.

Heterogeneous nucleation occurs when constituents of a crystal array themselves on a preexisting substance or at a defect (Sec. 1-6). Nucleation and growth on a substrate may be epitactic involving only one crystallographic surface or it may be syntactic involving three nonparallel planes. An example of epitaxy is nucleation and growth of halite crystals on a mica substrate, because the pattern and spacing of ions on a basal plane of mica closely match those on a (111) plane of halite. Seeding supercooled air with crystals of AgI to nucleate ice crystals, because these unit cells are approximately the same size, is an example of syntaxy. Growth of aragonite crystals from aqueous solutions at pressures and temperatures where calcite is the stable polymorph of $CaCO_3$ may be attributed, in part, to syntaxy. Some aragonite oolites (spherules) from the Bahama Banks, for instance, have different nuclei on which aragonite grew in turbulent waters.

Nucleation of a stable (or metastable) crystalline phase within a host crystal structure rendered unstable by passage into a new stability field may be homogeneous or heterogeneous. Displacive transformations of secondary coordination, such as the high-low transformation of quartz are extremely rapid and impossible to quench because thermal vibration in a structure at a transformation temperature permit many individual bond angles to assume stable configurations immediately (Sec. 1-7)

As quartz cools through its inversion temperature at 573°C, spontaneous homogeneous nucleation occurs at many locations within this structure, and growth of its low-temperature phase proceeds rapidly outward from these nuclei until boundaries from each nucleus meet. Since two directions of inversion to lower symmetry are possible in quartz, these two orientations of low-temperature nuclei are equally probable and form simultaneously in different parts of its high-temperature structure. When boundaries in parallel orientation meet, they are mutually annihilated. Meeting of antiparallel zones gives rise to a twin plane, called Dauphiné twinning in quartz. Twin composition planes formed by inversion to lower symmetry may be highly irregular, as in Dauphiné twinning, or planar and parallel, as in albite twinning in plagioclase.

Reconstructive transformations involving primary (quartz-stishovite) or secondary (quartz-cristobalite) coordination changes require activation energies considerably greater than those provided by thermal vibrations at near-surface conditions of the earth. Formation of a stable nucleus requires breaking and remaking chemical bonds. In these and similar cases, nucleation proceeds heterogeneously, if at all (stishovite and cristobalite are found in rocks at the earth's surface). Such nucleation requires a presence of structural defects or chemical impurities in order to occur.

Growth Topography Once nuclei of a stable phase exist, growth can then occur. Assuming for a moment that a stable nucleus is a submicroscopic perfect crystal with a source of constituents for growth, a problem similar to that of homogeneous nucleation appears immediately. Addition of a first atomic particle to a crystallographic surface is nearly as energetically improbable as formation of a nucleus in the first place. Additions may be individual ions or clusters called adatoms.

Experiments with synthetic materials indicate that impurities, grain boundaries, lineages, and screw dislocations are all important factors in growth of crystalline phases (Sec. 1-5). Matter in the vicinity of chemical and structural defects is in a higher energy state than that in places of crystalline perfection. Hence, they are in a state closer to a threshold of an energy barrier between these states and have a higher probability of being activated. In addition, where chemical composition of a growing phase is different from a host or parent phase or phases, growth rates may be limited by rates of diffusion both toward and away from an advancing face of a growing crystal.

A growing crystal face is not a simple plane, but has on it terraces, steps, kinks, vacancies, and adatoms (Sec. 4-6, Figs. 4-9, 7-2, Prog. 7-1).

FIGURE 7-2 Schematic growing crystal surface. A growing crystal surface shows, from left to right, a hole in a terrace, a kinked step between terraces, and an adatom on a terrace.

An adatom releases surface energy when it attaches itself anywhere on a growing crystal face. It releases more surface energy if its point of attachment is at a step and more yet at a kink. In some cases an adatom on a terrace can migrate to a step and along a step to a kink, each time releasing more surface energy. By filling kinks and steps, a terrace grows across a crystal face. Difficulty in beginning a new terrace is eliminated if a growing crystal face has one or more screw dislocations permitting steps to sweep helically around an axis.

Crystal Faces Without delving deeper into theories of crystal growth beyond the scope of this section, we may observe certain empirical generalizations concerning habits of crystals and controls of their crystallographic orientation. A crystal of a mineral in a rock is euhedral if it is bounded by well-developed crystal faces and anhedral if no faces occur. Intermediate conditions are subhedral. Rapid undercooling, or quenching, of a volcanic lava causes many rapidly growing nuclei resulting in many small, mutually sutured grains. A small degree of undercooling and slow crystal growth permit long-range diffusion of chemical constituents and development of faces on a few crystals.

More importantly, perhaps, in development of well-formed crystals, are differences in surface tension between an unstable parent material and a growing stable or metastable phase, which govern degrees to which crystal faces may develop. Surface tension γ indicates the amount of work dw necessary to extend a surface dA, so $dw = \gamma dA = dG$, where G is the free energy. The greater the difference in surface tension between two media, the better the development of crystal faces. The great difference in surface tension between an aqueous fluid phase and a crystalline phase may account for the well-developed crystals found in some veins, pegmatites, and evaporites.

Angular relationships between crystal faces depend on structural symmetry of a crystalline phase. Stensen's observation (Steno's law) of constancy of interfacial angles is noted in Chap. 3, as are forms possible for each crystal class (Sec. 3-8). Even before an atomistic theory of crystalline materials was confirmed by X-ray diffraction (Secs. 1-4 and 5-6), August Bravais formulated a rule that importance of a face on a crystal is proportional to interplanar spacing of lattice planes parallel to that face. (A crystal face is important in a mineral species if it occurs commonly and if it is large relative to other crystal faces.) Planes of highest lattice-point density, hence the largest number of structural units corresponding to each lattice point, should be the slowest to advance on a growing crystal. And faces normal to slow-growing directions are ones commonly found bounding crystals (Fig. 7-3). Fast-growing faces simply grow themselves out of existence.

Some apparent exceptions to Bravais' rule are made to conform to it when subtranslations of a lattice—glide planes and screw axes—are included in addition to interplanar spacing as such. The variety of existing crystal forms that do not conform to this modified Bravais rule arise, in part, from environment of growth. Thus, the typical cubic habit of halite may be suppressed by the presence of urea in the growth solution suppressing growth in the [111] direction and leading to development of octahedral faces. Highly supercooled atmospheric water vapor produces needles of ice elongated parallel to the **c** axis at around $-5°C$, but flakes of ice dendrites at right angles to **c** in the range $-10°$ to $-20°C$.

Another generalization is that minerals with tabular unit cells tend to produce acicular (needlelike) crystals, whereas those with elongate unit cells produce tabular crystals. For example, tourmaline (**a** = 160 pm, **c** = 70 pm) typically grows in elongate prisms, whereas ilmenite (**a** = 51 pm, **c** = 141 pm) commonly grows in flat plates. Zoisite (**a** = 162 pm, **b** = 59 pm, **c** = 101 pm) crystals are typically elongate in the **b** direction.

In some cases, gross morphology of a crystal is not the same as actual crystal faces present. Inspect with a hand lens a striated cube {100} face of pyrite to reveal alternating pyritohedral {210} faces. Similarly, striated quartz prisms $\{10\bar{1}0\}$ may consist only of alternating positive $\{10\bar{1}1\}$ and negative $\{01\bar{1}1\}$ rhombohedral faces.

Where a parent phase converting to another phase is crystalline, the crystallographic orientation of the new phase to the parent commonly controls orientation of a growing crystal. This topotaxy applies to many polymorphic transitions, to intergrowths resulting from exsolution, and to other crystalline-state reactions. When goethite dehydrates to hematite, spatial arrangement of O^{2-} ions suffers little change; the orthorhombic **a** axial direction becomes the trigonal **c** axes with a tripling of length, and the orthorhombic **b** axis becomes the trigonal **a** with a halving of its

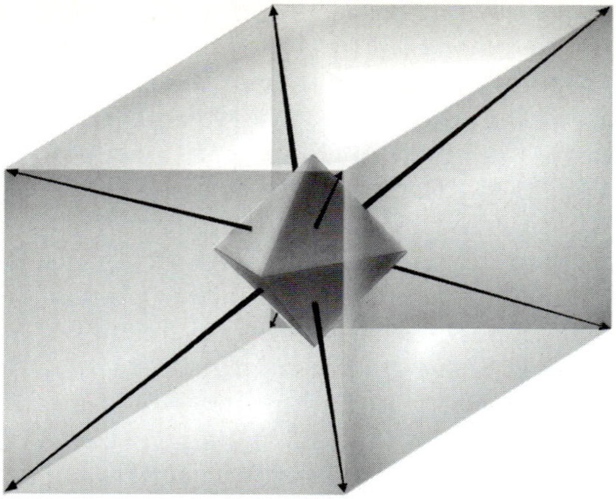

(a)

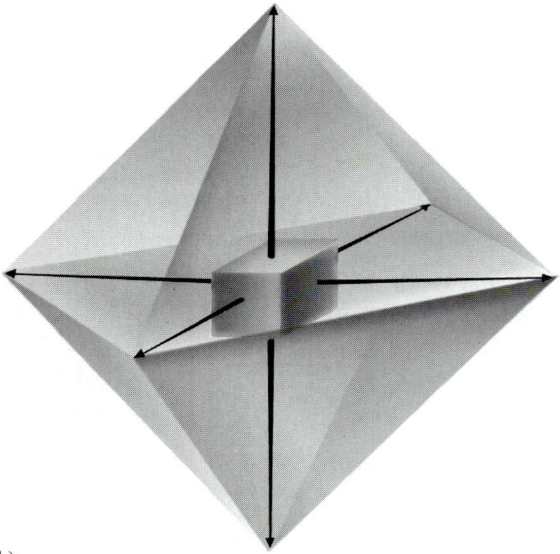

(b)

FIGURE 7-3 Growth rates and resulting crystal faces. (a) Octahedral faces are represented as fast-growing with the external form of a cube resulting. (b) Cube faces are represented as fast-growing with the external form of an octahedron being the result.

length. Although not all crystalline-state reactions are topotactic, many are and, thus, give further information about genesis of a particular mineral specimen.

7-2 MAGMAS AND CRYSTALLIZATION

An igneous rock is one crystallized from a magma, a mobile rock material with a noteworthy amount of melt phase. Interpretation of geophysical data indicates that nearly all terrestrial lithosphere is solid, presumably crystalline, and that its asthenosphere contains a small percentage of interstitial melt. Local concentrations of heat sufficient to keep rocks molten must exist to provide for volcanic activity. Interpretation of various rock textures and structures, plus a large amount of laboratory experimental data, leads to an inference that many rocks have formed within or upon the earth's crust by crystallization of a magma. These interpretations of field observations and of experimental results also lead to a conclusion that the rules of heterogeneous phase equilibria can apply to such rocks.

Classification Before looking at crystallization of magmas, some terminology of igneous rocks needs to be established. Various schemes have been set forth for purposes of providing a rational system for naming igneous rocks on a basis of their composition. Two principal methods of identifying components of igneous rocks are in terms of weight percentage of oxides of elements present and in terms of volumetric percentages of minerals present.

Although chemical analyses of a rock can be precise and accurate in terms of major and minor elements, most geologists find it difficult to relate 10 or more reported oxide percentages to rock mineralogy. To bridge this difficulty, petrologists have advanced formal procedures for calculation from oxide components to a set of standard components called normative minerals. In 1904, W. Cross, J. P. Iddings, L. V. Pirsson, and H. S. Washington proposed a set of calculations to arrive at a norm of an igneous rock, now called the CIPW norm. In most cases, correlation between normative minerals and modal (actual) minerals is good when volumetric modes are converted to weight modes by taking into account mineral density.

A scheme for classification of plutonic rocks was recommended in 1972 and of volcanic rocks in 1979 by the Subcommission of the Systematics of Igneous Rocks created by the International Union of Geological Sciences (Figs. 7-4, 7-5) and commonly referred to as the Streckeisen classification in respect for its main author and proponent. Apices of these triangles represent modal minerals of igneous rocks; ratios within triangles are in volume percentages.

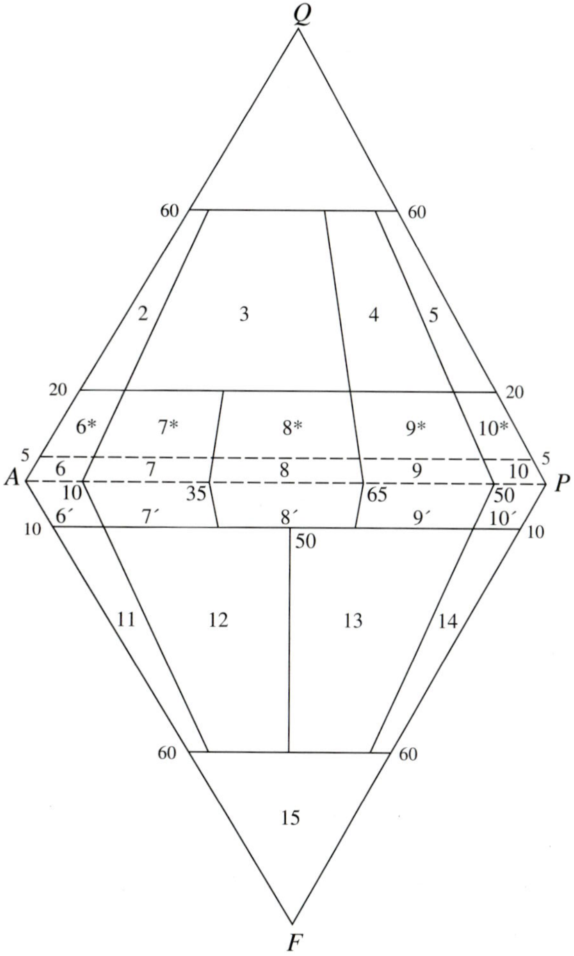

FIGURE 7-4 Rocks with less than 90% mafic minerals. The major divisions in fields **9** and **10** are among diorite, gabbro, and anorthosite and between andesite and basalt. Anorthosites are plutonic rocks composed of more than 90 vol% plagioclase, generally between *An* 35 and *An* 74. Gabbros may be distinguished from diorites on the basis of their plagioclase composition, gabbros having *An* greater than and diorite less than 50%. The same distinction may be made between basalt and andesite, although presence of *An*-rich phenocrysts in an extremely fine groundmass may be midleading. If a chemical analysis is available, andesite has more and basalt less than 52% SiO_2. For a complete discussion of rock names, see the reports of the International Union of Geological Sciences Subcommission on the Systematics of Igneous Rocks in *Geotimes* (Oct., 1973, p. 26) and in *Geology* (vol. 7, p. 331, 1979).

Key to figure (capital letters = plutonic rocks; lower case = volcanic): **2**, ALKALI-FELDSPAR GRANITE, alkali-feldspar rhyolite; **3**, GRANITE, rhyolite; **4**, GRANODIORITE, dacite; **5**, TONALITE, dacite; **6***, ALKALI-FELDSPAR QUARTZ SYENITE, quartz-alkali-feldspar trachyte; **6**, ALKALI-FELDSPAR SYENITE, alkali-feldspar trachyte; **6′**, FOID-BEARING ALKALI-FELDSPAR SYENITE, foid-bearing alkali-feldspar trachyte; **7***, QUARTZ SYENITE, quartz trachyte; **7**, SYENITE, trachyte; **7′**, FOID-BEARING SYENITE, foid-bearing trachyte; **8***, QUARTZ MONZONITE, quartz latite; **8**, MONZONITE, latite; **8′**, FOID-BEARING MONZONITE, foid-bearing latite; **9***, QUARTZ MONZODIORITE or QUARTZ MONZOGABBRO, andesite or basalt; **9**, MONZODIORITE or MONZOGABBRO, andesite or basalt; **9′**, FOID-BEARING MONZODIORITE or MONZOGABBRO, andesite or basalt; **10***, QUARTZ DIORITE or QUARTZ GABBRO or QUARTZ ANORTHOSITE, andesite or basalt; **10**, DIORITE or GABBRO or ANORTHOSITE, andesite or basalt; **10′**, FOID-BEARING DIORITE or GABBRO, andesite or basalt; **11**, FOID SYENITE, phonolite; **12**, FOID MONZOSYENITE, tephritic phonolite; **13**, ESSEXITE, phonolitic tephrite; **14**, THERALITE, tephrite; **15**, FOIDOLITE, foidite; **Q**, quartz; **A**, alkali feldspars *or* + *ab*; **P**, plagioclases *An* 5 − *An* 100 + scapolites; **F**, feldspathoids (foids).

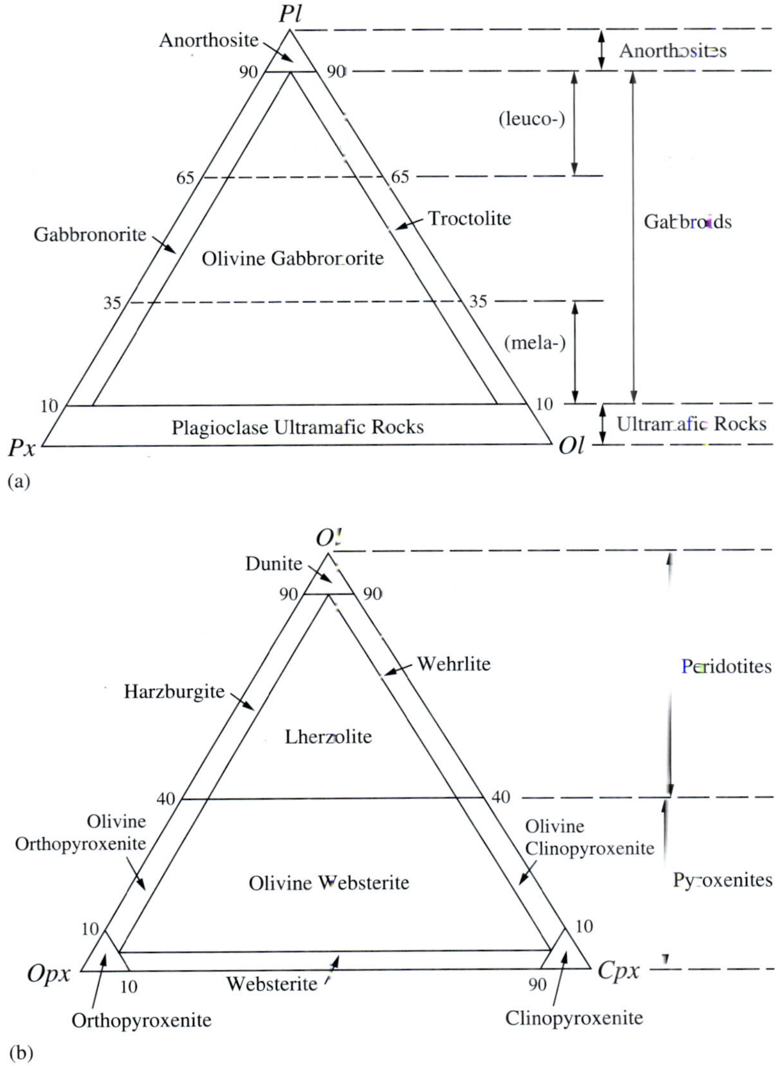

FIGURE 7-5 Classification of some mafic and ultramafic rocks. Abbreviations: *Ol*—olivine; *Pl*—plagioclase; *Px*—pyroxene; *Cpx*—clinopyroxene; *Opx*—orthopyroxene. In gabbros, clinopyroxene makes up more than 95% of pyroxene present. In norites, orthopyroxene makes up more than 95% of pyroxene present. When neither clinopyroxene nor orthopyroxene makes up less than 5% of pyroxene, the rock is gabbronorite. (a) Classification of gabbroic rocks. (b) Classification of ultramafic rocks (mafic minerals greater than 90%).

In addition to mineralogic criteria, rock texture is used in classification. An igneous rock is phaneritic if its individual mineral grains are visible to an unaided eye or aphanitic if they are not (*phaneros* = visible; *a* = not). Most plutonic rocks are phaneritic and most volcanic rocks are

TABLE 7-2 Igneous Minerals*

Silica	
Quartz, tridymite, cristobalite	SiO_2
Feldspars	
Plagioclase series	
Albite	$NaAlSi_3O_8$
Anorthite	$CaAl_2Si_2O_8$
Microcline, sanidine, orthoclase	$KAlSi_3O_8$
Feldspathoids	
Nepheline	$KNa_3(AlSiO_4)_4$
Leucite	KAl_2O_6
Sodalite	$Na_8(AlSiO_4)_6Cl_2$
Cancrinite	$Na_6Ca_2(AlSiO_4)_6(CO_3)_2$
Olivine series	
Forsterite	Mg_2SiO_4
Fayalite	Fe_2SiO_4
Tephroite	Mn_2SiO_4
Pyroxenes	
Augite	$(Ca,Na)(Mg,Fe,Al,Ti)(Si,Ti)_2O_6$
Hypersthene	$(Mg,Fe)_2Si_2O_6$
Acmite (aegirine)	$NaFe^{3+}Si_2O_6$
Spodumene	$LiAlSi_2O_6$
Amphiboles	
Hornblende	$Ca_2(Mg,Fe)_4Al(Si_7Al)O_{22}(OH,F)_2$
Riebeckite	$Na_2(Fe,Mg)_3Fe_2^{3+}Si_8O_{22}(OH)_2$
Micas	
Biotite	$K(Mg,Fe)_3(Al,Fe^{3+})Si_3O_{10}(OH,F)_2$
Muscovite	$KAl_2(AlSi_3)O_{10}(OH,F)_2$
Lepidolite	$K(Li,Al)_3(Si,Al)_4O_{10}(F,OH)_2$
Accessories	
Apatite	$Ca_5(PO_4)_3F$
Zircon	$ZrSiO_4$
Magnetite	$FeOFe_2O_3$
Ilmenite	$FeTiO_3$
Pyrite	FeS_2
Sphene	$CaTiSiO_5$
Fluorite	CaF_2
Calcite	$CaCO_3$
Corundum	Al_2O_3

*Within each mineral group, the more common minerals come before the less common ones.

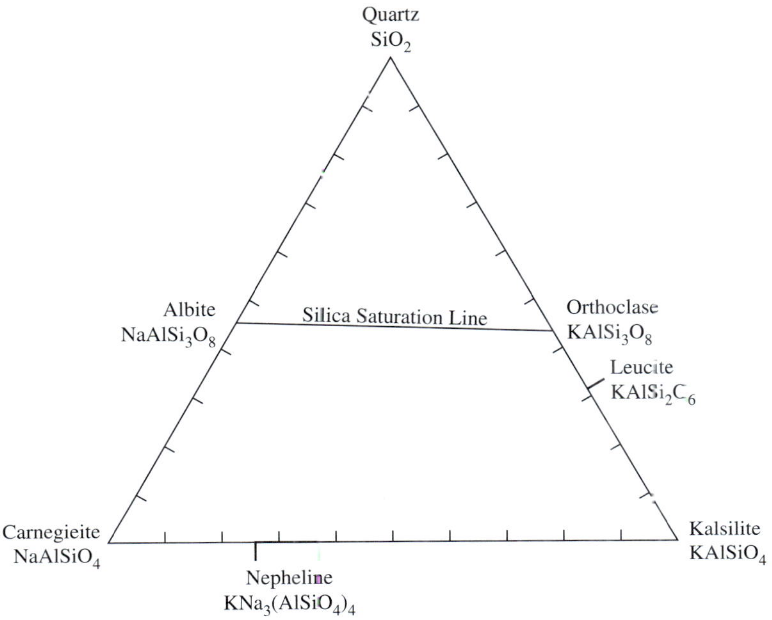

FIGURE 7-6 Silica saturation in the system carnegieite-kalsilite-quartz. Rocks containing free quartz are silica oversaturated; those containing carnegieite, nepheline, kalsilite, or leucite are undersaturated (weight percent).

aphanitic in texture. A volcanic rock with visible phenocrysts set in an aphanitic matrix has a porphyritic texture. Since grain size is not generally significant in heterogeneous equilibria, most discussion of genesis of igneous minerals uses a rock name to refer to rock composition without regard to its texture. Thus, granitic magma crystallizes to a rock that is predominantly alkali feldspar and quartz, called granite if intruded into the earth's crust but rhyolite if extruded upon it.

Most minerals in these classification schemes are silicates (Figs. 7-4, 7-5, Table 7-2), an indication that most igneous rocks are predominantly silicate. Relatively rare nonsilicate igneous rocks are treated at the end of this section.

Saturation In the earth's lithosphere, feldspar is predominant; hence, feldspar composition is used as a reference in chemical characterization of rocks and minerals. This usage may be illustrated by the system $NaAlSiO_4$—$KAlSiO_4$—SiO_2, which includes alkali feldspars (Fig. 7-6). The join $NaAlSi_3O_8$—$KAlSi_3O_8$ is a line of silica saturation; all compositions above it are silica oversaturated, and all below are silica undersaturated.

Presence of modal or normative quartz indicates (not always correctly, however) oversaturation, whereas presence of feldspathoids, such as nepheline and leucite, indicates undersaturation with respect to silica. Feldspathoids and quartz do not coexist in a stable plutonic assemblage, although in volcanic lava above the dissociation temperature of K-feldspar, quartz and leucite exist as a stable assemblage (Fig. 7-13).

In terms of oxide components, a rock is acid if it is substantially oversaturated with silica (quartz in the norm) and basic if substantially undersaturated. These chemical terms have counterparts based on mineralogic criteria, for example, felsic (from feldspar) or salic (from Si and Al), in which feldspars, feldspathoids, and quartz predominate, and mafic (from ma Fe) or femic (from Fe ma) rocks, in which ferromagnesian minerals (such as pyroxenes and amphiboles) predominate. Note that these two sets of terms (chemical normative and modal) are not precisely equivalent.

Alumina saturation is also based on feldspar compositions. All rocks in which the mole ratio of (K + Na)/Al is greater than 1 are alumina undersaturated; if the ratio is less than 1, they are oversaturated. Muscovite is an indicator of alumina oversaturation, although biotite is not. Riebeckite and acmite (aegirine) indicate that a rock is undersaturated with respect to alumina.

Magmas exist at surface pressure in the form of lava flows and are inferred from geophysical data to constitute between 0.001 and 1% of the earth's asthenosphere. Magmatic temperature extends from approximately 650°C, a temperature at which hydrous granite can be melted in a laboratory, to 1200°C, as actually measured in basaltic lava pools of active volcanos (Fig. 7-7). Molten material in the asthenosphere may be somewhat hotter. Momentary temperatures in excess of 2000 K under extremely reducing conditions are recorded by the presence of carbide and silicide phases in rock melts produced by lightning strikes.

Felsic Rocks The most abundant plutonic rocks in the continental crust are granitic (granites, granodiorites, quartz monzonites) that constitute most batholiths, the exposed roots of eroded mountain chains. Felsite, their volcanic equivalent, is at least as abundant in continental volcanic eruptions as is basalt, but is less well represented in geologic records because its pyroclastic eruptions produce more easily weathered and eroded rock than do basalt flows. Essential minerals for these granitic rocks are K-feldspar, Na-feldspar, and quartz, with muscovite, biotite, hornblende, apatite, fluorite, sphene, zircon, and magnetite occurring as common accessory minerals.

A contour plot of chemically analyzed plutonic rocks reduced to calculated amounts of albite, orthoclase, and quartz reveals a strong concentration of rock compositions near the center of this triangle (Fig. 7-8). Analyses of extrusive rocks plot similarly. In addition to rejecting inferior published chemical analyses, only two criteria were used to select these analyses from all other published rock analyses. First, these rocks

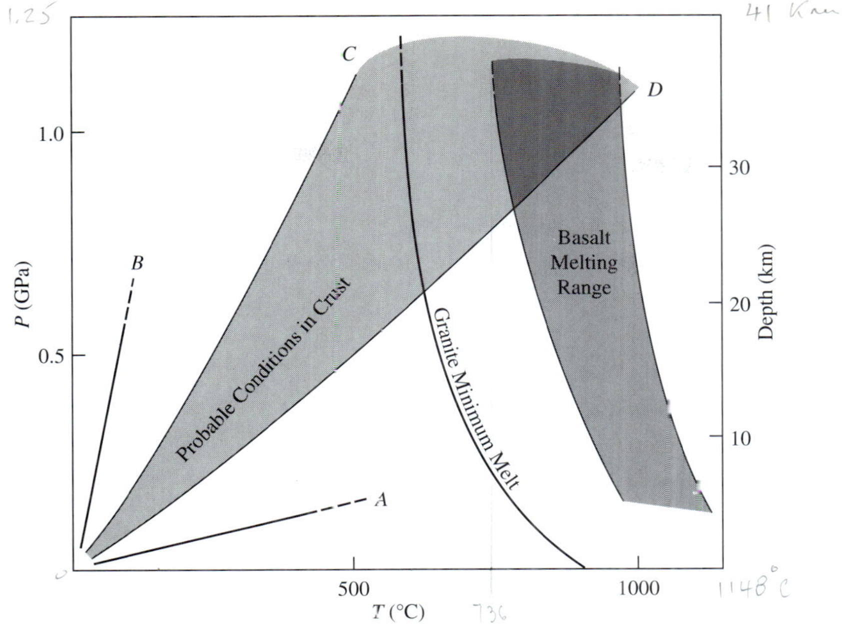

FIGURE 7-7 Pressures and temperatures in the earth's crust. Rock temperatures increase with depth. Curves *A* and *B* represent extreme values for measured geotherms, *A* for areas of recent vulcanism and *B* for geosynclinal areas of rapid sediment deposition. Probable geotherms lie between *C* and *D* in most continental areas. Granite minimum melting curve and basalt melting range are shown for reference (10 km = 0.3 GPa = 3 kbar).

all contain more than 80% normative *ab* + *or* − *qz*, and, second, they contain no normative nepheline, which is silica undersaturated (compare Fig. 7-6). From this concentration of compositions, N. L. Bowen and O. F. Tuttle concluded that granites and rhyolites represent low-temperature melts in the earth's continental crust.

Haplogranites The relevant system studied by Bowen and Tuttle is albite-orthoclase-quartz-water. A polythermal, polybaric, composition tetrahedron represents this system with arrows indicating directions of falling temperature (compare Fig. 6-14). First consider the six edges of this composition tetrahedron (Fig. 7-9). Edges *ab*-*w*, *or*-*w*, and *qz*-*w* are binary systems with liquid miscibility and crystalline immiscibility (compare Fig. 6-2) with a binary eutectic composition vanishingly close to *w* in equilibrium with *ab*, *or*, or *qz* and water ice. Edges *ab*-*qz* and *or*-*qz* are similar but show eutectic compositions at *N* and *O*, respectively. Edge *or*-*ab* is a binary system with a subsolidus solvus dome and a minimum on the liquidus-solidus loop (compare Fig. 6-5).

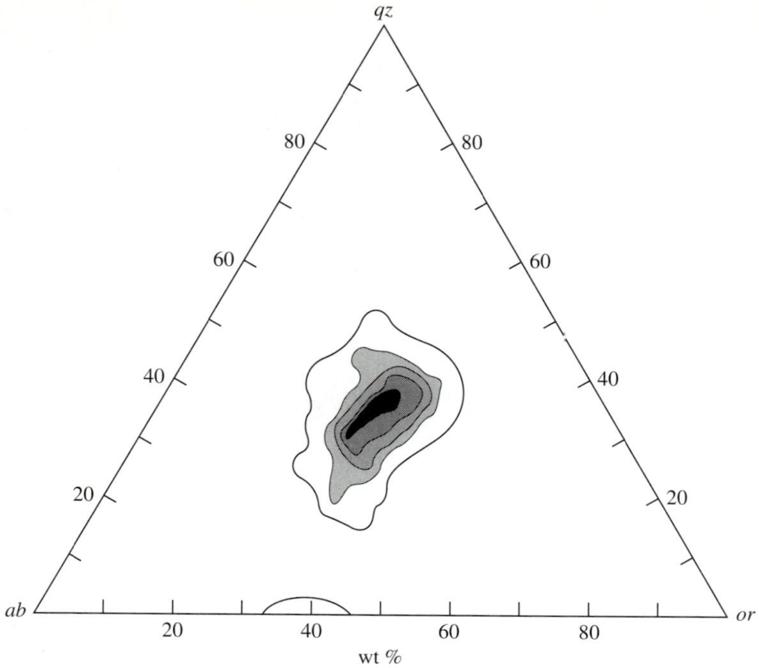

FIGURE 7-8 Contour diagram for compositions of siliceous plutonic rocks. Rocks selected on the basis of having more than 80% *ab* + *or* + *qz* as calculated from chemical analyses and normalized to 100%. Most rock compositions plot near the center of this diagram, which is best explained if granite magmas form by fractional crystallization or fractional melting of a parent rock.

Now consider the four ternary faces that bound this composition tetrahedron. Phase relationships of its anhydrous base are similar to those illustrated in Fig. 6-9b. Curve *ON* is a cotectic field boundary with a minimum between primary fields of quartz and of alkali feldspar. Face *ab-qz-w* is a ternary system with a ternary eutectic composition vanishingly close to *w* where albite, quartz, water, and ice coexist stably (compare Fig. 6-8b). This face may also be represented by a pseudobinary system where phase relationships are projected onto the anhydrous face of its polythermal composition prism (Fig. 7-9b). The positions of these pseudobinary liquidus curves are shown for several pressures. Note that increased pressure depresses its eutectic temperature, as shown, because of increased water in its predominantly silicate melt that cannot be shown in this kind of projection except for changes in *ab*:*qz* ratios. Face *or-qz-w* is similar if the dissociation of K-feldspar to leucite plus quartz is ignored.

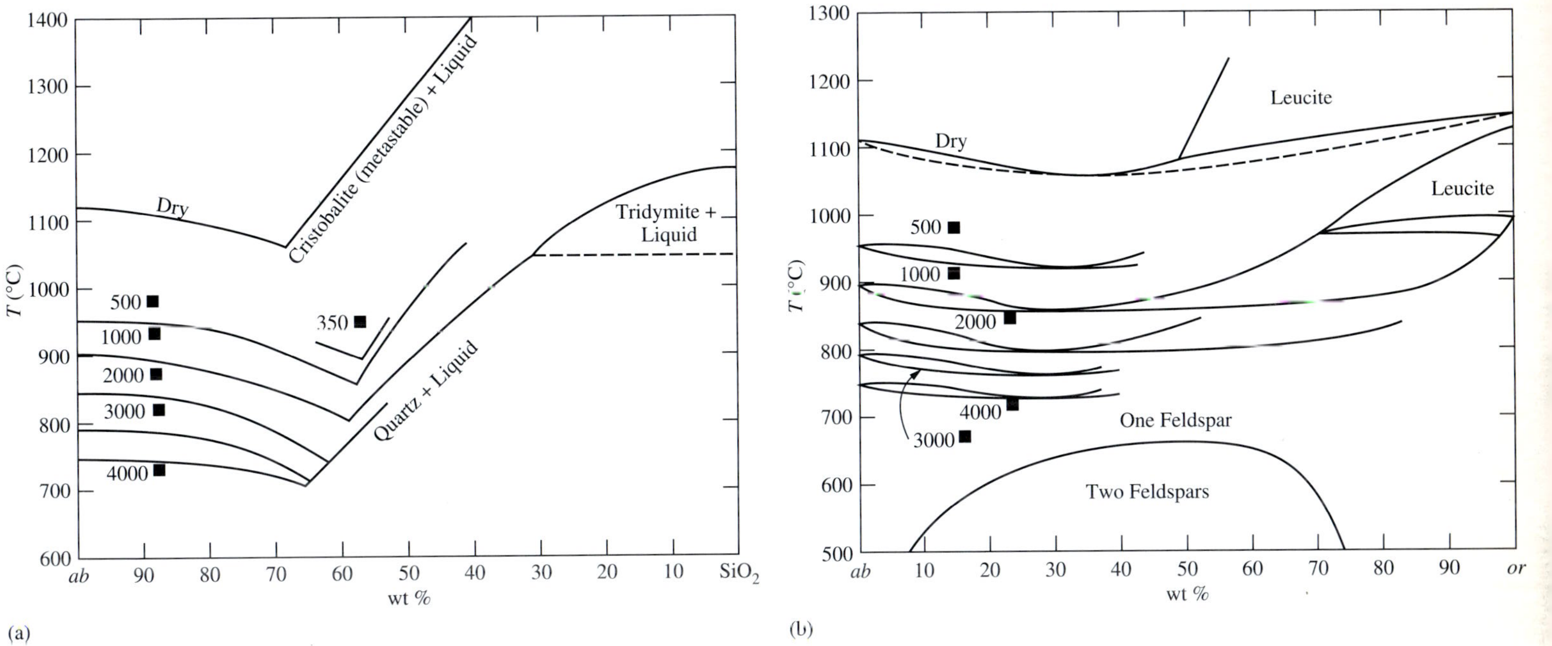

FIGURE 7-9 Systems boundary to the granite system. (a) The system $ab - qz - w$ projected onto the anhydrous plane. This system shows a eutectic composition that shifts toward the albite corner with lower temperatures with increased pressure in the presence of excess water. (b) The system $ab - or - w$ projected onto the anhydrous plane. This system shows a minimum that shifts to lower temperatures and toward the albite corner with increased pressure in the presence of excess water. Note the exsolution solvus dome in the subsolidus region. (After O. F. Tuttle and N. L. Bowen, *Origin of Granite in the Light of Experimental Studies*, Memoir 74. Boulder, CO: The Geological Society of America, 1958, Figs. 17, 20.)

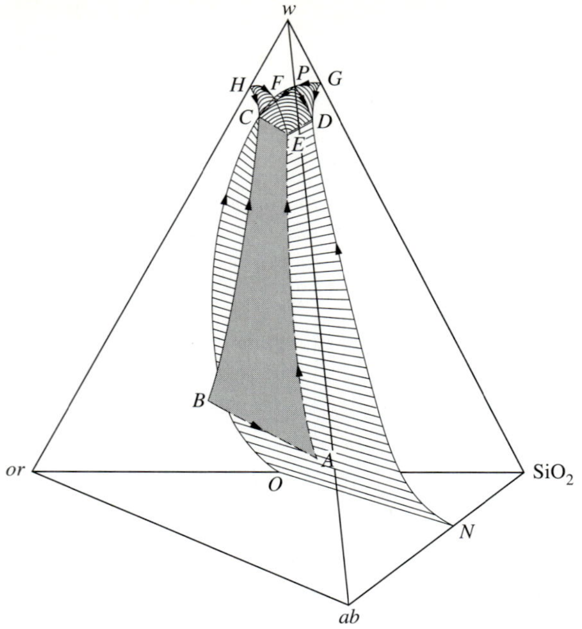

FIGURE 7-10 Schematic equilibrium phase diagram for the quaternary system albite (*ab*)-orthoclase (*or*)-silica (SiO_2)-water (*w*). (After O. F. Tuttle and N. L. Bowen, *Origin of Granite in the Light of Experimental Studies*, Memoir 74. Boulder, CO: The Geological Society of America, 1958, Fig. 29.)

Face *ab-or-w* may also be projected onto the anhydrous face of its polythermal composition prism (Fig. 7-9a). Pseudobinary ternary minimum liquid compositions also shift their *ab*:*or* ratios with increasing water in predominantly silicate melts resulting from increase in pressure. At water pressures higher than those shown, the liquidus-solidus loop intersects the solvus dome, converting the low-pressure minimum into a high-pressure ternary eutectic point. Note that these projections apply only to cases where melts are saturated with water and where a vapor phase is present. This experimental fact is often reported as $P_{H_2O} = P_{total}$, but treating a component as an intensive variable does not make it one.

Now consider quaternary relationships with regard to these ternary faces (Fig. 7-10). As water contents of melts in equilibrium with alkali feldspar crystal solution and quartz increase with increasing pressure, boundary *ON* generates a plane in this composition tetrahedron representing compositions of silicate melts with dissolved water in equilibrium with alkali feldspar and quartz. Point *A* represents the composition of a quaternary liquid that is in equilibrium with alkali feldspars at the maximum on the solvus dome and with quartz. At pressures and water

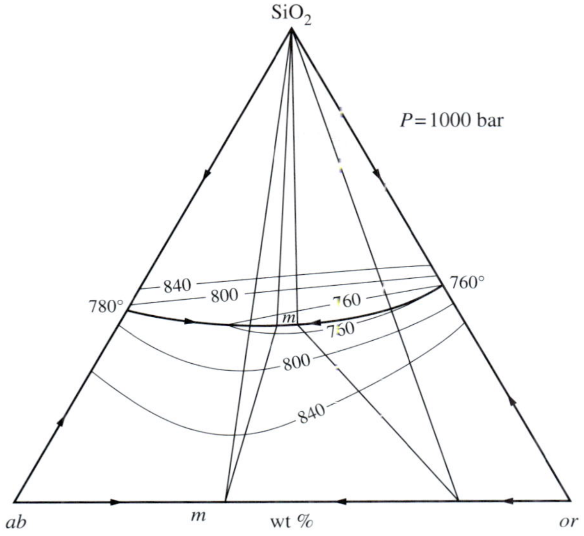

FIGURE 7-11 Liquidus surface for the system *ab-or-qz-w*. Liquid compositions are projected onto the anhydrous base of the composition tetrahedron. Liquidus surface in the presence of excess water at a pressure of 10 MPa (1 kbar). A cotectic thermal valley with a minimum connects eutectic compositions in *ab-qz-w* and *or-qz-w*. Liquidus surface indicated by isothermal contour lines. Two three-phase triangles for feldspar-quartz-liquid indicate the location of the minimum. Increased water pressure shifts the minimum away from SiO_2 and toward lower temperatures (After O. F. Tuttle and N. L. Bowen, *Origin of Granite in the Light of Experimental Studies*, Memoir 74. Boulder, CO: The Geological Society of America, 1958, Fig. 23.)

contents higher than this point, this system has a cotectic curve where the aqueous phase is in equilibrium with albite-rich alkali feldspar, orthoclase-rich alkali feldspar, quartz, and water vapor.

Plane *ABCE* represents liquid compositions in equilibrium with two alkali feldspar crystal solutions. Line *AE* represents liquid compositions in equilibrium with two alkali feldspars and quartz. Crystallization of anhydrous minerals drives liquid compositions along this line to lower and lower temperatures. Point *E*, in actuality very close to *w*, is the quaternary eutectic point involving six phases: albite, orthoclase, quartz, ice, water, and water vapor. Note that all compositions not on the anhydrous base of this composition tetrahedron are in equilibrium with a vapor phase.

This haplogranite system may also be portrayed as a pseudoternary system by projecting liquid compositions from the water apex to the anhydrous base of this composition tetrahedron (Fig. 7-11). In this case water, a chemical component is incorporated into pressure, an intensive

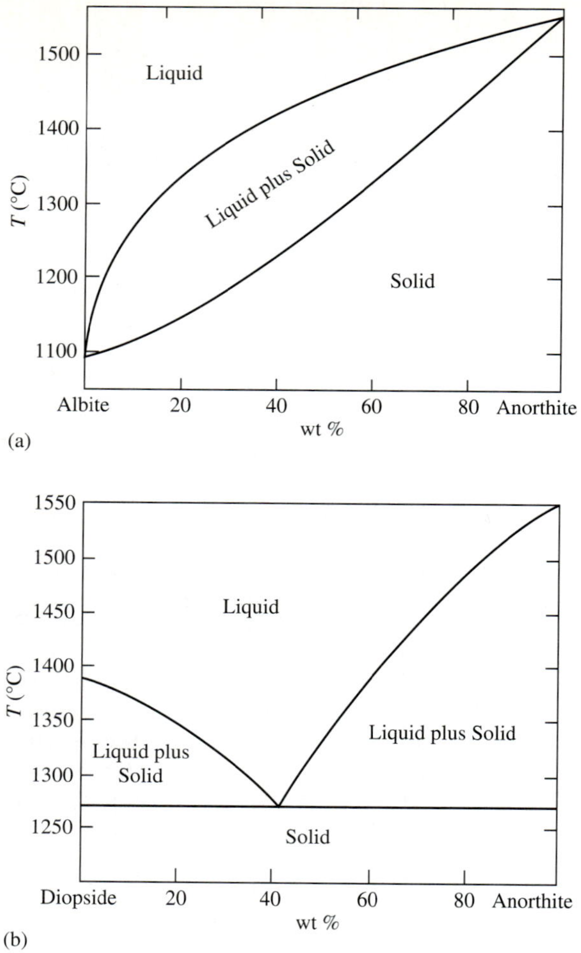

FIGURE 7-12 **Binary systems albite-anorthite and anorthite-diopside. (a) Phase relationships for plagioclase at atmospheric pressure. Upper curve is the liquidus, representing the highest temperature at which solids can exist, and lower curve is solidus, representing the lowest temperature at which liquids can exist. (b) Melting curves for diopside-anorthite at atmospheric pressure. Crystallization drives liquid compositions toward the eutectic point. (After N. L. Bowen, *The Evolution of the Igneous Rocks*. Princeton: Princeton University Press, 1928.)**

variable, as P_{H_2O} (= P_{total}). Projected phase relationships may then be plotted for a variety of pressures. Projected minima at various pressures plot along the axis of most abundant rock compositions as determined by Bowen and Tuttle. One may reasonably conclude cause and effect; most felsic rocks represent crystallization from crustal magmas having minimum melt compositions. Felsic igneous rocks not lying along this trend commonly contain undissolved crystals, called xenocrysts, in equilibrium with a minimum melt.

Haplobasalt Basalt is the most abundant igneous rock in the earth's crust, constituting most of the oceanic crust, and occurring as extensive flows on the continental crust. Gabbro, its phaneritic counterpart, intrudes crustal rocks as dikes, sills, and plutons in many parts of the crust. Essential minerals of basalt-gabbro are plagioclase and pyroxene with olivine, magnetite, a feldspathoid, or quartz as accessory minerals. N. L. Bowen first presented experimental results on basalt crystallization based on phase relationships in the ternary system albite-anorthite-diopside, a haplobasalt. This simplified system is a reasonable first approximation to real basalts even though it ignores iron and silica saturation.

Consider first the three boundary binary systems, *ab-an*, *ab-di*, *an-di*, to the ternary system *ab-an-di*. At atmospheric pressure the system *ab-an* shows complete crystalline miscibility (Fig. 7-12, compare Fig. 6-4). Although details of this phase diagram are different at high pressures with H_2O or CO_2 dissolved in the liquid, the general relationships are the same, making this diagram applicable to basalts and gabbros. This liquidus-solidus loop indicates that whenever plagioclase crystals are in equilibrium with a plagioclase melt, crystals are *an*-rich, compared with *ab*-rich liquids.

The system *an-di* shows crystalline immiscibility with a eutectic composition and temperature at atmospheric pressure (Fig. 7-12, compare Fig. 6-2). Phase relationships between *ab* and *di* are similar to those between *an* and *di*, except that this eutectic composition is close to *ab* at a temperature of 1100°C at atmospheric pressure.

Consider now a liquidus surface in the haplobasalt ternary system *ab-an-di* (Fig. 7-13). A cotectic thermal valley divides this liquidus surface into two fields of primary crystallization. On the *ab-an* side, a plagioclase crystallizes first and drives liquid compositions toward the cotectic thermal valley. If crystallization results from cooling, plagioclase crystals continuously change composition toward *ab*, liquid compositions follow a curving path across this liquidus surface (compare Fig. 6-9a). Melt compositions on the *di* side are also driven toward this cotectic thermal valley directly away from the *di* apex. A melt composition on the cotectic thermal valley is in equilibrium with two crystalline phases, pure *di* and a plagioclase. These relationships may be represented by three-phase triangles, two of which are shown in Fig. 7-13.

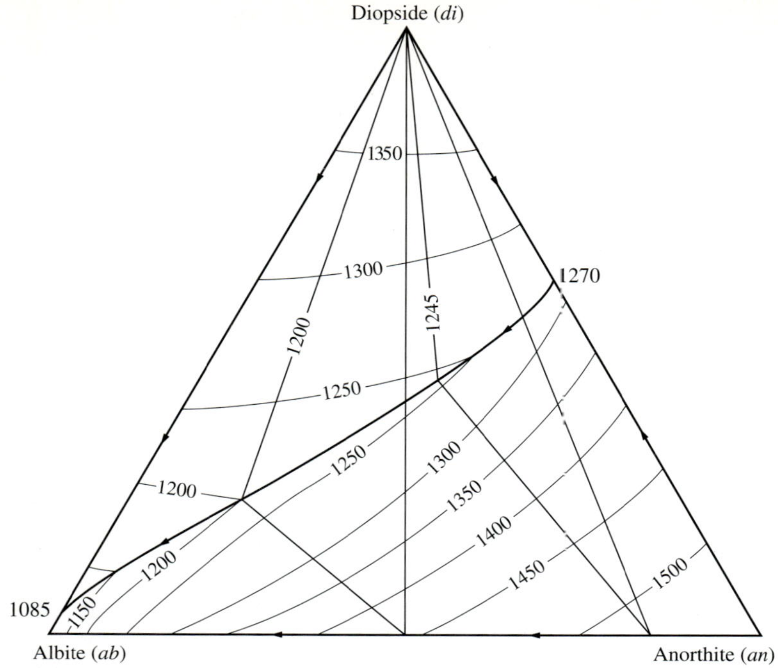

FIGURE 7-13 Haplobasalt system albite-anorthite-diopside at atmospheric pressure. Liquidus surface contoured isothermally. A cotectic thermal valley that represents the boundary between fields of primary crystallization of plagioclase and of diopside extends from eutectic compositions in *di-an* and in *di-ab*. Two isothermal three-phase triangles are shown. (After N. L. Bowen, *The Evolution of the Igneous Rocks*. Princeton: Princeton University Press, 1928.)

Note several petrologic relationships evident from this liquidus surface of a haplobasalt. First, equilibrium crystallization in this system yields mineral assemblages resembling real basalts and gabbros. Second, fractional crystallization with segregation of early plagioclase crystals can produce a relatively pure plagioclase rock, anorthosite. Third, residual melts produced by fractional crystallization become progressively more siliceous and feldspathic, a trend observed in successive rocks in many magma series.

Quaternary (Four-Component) Basalts Natural basalts, and closely related andesites, differ significantly among themselves because of silica over- and undersaturation and the presence of iron, which may be either divalent and mimic Mg^{2+} or trivalent. Silica oversaturation leads to quartz as an accessory, whereas undersaturation leads to olivine or a feldspathoid mineral as an accessory. Although some ferric iron follows Mg, it also

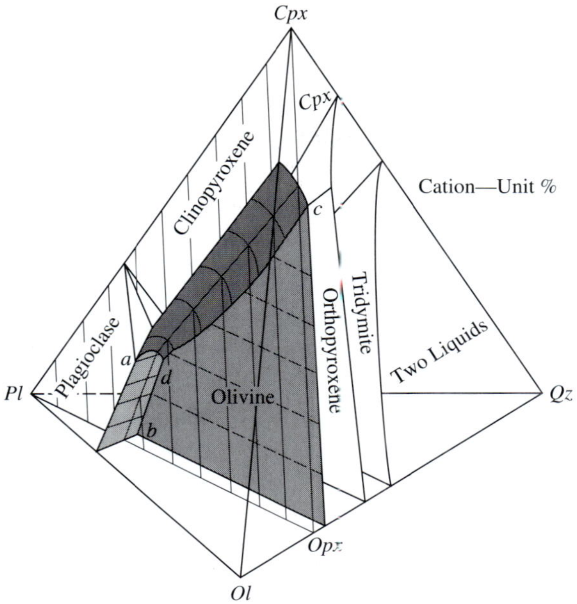

FIGURE 7-14 **Basalt system. (After T. N. Irvine, in H. S. Yoder (ed.), *The Evolution of the Igneous Rocks*. Princeton: Princeton University Press, 1979, Fig. 9-1, p. 249.)**

substitutes for Al or leads to the presence of magnetite, which lowers that amount of Fe^{2+} available for ferromagnesian minerals.

Some of these differences in natural basalts and andesites may be represented by the pseudoquaternary system olivine-clinopyroxene-plagioclase-quartz (Fig. 7-14). This system is not truly quaternary since plagioclase has variable *an* content that changes during crystallization and since Fe^{2+}:Mg ratios vary. In addition, clinopyroxene (augite) contains Ca. In constructing this pseudoquaternary composition tetrahedron, however, T. N. Irvine took into account abundant laboratory phase equilibria results and field observations of real mineral and rock assemblages to adjust phase boundaries so as to represent best a large variety of basalts and andesites under near surface conditions.

Consider first the four faces of this composition tetrahedron (compare Fig. 6-15). Faces *qz-pl-cpx* and *pl-ol-cpx* are liquidus surfaces with ternary eutectic points (compare Fig. 6-8b). Faces *qz-pl-ol* and *qz-cpx-ol* each have an incongruently melting binary compound, *opx* (hypersthene), along their common *qz-ol* edge (compare Fig. 6-9a). Thus, *opx* composition does not lie within the primary crystallization area for *opx* on either of these faces.

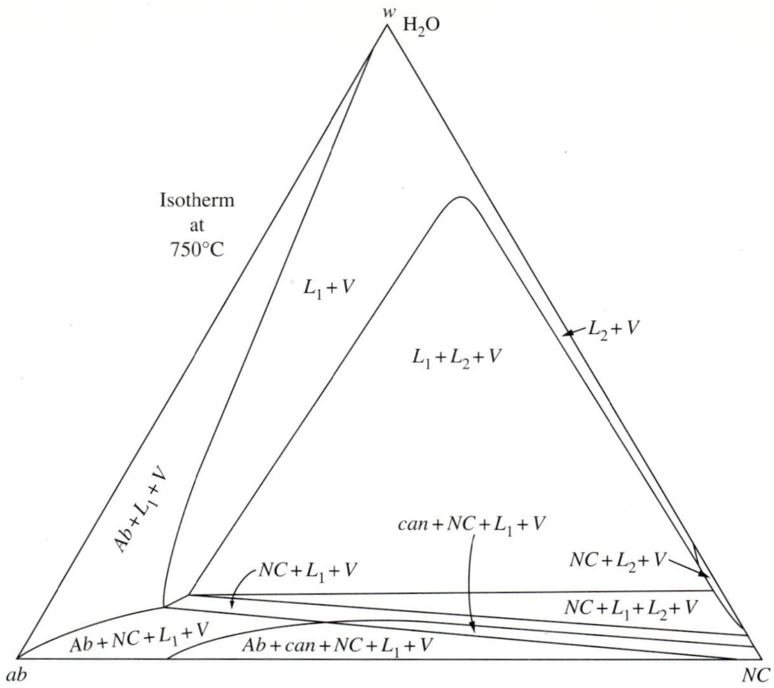

FIGURE 7-15 Immiscibility between silicate and carbonate magmas. Isothermal, isobaric section through the system *ab-NC-w* at 100 MPa (1000 bar) and 750°C is shown. Abbreviations: *NC* = Na_2CO_3; *can* = cancrinite; *ab* = albite; L_1 = silicate magma; L_2 = carbonate magma. The miscibility gap between these two magmas disappears below 700°C. (After A. F. Koster van Groos and P. J. Wyllie, *Amer. Jour. Sci.* 266(1968): p. 957.)

Most basalt and andesite (gabbro and diorite) compositions lie near the five-phase invariant point within this tetrahedron (*d* in Fig. 7-14), where magma coexists with olivine, plagioclase, orthopyroxene, and clinopyroxene. Therefore, only small changes in rock composition can cause significant changes in the order of mineral appearance during crystallization; any one of these four mineral phases can crystallize first. Under conditions of fractional crystallization, large differences in evolving melts can result from small differences in initial magma composition because different crystals fractionate early. Such diversity is found in basalts and basalt-related rocks.

Immiscible Melts Some liquids, such as alcohol and water, mix in all proportions; others, such as oil and water, separate into two immiscible liquid phases. A concept of liquid immiscibility in magmas has been invoked repeatedly, but disputed widely, in attempts to account for some rock and mineral associations not in apparent accordance with concepts of fractional melting and crystallization. Sulfide mineral accumulations toward the bottom of some gabbro plutons have long been interpreted as resulting from coagulation and sinking of dense, immiscible sulfide droplets exsolved from a parent silicate melt.

Where carbonatite lavas have been observed and where carbonatite plutons have been studied in detail, they are found in association with silicate rocks very low in silica and rich in alkalis and with host rocks pervasively altered, or fenitized, by alkali-rich hydrous fluorocarbonate fluids. Alkali magmatic rocks, carbonatites, and fenitized country rocks are distinct, which leads to a possible existence of three distinctly different fluid phases.

Three immiscible fluid phases in the system $NaAlSi_3O_8—Na_2CO_3—H_2O$ are (1) silicate melt saturated with vapor and carbonate, (2) carbonate melt saturated with silicate and vapor, and (3) vapor saturated with silicate and carbonate (Fig. 7-15). Silicate and carbonate liquids could crystallize as alkali-rich silicate igneous rock and alkali-rich carbonate igneous rock, respectively, while vapor given off fenitizes the country rock with Na_2O, H_2O, and CO_2 (plus F, which is generally associated with such processes, but ignored in this experimental treatment).

Although for many years geologists working on Lapland's Kiruna and associated magnetite deposits reported intrusive relationships between this magnetite and host silicate rocks, doubts about a possibility of existence of magnetite-rich magmas at geologically reasonable temperatures and pressures persisted. These doubts continued even after other geologists reported magnetite lava flows high in the Chilean Andes. Phase relationships on a liquidus surface in the system Fe—C—O at 50 MPa (500 bar) pressure reveal magnetite-rich melts at temperatures as low as 815°C (Fig. 7-16). Crystallization of such melts would yield igneous rocks composed predominantly of magnetite with a small amount of graphite. At temperatures below the solidus, graphite can react with CO_2 to form siderite, a common accessory mineral in magnetite deposits of alleged igneous origin.

Field relationships indicate that nelsonites, which are dikes of apatite-rutile or apatite-ilmenite, intrude silicate host rocks. Laboratory experiments reveal compositions of liquid immiscibility when either TiO_2 or P_2O_5 is present in silicate melts in excess of a few weight percent. Laboratory experiments do not prove that a chemical process, such as fractional crystallization or unmixing of immiscible liquids, occurred during formation of some rock, only that it is possible. When coupled with substantiating field observations, they lend credence to theories about origins of rocks. Such experiments demonstrate that associations of minerals found in igneous rocks may be interpreted as the result of crystallization from a magma, according to laws of chemistry and physics, and that such crystallization can be approximated and illustrated by laboratory experiments. This discussion of igneous mineral genesis is not exhaustive, as

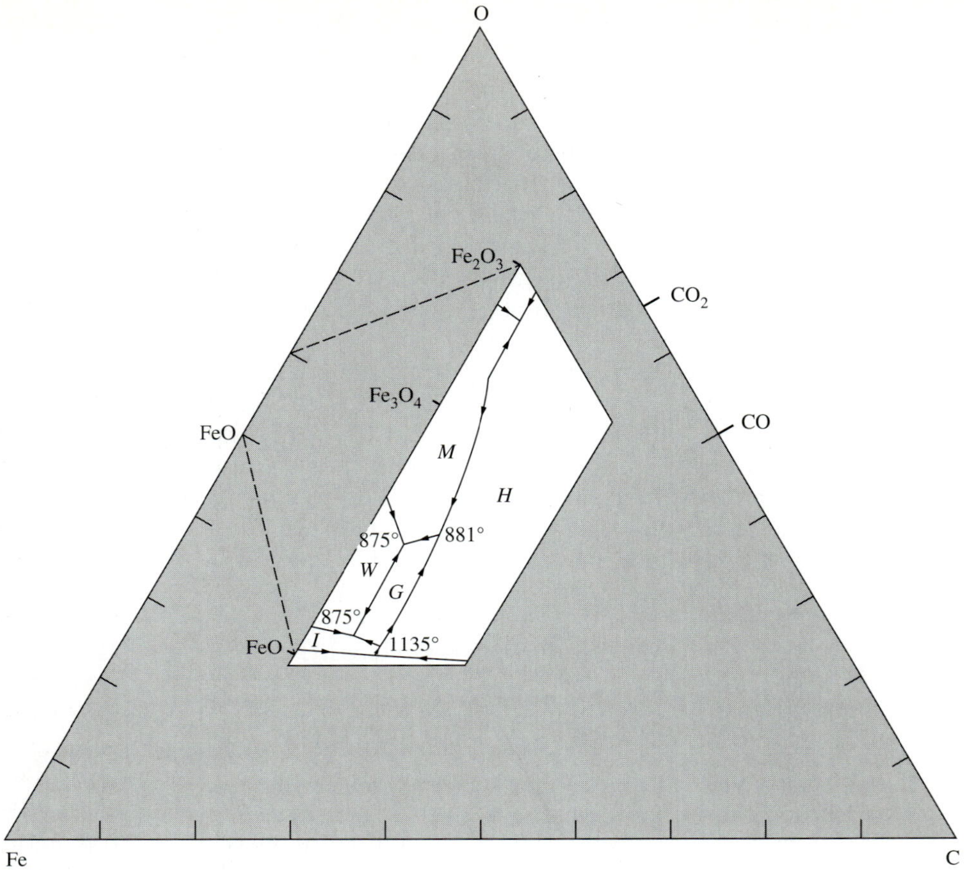

FIGURE 7-16 Liquids in the system Fe—C—O. Abbreviations: *I* = iron; *G* = graphite; *W* = wustite; *M* = magnetite; *H* = hematite. Cotectic thermal valleys are shown with arrows indicating falling temperatures. Low temperatures of eutectic compositions indicate that iron-rich liquids can exist in this system at geologically reasonable temperatures. Pressure is 50 MPa (500 bar). (After J. R. Weidner, *Can. Min.* 20(1982): p. 555.)

no mention has been made of many igneous rocks classified in Fig. 7-4 or of many rare igneous rocks found in the earth's crust. However, the laws of heterogeneous equilibria may be used to account for their origins as well. Nor are these principles confined to earth, since much of what we know about the history of the moon also derives from analyses of lunar samples and experimental simulations of these rocks.

Magma Sources Consider now sources of magmas. Two sites may be considered for magma genesis—specific locations in the earth's crust and mantle. Many sediments (Sec. 7-3) and sedimentary rocks contain the constituents of granite. The granite minimum melting curve intersects continental geotherms where crust has been tectonically thickened or has rifted to be heated from below by rising mantle basaltic magma. Under these conditions, partial melting of continental rock yields a magma having a composition corresponding to a minimum in the system *ab-or-qz-w*. If pressure remains constant, additional heat increases magma amounts isothermally until, under equilibrium conditions, one phase (for instance, orthoclase) disappears. Fractional melting, however, continues until one component (for instance, potassium) is consumed, a process producing more minimum-melt magma from a rock than does equilibrium melting.

Magmas thus generated may then rise to higher levels in the crust and there crystallize as granites or to the surface to extrude as rhyolites. Crustal temperatures are too low to yield much magma more mafic than granite, but minimum-melt granite magma, carrying with it undissolved plagioclase and mafic minerals, may crystallize as igneous rock intermediate in composition between granite and gabbro.

Studies of xenoliths from kimberlites and basalts, of stony meteorites, and of synthetically produced assemblages in experimental laboratories, along with seismic and gravitational properties, indicate that the upper mantle is composed predominantly of peridotite (Fig. 7-4). Most mantle-derived xenoliths are eclogites and garnet- and spinel-bearing lherzolites (a peridotite containing orthopyroxene and clinopyroxene). Eclogites, which consist of garnet and pyroxene, have the chemical composition of basalt. Other mantle minerals of importance include olivine, amphibole, phlogopite, and dolomite.

Evidence for mantle vapor phases necessary for stability of hydroxyl and carbonate phases comes from studies of fluid inclusions in xenolith minerals. Experiment results can be interpreted to indicate that solidii for peridotite plus vapor intersects geotherms at the very depths where geophysical data may be interpreted to indicate that interstitial molten material occurs. This is the asthenosphere.

Variations in depth of source as well as variations in vapor composition thus give rise to observed variation in basaltic magmas rising from the mantle to the earth's surface (Fig. 7-17). Data indicating that kimberlite, lamproite, and carbonatite magmas are also generated in the asthenosphere suggest horizontal and vertical variations in mantle composition. Additional chemical and mineralogical variations arise where oceanic crustal rock is subducted into the mantle where it compresses into eclogite. Distinctive magmas of island arcs appear to be generated when siliceous aqueous fluids, liberated by dehydration of subducted oceanic basaltic crust, interact with overriding spinel peridotite to permit partial melting yielding andesitic magmas.

Although different geologic processes are involved in magma generation, partial fusion according to the laws of heterogeneous equilibrium may be employed to account for their composition. Fractional or equilibrium crystallization processes, as outlined in this section and in Chap. 6, may be used to account for mineral assemblages found in igneous rocks.

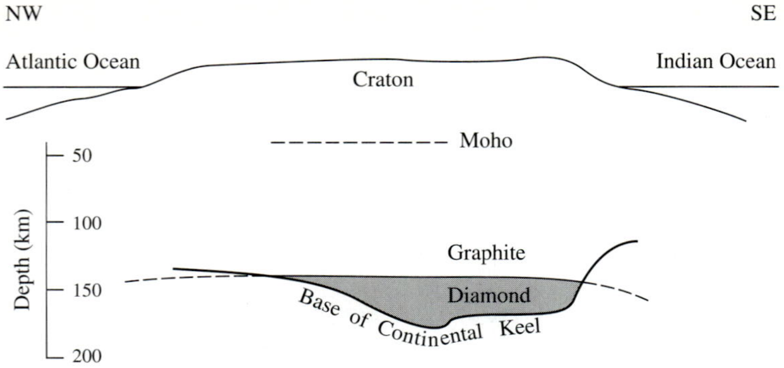

FIGURE 7-17 Cross section of African crust showing locations of magma sources. (After F. R. Boyd and J. J. Gurney, *Science* 232(1986): 472.)

Trace Element Distribution A modern method of tracking magmatic evolution of rocks involves detecting and measuring increase and decrease of trace elements in an evolved rock series. During melting or crystallization some trace elements concentrate in crystal structures, whereas others concentrate in the melt phase; hence, trace-element contents can tell us something about degree of melting of a magma source area. This trace-element partitioning may be represented by a distribution coefficient (K_D), the ratio of the concentration of an element (X) in a mineral to its concentration in an adjacent melt:

$$K_D = X(\text{mineral})/X(\text{melt}).$$

When $K_D < 1$, an element concentrates in the melt phase; when $K_D > 1$, an element is depleted from a melt. For example, when olivine and pyroxene are crystallizing from a magma, potassium ($K_D \approx 0.001–0.1$) is excluded from those crystalline phases to concentrate in the melt phase. On the other hand, Ni ($K_D \approx 1–10$) is depleted from a melt to concentrate in those crystalline phases. The same is true for partial melting, since these distribution coefficients are the same. Consider the behavior of Ba. If the crystallizing phase is hornblende, Ba ($K_D \approx 0.5$) tends to concentrate in the melt phase. If the crystallizing phase is K-feldspar, however, Ba ($K_D \approx 6$) is depleted from the melt and concentrates in the feldspar structure.

By monitoring trace-element distributions in minerals, mineral scientists can decipher details about melting and crystallization histories of magmas and rocks that are otherwise obscure from studies of mineral assemblages alone.

7-3 SEDIMENTARY MINERAL AND ROCK FORMATION

Minerals formed in magmatic and other high-temperature environments are not, in general, stable near the earth's surface in the presence of molecular oxygen and water. Reduced ions oxidize, anhydrous minerals hydrate, and soluble ions dissolve, each process causing destruction of crystal structures of high-temperature minerals. New minerals stable near the earth's surface form from remnants of unstable minerals (Table 7-3).

Ionic Potentials Understanding mineral behavior near the earth's surface may be approached from a view of geochemical behavior of their constituent ions. This behavior may be summarized by their ionic potential—ionic charge divided by ionic radius (Fig. 7-18). Chemical elements having ionic potentials less than 3 tend to be soluble in waters near the earth's surface, whereas those with potentials greater than 12 tend to form soluble hydroxyl complexes. Hydrolysate elements have ionic potentials ranging from 3 to 12 and tend to be relatively insoluble. Native elements exist because they, too, are relatively insoluble in near-surface waters.

Minerals containing water-soluble ions lose them to rain and groundwater, causing collapse of any remaining insoluble crystal structure. Ions having more than one valence state, of which Fe predominates (but Mn, U, and S are also included), react with free oxygen to go from a lower to a higher oxidation state. Removal of one or more electrons from an ion not only increases its charge but also reduces its size. Oxidation upsets structural electrostatic neutrality and decreases ionic coordination with a single operation, either result being sufficient to break up a crystal structure.

Some minerals formed in an anhydrous environment react directly with water to become hydrated minerals. Although such simple hydration reactions between high-temperature minerals and water are rare, minerals formed near Earth's surface from breakdown products of anhydrous high-temperature minerals include many hydrated silicates, predominantly layered silicates, such as clays and micas.

Rock Weathering Processes that convert high-temperature minerals to sedimentary minerals may be illustrated by chemical weathering of a granodiorite, the continental crust's average rock. Minerals to be considered, then, are quartz, microcline, a plagioclase, and a ferromagnesian mineral such as biotite, hornblende, or hypersthene. Quartz is relatively insoluble; Si^{4+} is an hydrolysate element. Both Al^{3+} and Si^{4+} in feldspars are hydrolysate elements, but K^+ is a soluble cation. Removal of K^+ from microcline causes collapse of this framework silicate structure, which, under humid temperate conditions rearranges itself into a layered structure. Microcline weathering may be represented simplistically by the equilibrium chemical reaction

$$2KAlSi_3O_8 + 2H_2O \rightarrow Al_2Si_2O_5(OH)_4 + K_2O + 4SiO_2,$$
$$\text{microcline} + \text{water} \rightarrow \text{kaolinite} + \text{potash}_{(sol'n)} + \text{silica}_{(sol'n)}.$$

TABLE 7-3 Sedimentary Minerals*

Sulfur	S_8
Carbon	C
Silica	
Quartz, chalcedony	SiO_2
Opal	$SiO_2 \cdot nH_2O$
Feldspars	
Microcline	$KAlSi_3O_8$
Albite	$NaAlSi_3O_8$
Micas	
Muscovite	$KAl_2(AlSi_3)O_{10}(OH,F)_2$
Smectite	$(Na,Ca)_{0.33}(Al,Mg)_2Si_4O_{10}(OH)_2 \cdot nH_2O$
Glauconite	$(K,Na)(Fe^{3+},Al,Mg)_2(Si,Al)_4O_{10}(OH)_2$
Vermiculite	$(Mg,Fe,Al)_3(Si,Al)_4O_{10}(OH)_2 \cdot 4H_2O$
Clays	
Kaolinite, nacrite, dickite	$Al_4Si_4O_{10}(OH)_8$
Halloysite	$Al_4Si_4O_{10}(OH)_8 \cdot nH_2O$
Oxides	
Hematite	Fe_2O_3
Pyrolusite	MnO_2
Romanechite	$BaMn^{2+}Mn_8^{4+}O_{16}(OH)_4$
Rutile	TiO_2
Magnetite	$FeOFe_2O_3$
Hydroxides and oxyhydroxides	
Goethite, lepidocrite	FeO(OH)
Diaspore, boehmite	AlO(OH)
Manganite	MnO(OH)
Gibbsite	$Al(OH)_3$
Sulfides	
Marcasite, pyrite	FeS_2
Sulfates	
Gypsum	$CaSO_4 \cdot 2H_2O$
Anhydrite	$CaSO_4$
Halides	
Halite	NaCl
Sylvite	KCl
Carnallite	$KMgCl_3 \cdot 6H_2O$
Carbonates	
Calcite, aragonite	$CaCO_3$
Dolomite	$CaMg(CO_3)_2$
Borates	
Borax	$Na_2B_4O_7 \cdot 10H_2O$
Phosphates	
Apatite, collophane	$Ca_5(PO_4)_3(F,OH)$

*Within each mineral group, more common minerals precede less common ones.

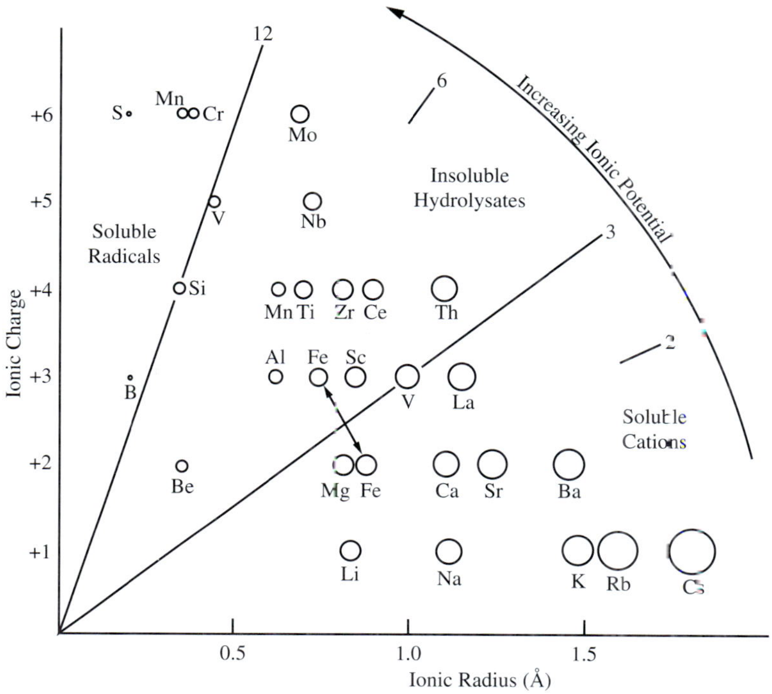

FIGURE 7-18 Ionic potentials of chemical elements. Ionic potential is ionic charge divided by ionic radius. Ionic potential less than 3 indicates soluble cations, greater than 12 soluble radicals, between 3 and 12 insoluble hydrolysates.

Consider a slight digression. Hydrocarbons burn according to the equation

$$CH_4 + 2O_2 \rightarrow CO_2 + 2H_2O,$$
$$\text{methane} + \text{oxygen} \rightarrow \text{carbon dioxide} + \text{water vapor}.$$

These gases are colorless, but look at a flame. You can see it because real combustion is never complete. Smoke, soot, nitrous oxides, and carbon monoxide are generated by any real flame, although varying burning conditions influence just how combustion takes place. Similar partial reaction occurs in real weathering of minerals.

Detailed analyses of minerals formed from K-feldspar reveal that a kaolin mineral is not the first phase to form during weathering. First, solution occurs preferentially at high-strain locations such as dislocations and twin boundaries. Removal of K^+ collapses this aluminosilicate framework to allophane, an amorphous hydrous material. From this allophane a smectite (Table 7-3) may form with its {001} parallel to the microcline {001}. This smectite in turn recrystallizes to a mica, possibly illite or sericite, plus kaolinite. Some of these recrystallizations have high enough activation energies that intermediate phases may persist for geologically long periods of time. Plagioclase weathering appears to follow a similar path but at higher rates; the higher proportion of alumina tetrahedra in intermediate plagioclase domains may be more rapidly attacked by weathering solutions than are alkali-feldspar end members with their 1:3 alumina : silica ratios.

Since weathering products include many layered silicates, you might expect that crystallographic orientation of parent micas and chlorites would control this orientation in their breakdown products. Muscovite weathers first by loss of K^+ from alternate interlayers resulting first in muscovite interlayered with vermiculite and subsequently with the smectite beidellite (Table 7-3). Further K^+ removal yields pure beidellite. Biotite follows a slightly different path because its octahedral layer contains soluble Mg^{2+} and oxidizable Fe^{2+}. As K^+ leaches from biotite, hydrobiotite layers form followed by biotite-vermiculite interlayering. Octahedral Fe^{2+} oxidizes and hydrates in situ to goethite with its octahedral chains parallel to those in the biotite parent structure. Octahedral Mg^{2+} may temporarily form brucitelike layers as tetrahedral layers rearrange themselves into kaolinite, still maintaining structural continuity.

Pyroxenes and amphiboles (single- and double-chain silicates) weather first to talclike layers in crystallographic continuity and then to talc plus goethite. Olivine, with its independent silica tetrahedra, weathers to iddingsite, a mixture of the smectite saponite (Table 7-3) plus goethite, generally beginning along channels parallel to the [010] direction of olivine. This smectite subsequently may alter to kaolinite.

All these weathering reactions have in common the fact that their initial and secondary products are not stable phases under surface or near-surface pressure, temperature, and geochemical conditions. Although smectites persist for geologically long periods of time, some evidence indicates that they may have no stability field at all. Why then do these and other metastable phases appear in most weathering reactions? When detailed studies reveal which phases are thermodynamically stable under a set of conditions, why do these reactions appear to behave so badly? Toward the end of the 19th century, W. Z. Ostwald suggested a reason in the form of the Ostwald step rule. He observed that when one reaction can result in several products, the phase most likely to appear is not the most stable one with the lowest free energy (G) but the next lowest one with the smallest change in free energy. Thus, reactions proceed downward toward stability stepwise in terms of free-energy change (ΔG) with mineral species of each step controlled by reaction rates (kinetics). In silicate weathering, you can understand this rule as a reaction product being governed by the least structural rearrangement occurring during the most favored reaction.

Since Fe^{2+} in ferromagnesian minerals is soluble and is unstable in the presence of free oxygen, two separate reactions may occur. Under reducing conditions, Fe^{2+} goes into aqueous solution, its ionic potential being between that of Mg^{2+} and Ca^{2+}. Organic acids in humid temperate soils keep Fe^{2+} reduced while it is carried away in solution. Under oxidizing conditions, Fe^{3+} is an hydrolysate element. Ideal oxidation of Fe^{2+} in igneous ferromagnesian minerals may be represented by

$$2FeO + (1/2)O_2 \rightarrow Fe_2O_3,$$
$$\text{ferrous iron} + \text{oxygen} \rightarrow \text{hematite}.$$

Several partial steps are possible when this reaction does not go to completion. The oxyhydroxides goethite [α-FeO(OH)], lepidocrocite [γ-FeO(OH)], or akaganeite [β-FeO(OH)] may crystallize as metastable phases. The rock limonite is a mixture of these and other hydroxides with adsorbed water. Additionally, Fe^{3+} may enter the structure of glauconite and vermiculite. Any Mn^{2+} behaves similarly to Fe^{2+}, although its oxides and oxyhydroxides are as yet poorly understood because of fine grain size, adsorbed cations, and admixed compounds.

Thus, minerals formed at and stable under conditions of high pressure and temperature weather to layered silicates, insoluble oxides or metastable oxyhydroxides, and soluble ionic species. Analysis of these phases is difficult because of their extremely fine particle sizes, commonly about 1 μm, and mixed layer stacking.

A kaolin mineral or other layered silicate has been considered so far to be the stable end product in chemical weathering. This is true for temperate and some tropical climates. For well-drained uplands in humid tropical climates, however, the end product is a mixture of gibbsite [$Al(OH)_3$], diaspore [α-AlO(OH)], and boehmite [γ-AlO(OH)]. This mixture, bauxite, is the major ore of aluminum. Bauxite mixed with hematite and clay is a residual tropical soil, laterite. Under conditions of alternate wetting and drying in tropical zones, bauxite minerals form directly from plagioclase as

$$2NaAlSi_3O_8 + CaAl_2Si_2O_8 + 6H_2O \rightarrow 4Al(OH)_3 + Na_2O + CaO + 8SiO_2,$$
$$\text{plagioclase} + \text{water} \rightarrow \text{gibbsite} + (\text{soda} + \text{lime} + \text{silica})_{(\text{sol'n})}$$

Carbonates Chemical reactions discussed in the foregoing paragraphs divide chemical elements of igneous minerals into two groups: soluble elements, which may be transported in solution, and insoluble elements and complexes, which may be left behind or transported physically.

Both Ca^{2+} and Mg^{2+} dissolve in aqueous solution as bicarbonate radicals. Atmospheric CO_2 reacts with rainwater to form carbonic acid:

$$CO_2 + H_2O \rightarrow H_2CO_3,$$

which dissociates in water as

$$H_2CO_3 \rightarrow H^+ + HCO_3^-.$$

Ca^{2+} leaches out of plagioclase and hornblende as

$$CaO + H_2CO_3 \rightarrow CaHCO_3^+ + OH^-.$$

Anything that tends to increase dissolved CO_2 thereby permits solution of more CaO. Anything that tends to decrease CO_2 causes precipitation of calcite from a saturated aqueous solution:

$$CaHCO_3^+ + HCO_3^- \rightleftharpoons CaCO_3 + CO_2 + H_2O$$

Addition of CO_2 drives this reaction to the left, and removal of CO_2 from a system drives it to the right. Cooling or increasing pressure promotes solution of Ca^{2+}, whereas warming or decreasing pressure causes carbonate precipitation from a saturated or supersaturated solution.

Sedimentary behavior of Ca^{2+} (and Mg^{2+}) is further complicated by living creatures that use it for carbonate skeletal material. Indeed, many limestones (and dolomites) are composed largely of accumulated skeletal material. Although ancient carbonate rocks are low-Mg calcite (<0.05 mole %) and dolomite, modern marine carbonate minerals are predominantly high-Mg (10–25 mole %) calcite and aragonite, derived mostly from skeletal materials. These modern minerals are not stable phases with respect to the ancient ones, another example of reaction rate rather than thermodynamic stability controlling product mineralogy.

Having established some chemical reactions by which sedimentary minerals weather from high-temperature and high-pressure minerals, now consider how these minerals combine to produce sedimentary rocks. Hydrolysate, intermediate, and end-produce minerals either concentrate as residual deposits or move by wind, water, or ice to shallow seas of continental margins or interiors. Soluble cations either crystallize in intermediate weathered minerals or move in solution to the world ocean. Where evaporation greatly exceeds water influx, dissolved ions concentrate to maximum solubility, then precipitate salts in evaporite deposits.

Diagenesis An unconsolidated sediment is not a rock. Changes must occur within a sediment to convert it into rock, the process of lithification. Diagenesis refers to all physical and chemical changes that may occur after sediment deposition but before onset of metamorphism or of another weathering cycle. Diagenetic temperatures and pressures range from those at the earth's surface to perhaps 300°C and 100 MPa (1 kbar), corresponding to less than approximately 10 km of burial in the earth's crust.

Early diagenesis occurs near the surface with chemical reactions occurring between sediments and bottom waters of oceans, estuaries, and lakes. These sediments also include any volcanic material brought in by wind or flowing water. Deep burial and compaction bring about chemical reactions between sediments and ascending pore waters; here diagenesis becomes transitional with metamorphism. Uplift and erosion of overlying sediment permits further diagenetic reaction resulting from descending meteoric waters carrying with them dissolved products of chemical weathering of overlying rock.

In sandstones, diagenetic changes are predominantly compaction and cementation. Common cements include quartz, carbonate minerals, and clay minerals. Pressure solution at contact areas releases silica for cementation as quartz, commonly occurring as overgrowths in crystallographic continuity with existing detrital quartz grains (oriented overgrowths).

Recrystallization may occur during diagenesis In limestones any sedimentary aragonite inverts to calcite. Originally magnesian calcite becomes purer by losing Mg^{2+} and gaining Ca^{2+} or converts to dolomite by gaining Mg^{2+} and losing Ca^{2+}. Volcanic glass devitrifies predominantly to montmorillonite and to zeolite minerals (Table 7-3). Evaporite deposits, which contain chemical precipitates resulting from evaporation of seawater or salt lakes, undergo simple to complex recrystallization and authigenesis. Authigenesis is nucleation and growth in situ of discrete grains, commonly euhedral, of new minerals. Hydrated minerals, such as gypsum, dehydrate, in this case to anhydrite.

Diagenetic changes in shales commonly produce authigenic minerals. Pyrite, calcite, dolomite, illite, palygorskite, sepiolite, chlorites, kaolinite, illite, glauconite, smectites, alkali-feldspars, and zeolites are common authigenic minerals. Sulfur may be present in sediments as SO_4^{2-}, H_2S, or HS^-. The reducing reactions that produce H_2S occur in the presence of organic matter and are bacterially mediated. Resulting anaerobic interstitial waters permit precipitation of sedimentary sulfide minerals, chiefly pyrite and marcasite [FeS_2], but mackinawite [$Fe_{1-x}S$] may be an intermediate phase. The source of iron is commonly metastable geothite or hematite.

Mineral Deposits Weathering and diagenesis of sulfide mineral deposits lead to distinctive iron-rich caps (*gossans* in Welsh, *colorados* in Spanish, or *Iseren Huts* in German) overlying enriched zones of ore. Oxidation of sulfide minerals produces H_2SO_4, which leaches soluble metals from ore minerals and transports them downward in aqueous solution. Neutralization under oxidizing conditions leads to deposition of nonsulfide minerals of these metals. For example, Cu dissolved from enargite [Cu_3AsS_4] or tetrahedrite-tennantite [$(Cu,Ag)_{10}(Fe,Zn)_2(Sb,As)_4S_{13}$] may be precipitated in atacamite [$Cu_2Cl(OH)_3$], azurite [$Cu_3(CO_3)_2(OH)_2$], or malachite [$Cu_2CO_3(OH)_2$]. Under reducing conditions, generally beginning at the water table, replacement of other sulfides by covelline (covellite) [CuS] or chalcocite [Cu_2S] forms a zone of supergene enrichment with metal contents of enriched ore up to 10 times that of any original vein.

Weathering of mineral deposits such as rare-element rich granite pegmatites results in concentration of resistate elements in soils above these rock bodies. Since granite pegmatites contain massive quartz cores, their presence is marked by accumulations of blocky quartz masses on the ground surface. Those pegmatites rich in Be, Sn, Li, and U, for instance, additionally have those elements concentrated in overlying residual soils. Thus, finding a few rare-element pegmatites among many barren ones is possible by means of soil samples instead of expensive drilling and trenching of each one.

7-4 METAMORPHIC MINERALS AND ROCKS

Metamorphism includes a range of processes, exclusive of weathering, which operate in the earth's crust and mantle to alter a solid rock, both mineralogically and texturally, as a result of changes from physical and chemical conditions of its origin. Metamorphism in response to rising temperatures is prograde; to falling temperatures, retrograde. At its low-temperature end, metamorphism is transitional with diagenesis of sedimentary rocks. At its high-temperature end, partial fusion of low-temperature melting components produces a rock that is partly metamorphic and partly magmatic, a migmatite. Indeed, determining whether a mineral crystallized from a magma or recrystallized in equilibrium with a magma without actually having dissolved in it may be extremely difficult in migmatites and some plutonic rocks of intermediate composition. These distinctions may be particularly difficult in the cases of sudden reactions such as those produced by meteorite impact. Sanidine spherules so produced are clearly igneous and deformation lamellae in quartz clearly metamorphic, but crystallization of coesite or stishovite may or may not involve an intervening melt phase.

Facies and Grades In addition to effects of pressure and temperature in metamorphic processes, chemical elements may move in or out of a rock during metamorphism. Transporting agents, metasomatic fluids, are predominantly H_2O with variable amounts of dissolved CO_2, HCl, HF, and H_2SO_4. Those chemical elements most susceptible to solution during weathering processes are the ones most commonly moved about during metasomatism. Thus, mineralogy of a metamorphic rock depends upon the chemical composition of its parent rock (sedimentary, igneous, or metamorphic protolith), the temperature and pressure under which it recrystallized, partial pressures of H_2O and CO_2, and any chemical changes wrought by metasomatism (Table 7-4). Note that if no iron-bearing mineral existed in its parent rock and if metasomatism brought in no iron, then no iron-bearing mineral is possible in a metamorphic rock regardless of physical conditions under which it formed.

Because a wide variety of igneous and sedimentary rocks and a wide variety of pressure-temperature environments exist in the earth's crust and mantle, an even wider variety of metamorphic rocks are derived from them. In 1915, Penti Eskola proposed a concept of metamorphic facies to

TABLE 7-4 Metamorphic Minerals*

Silica	
Quartz, coesite, stishovite	SiO_2
Feldspars	
Microcline, orthoclase	$KAlSi_3O_8$
Plagioclase series	
Albite	$NaAlSi_3O_8$
Anorthite	$CaAl_2Si_2O_8$
Pyroxenes	
Diopside	$CaMg(SiO_3)_2$
Enstatite	$MgSiO_3$
Augite	$Ca(Mg,Fe)(SiO_3)_2$
Jadeite	$NaAl(SiO_3)_2$
Hypersthene	$(Mg,Fe)SiO_3$
Pyroxenoid	
Wollastonite	$CaSiO_3$
Amphiboles	
Tremolite-actinolite	$Ca_2(Mg,Fe)_5Si_8O_{22}(OH)_2$
Anthophyllite	$(Mg,Fe)_7Si_8O_{22}(OH)_2$
Cummingtonite	$(Fe,Mg)_7Si_8O_{22}(OH)_2$
Hornblende	$Ca_2(Mg,Fe)_4Al(Si_7Al)O_{22}(OH,F)_2$
Glaucophane	$Na_2(Mg,Fe)_3Al_2Si_8O_{22}(OH)_2$
Olivine series	
Forsterite	Mg_2SiO_4
Fayalite	Fe_2SiO_4
Layered silicates	
Muscovite	$KAl_2(Si_3Al)O_{10}(OH,F)_2$
Biotite	$K(Mg,Fe)_3(Al,Fe)Si_3O_{10}(OH,F)_2$
Serpentine	$Mg_6Si_4O_{10}(OH)_2$
Chlorite group	$Mg_5Al(Si_3AlO_{10})(OH)_8$
Talc	$Mg_3Si_4O_{10}(OH)_2$
Garnets	
Almandine	$Fe_3Al_2(SiO_4)_3$
Grossular	$Ca_3Al_2(SiO_4)_3$
Pyrope	$Mg_3Al_2(SiO_4)_3$
Andradite	$Ca_3Al_2(SiO_4)_3$
Aluminum silicates	
Kyanite, andalusite, sillimanite	Al_2SiO_5
Epidotes	
Clinozoisite, zoisite	$Ca_2Al_3(SiO_4)(Si_2O_7)O(OH)$
Epidote	$Ca_2(Al,Fe)_3(SiO_4)(Si_2O_7)O(OH)$
Carbonates	
Calcite	$CaCO_3$
Dolomite	$CaMg(CO_3)_2$
Other silicates	
Analcime	$NaAlSi_2O_6 \cdot H_2O$
Zeolites	
Chabazite	$Ca_2Al_4Si_8O_{24} \cdot 13H_2O$
Laumontite	$Ca_4Al_8Si_{16}O_{48} \cdot 16H_2O$
Heulandite	$(Ca,Na_2)_4Al_8Si_{28}O_{72} \cdot 24H_2O$

*Within each mineral group, the more important minerals are listed before the less important ones.

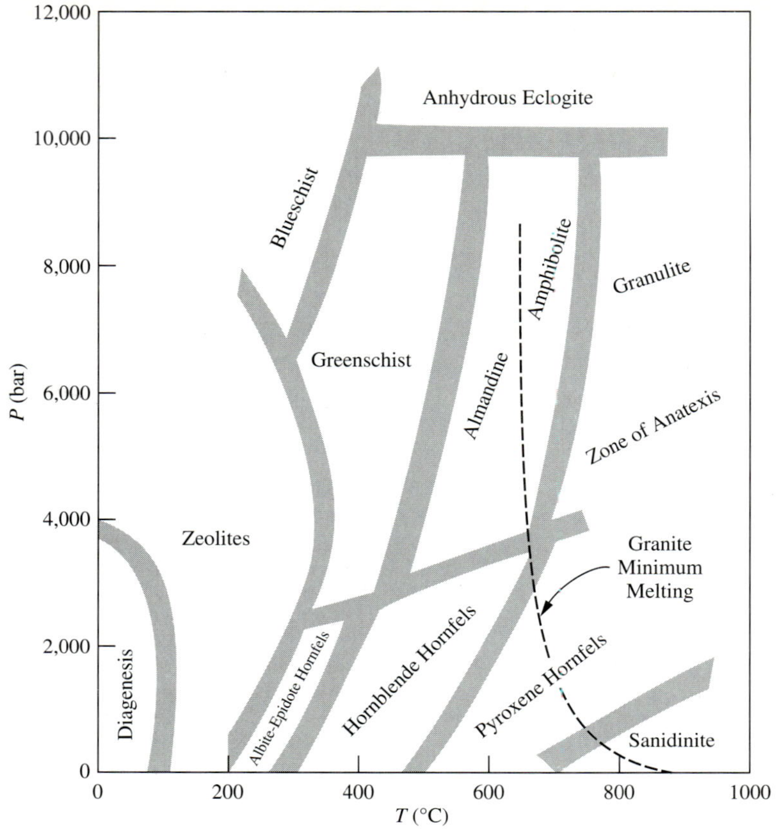

FIGURE 7-19 Schematic pressure-temperature diagram for different types of metamorphism. Depths and pressures are maximum values; actual pressures may be somewhat less. The presence of a fluid phase is assumed. (After H. G. F. Winkler, *Petrogenesis of Metamorphic Rocks*, 5th ed. New York: Springer-Verlag, 1979, Fig. 1-1, p. 5.)

classify and group metamorphic rocks in a systematic fashion. A facies comprises all rocks formed under the same set of physical conditions (Fig. 7-19). All rocks of the same chemical composition have the same mineralogical composition if they belong to the same facies. Different chemical composition within a facies, however, yields a different mineralogy. This facies concept requires that conditions of heterogeneous equilibrium existed during metamorphic processes.

In actual mapping of a metamorphic terrane, however, we do not map facies; we map rocks, which are assemblages of minerals, noting especially the first or last appearance with increasing grade of indicator minerals such as biotite or sillimanite within these assemblages (Table 7-5). With increasing metamorphic grade, that is, increasing pressure and temperature of metamorphism, reactions occur between minerals in these assem-

TABLE 7-5 Indicator Metamorphic Minerals

Very low grade	Medium grade
Zeolites, albite, lawsonite, serpentine, analcime, heulandite; at high pressures jadeite, aragonite, glaucophane	Cordierite, staurolite, margarite, Ca/Na plagioclase, grossular
Low grade	**High grade**
Zoisite, clinozoisite, epidote, Na plagioclase, biotite, muscovite, forsterite, hornblende, stilpnomelane; at high pressures almandine	Kyanite, anthophyllite, hypersthene, Ca plagioclase, partial melting to granite magma; at high pressures kyanite, pyrope

blages. Within a given volume of rock containing a change in metamorphic grade, a surface (or a transitional zone) divides one assemblage from another. The intersection of this surface (or zone) between assemblages with the earth's surface is a mappable line (or band), an isograd. Combined with experimental data on mineral reactions, we can infer temperatures and pressures of metamorphism from configurations of isograds on geologic maps.

Siliceous Carbonates Application of heterogeneous phase equilibria to metamorphic assemblages can be illustrated by progressive mineral-assemblage changes during metamorphism of siliceous carbonate rocks when water is present. Such rocks are common, and the system $CaO—MgO—SiO_2—CO_2—H_2O$ can be represented in a relatively simple fashion. For these reasons, this system was one of the first to be studied experimentally in detail by N. L. Bowen and one of the first to have experimental results applied to real rocks.

Under sedimentary conditions, four minerals—calcite, dolomite, magnesite, and quartz—are stable (Fig. 7-20). Two ternary assemblages are possible—calcite-dolomite-quartz and magnesite-dolomite-quartz. Calcite and magnesite cannot coexist stably because of a stable intermediate mineral, dolomite. Each mineral may exist by itself, and five two-mineral assemblages are stable.

Tremolite [$Ca_2Mg_5Si_8O_{22}(OH)_2$] and talc [$Mg_3Si_4O_{10}(OH)_2$] become additional stable phases in this siliceous carbonate system during first stages of low-grade metamorphism (Fig. 7-21). Formation of these silicates can be expressed as

$$3MgCO_3 + 4SiO_2 + H_2O \rightleftharpoons Mg_3Si_4O_{10}(OH)_2 + 3CO_2,$$
$$\text{magnesite} + \text{quartz} + \text{water} \rightleftharpoons \text{talc} + \text{carbon dioxide},$$

and

$$5CaMg(CO_3)_2 + 8SiO_2 + H_2O \rightleftharpoons Ca_2Mg_5Si_8O_{22}(OH)_2 + 3CaCO_3 + 7CO_2,$$
$$\text{dolomite} + \text{quartz} + \text{water} \rightleftharpoons \text{tremolite} + \text{calcite} + \text{carbon dioxide}.$$

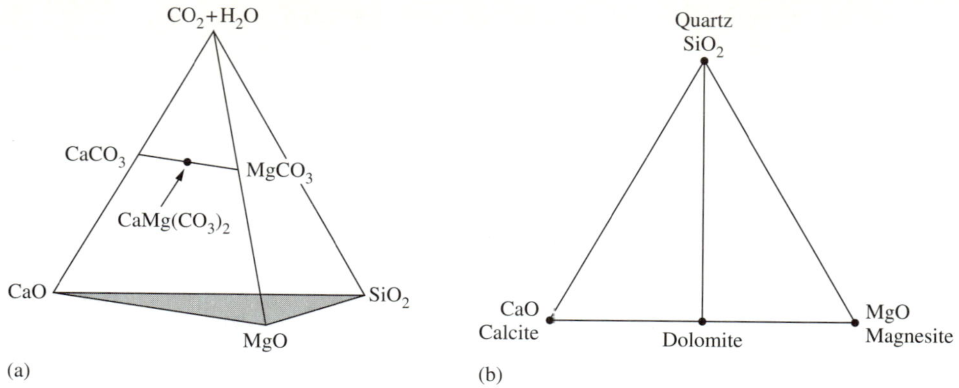

FIGURE 7-20 Mineral phases in the system MgO—CaO—SiO_2—CO_2—H_2O at the earth's surface. (a) Composition tetrahedron showing stable phases. (b) Projection of stable phases onto the anhydrous, carbonate-free base of the composition tetrahedron. Two possible three-phase assemblages shown. (After H. G. F. Winkler, *Petrogenesis of Metamorphic Rocks*, 5th ed. New York: Springer-Verlag, 1979.)

Five three-phase assemblages are stable under these conditions of metamorphism: calcite-dolomite-tremolite, dolomite-tremolite-talc, dolomite-talc-magnesite, calcite-tremolite-quartz, and quartz-tremolite-talc. Note that the common sedimentary assemblage, dolomite-quartz, is no longer stable under conditions of low-grade metamorphism.

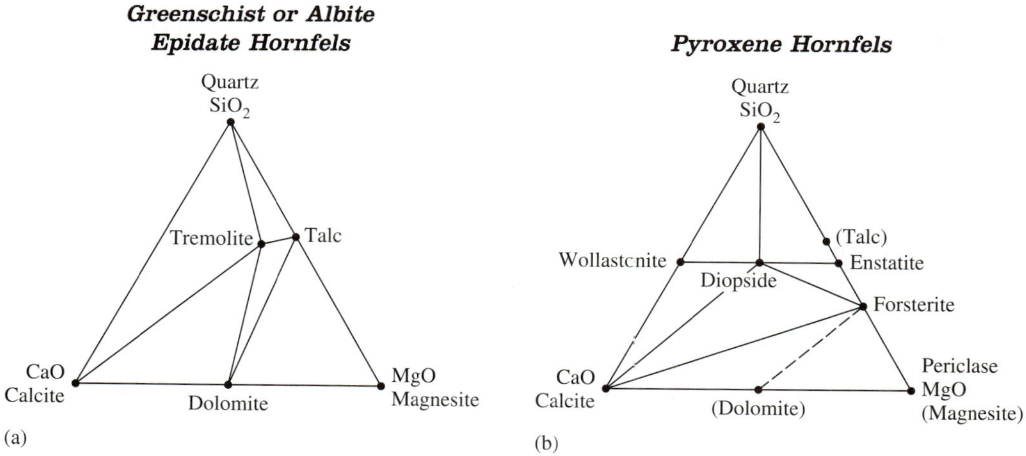

FIGURE 7-21 Mineral phases in the system MgO—CaO—SiO_2—CO_2—H_2O at elevated temperatures and pressures. (After H. G. F. Winkler, *Petrogenesis of Metamorphic Rocks*, 5th ed. New York: Springer-Verlag, 1979.)

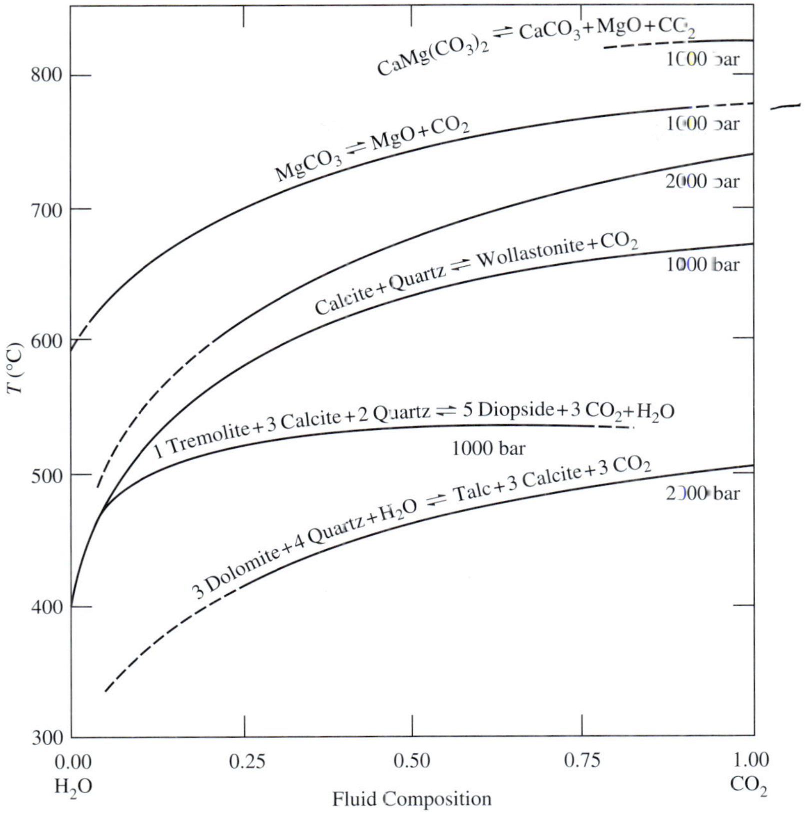

FIGURE 7-22 Isobaric temperatures for decarbonation reactions. (After H. G. F. Winkler, *Petrogenesis of Metamorphic Rocks*, 5th ed. New York: Springer-Verlag, 1979.)

Further increase in metamorphic grade stabilizes the minerals diopside and forsterite. Talc and magnesite dehydrate and decarbonate to form forsterite; diopside can crystallize according to

$$Ca_2Mg_5Si_8O_{22}(OH)_2 + 3CaCO_3 + 2SiO_2 \rightleftharpoons 5CaMgSi_2O_6 + 3CO_2 + H_2O,$$
$$\text{tremolite} + \text{calcite} + \text{quartz} \rightleftharpoons \text{diopside} + \text{carbon dioxide} + \text{water}.$$

Note that the assemblage quartz-tremolite-talc is common to both grades of metamorphism.

Temperatures and pressures have not been assigned to these reactions and, in general, cannot be assigned precisely to metamorphic boundaries. Reaction temperatures are strongly pressure-dependent (Fig. 7-22). Even with the assumption that $P_{vapor} = P_{total}$, which cannot be verified, reaction temperatures and pressures depend on the $H_2O:CO_2$ ratio in the vapor phase at peak grades of metamorphism, a number not readily available.

This sequence of mineral assemblages for progressive contact metamorphism of siliceous carbonate rocks has been carried through in some detail to illustrate how assemblages and reactions are used to establish metamorphic grade. Any rock can be metamorphosed, but assemblages and reactions will be different because starting materials are different. These principles, however, are the same regardless of the rocks involved.

Pseudo-Phase Diagrams In cases where compositional variables are so extensive as to preclude simple representation of possible stable mineral assemblages as a function of composition, a kind of pseudo-phase diagram may be employed. One such is an *ACF* diagram (Fig. 7-23), first proposed by Eskola. An *ACF* diagram simplifies mineral compositions by omitting from consideration those constituents either commonly present in excess or having little effect on the resulting representation. The *A* apex of an *ACF* diagram represents Al_2O_3 in a rock along with Fe_2O_3, which behaves very similarly mineralogically. The *C* apex represents CaO in a rock, but corrected for apatite or fluorite for rocks containing phosphate or fluoride. The *F* apex represents FeO + MgO, which generally proxy fairly well for one another (Table 1-6).

Silica is the main constituent not overtly represented on an *ACF* diagram. Since those rocks typically represented on *ACF* diagrams are oversaturated with silica (quartz being present), stipulation of this fact suffices. Soda for plagioclase and potash for micas may also be stipulated.

An *A'FK* plot complements *ACF* plots for mineral assemblages stable at different metamorphic grades (Fig. 7-24). Here, *A'* represents $A - (Na_2O + K_2O + CaO)$, that is, adjusted for alumina in feldspars. The *K* apex represents K_2O in a rock, and *F* is common to both diagrams. Other plots may be used to take account of other constituents or where neither *ACF* nor *A'FK* is sensitive to particular assemblages. One such relates *an* and *ab* contents of plagioclase as an indicator of metamorphic grade.

These pseudo-phase diagrams read exactly as if they were true phase diagrams. Different rock compositions fall into different three-phase triangles, actually four-phase since the presence of quartz is stipulated. Minerals with variable composition, such as hornblende and biotite, plot as areas rather than as points, resulting in two-phase areas in these diagrams. As with true phase diagrams, some assemblages are sensitive to metamorphic grade while others are not.

Petrogenetic Grids Metamorphic reactions may be plotted in pressure-temperature space as a petrogenetic grid. Plotting all metamorphic reactions on a single pressure-temperature diagram results in hopeless confusion of reaction lines; hence, appropriate reactions for common protoliths are plotted separately. As with projections and pseudo-phase diagrams, exact pressures and temperature of these reaction curves shift with changes in fluid pressure and composition. For example, dehydration

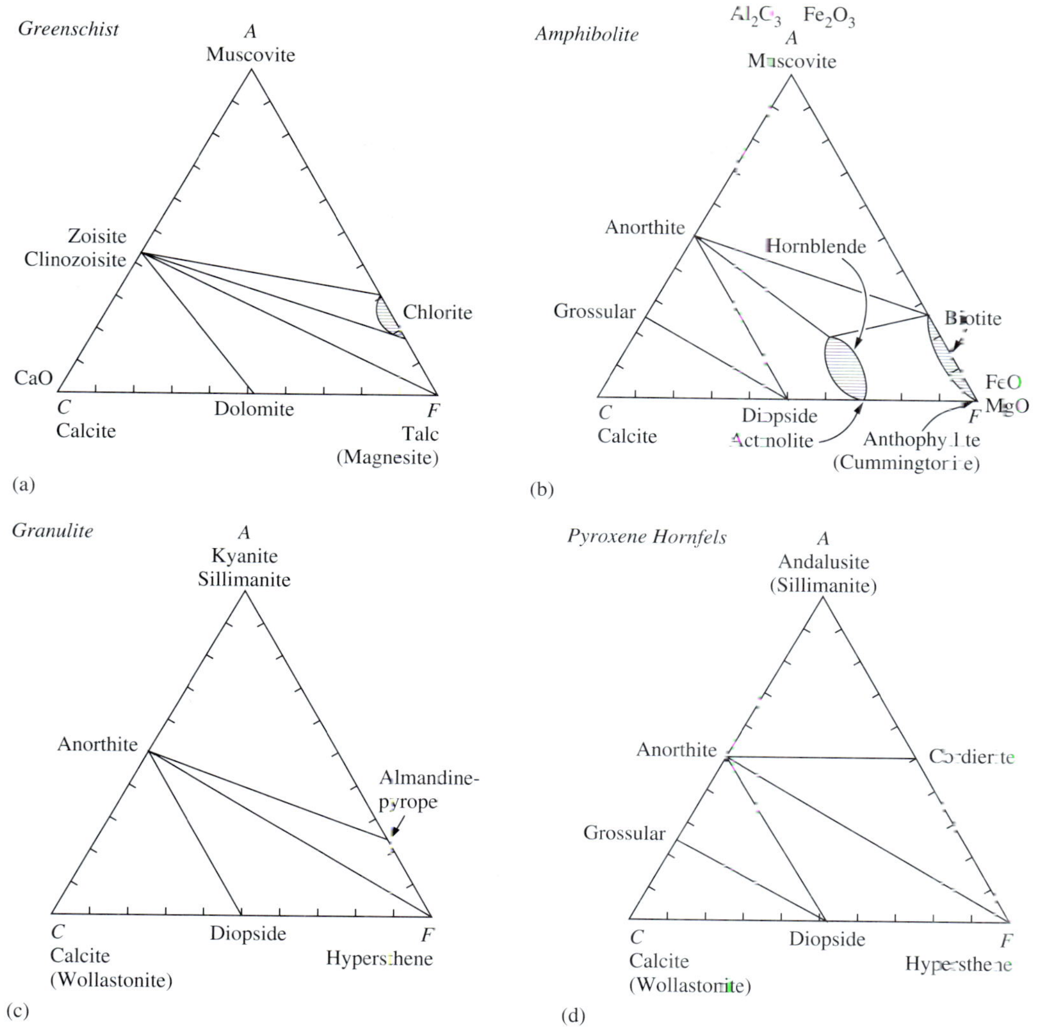

FIGURE 7-23 ***ACF*** **diagrams for different metamorphic conditions. (After H. G. F. Winkler, *Petrogenesis of Metamorphic Rocks*, 5th ed. New York: Springer-Verlag, 1979.)**

reactions generally proceed at temperatures lower than indicated when $P_{fluid} < P_{total}$ or when $P_{H_2O} < P_{fluid}$. On the other hand, onset of melting shifts to higher temperatures than indicated whenever a rock is less than saturated with H_2O.

Several reaction curves for metabasites, a collective name for metamorphosed basalts and andesites, typify this sort of representation of petrologic data (Fig. 7-25). Some curves represent reactions, such as pumpelley-

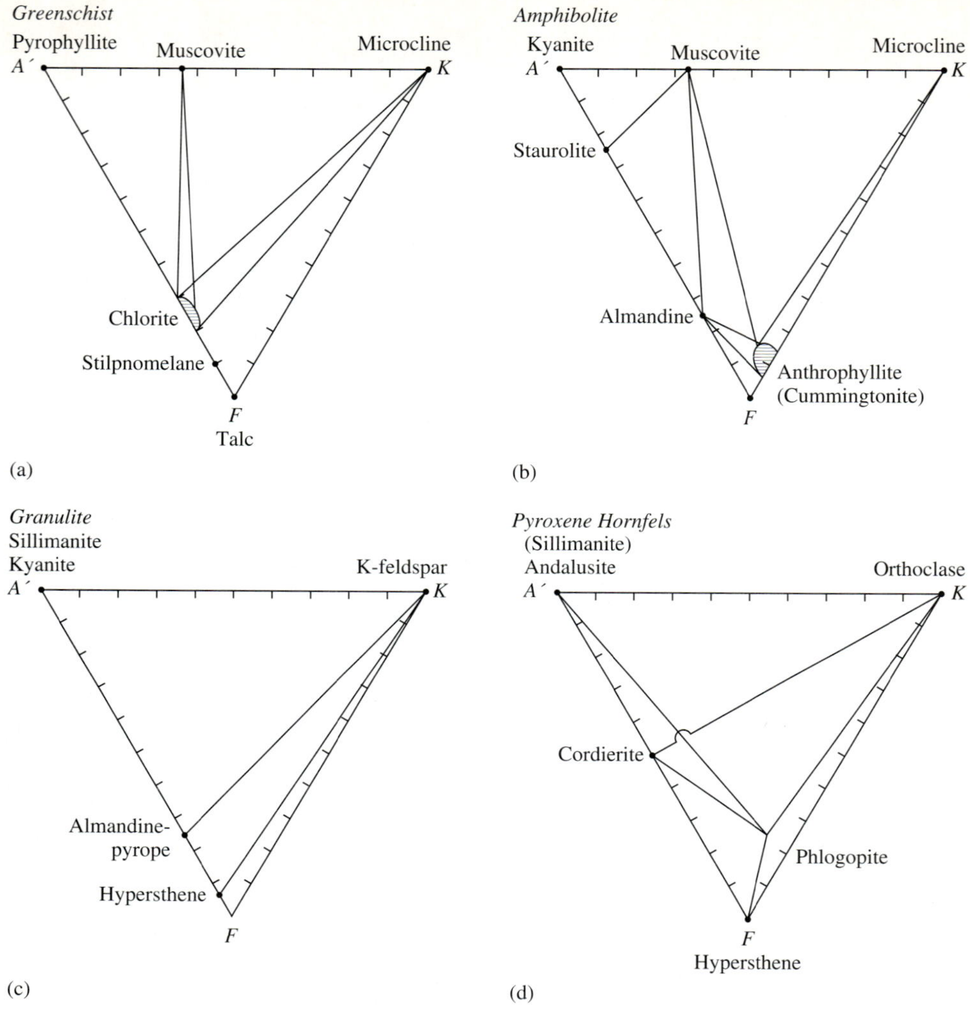

FIGURE 7-24 ***A′FK* diagrams for different metamorphic conditions.**

ite + chlorite + quartz = zoisite + actinolite and zoisite = anorthite + grossular + corundum + water. Other curves represent the highest temperatures and pressures of stability of a mineral phase, regardless of overall rock composition, and are labeled "mineral-out." Depending on rock composition, lawsonite may react with other minerals at lower pressures and temperatures, but the lawsonite-out curve represents the highest conditions at which lawsonite can occur.

Curves such as *An* 17 + hornblende represent the onset of a particular assemblage. Below this curve, plagioclase occurs with a maximum *An* content of *An* 5. Because of a peristerite solvus between *An* 5 and *An* 17,

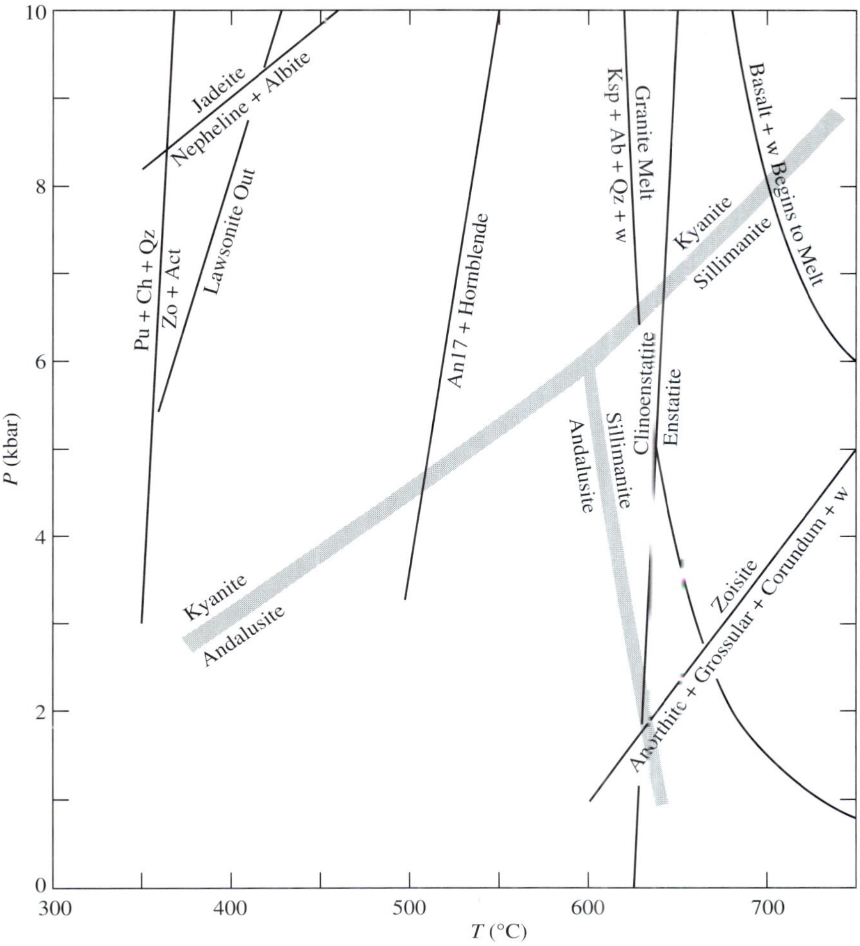

FIGURE 7-25 Petrogenetic grid for felsic metamorphic reactions.

albite cannot take on any additional CaO until these conditions are reached during progressive metamorphism. The granite and basalt melting curves represent minima for the onset of melting for these compositions under conditions of water saturation.

Reference curves for the aluminum silicate polymorphic transitions are plotted as broad reference bands because experimental and field data do not yet permit their precise placement in pressure-temperature space. Although they are common phases in aluminum-oversaturated metamorphic rocks, factors other than pressure and temperature appear to influence strongly their ranges of appearance.

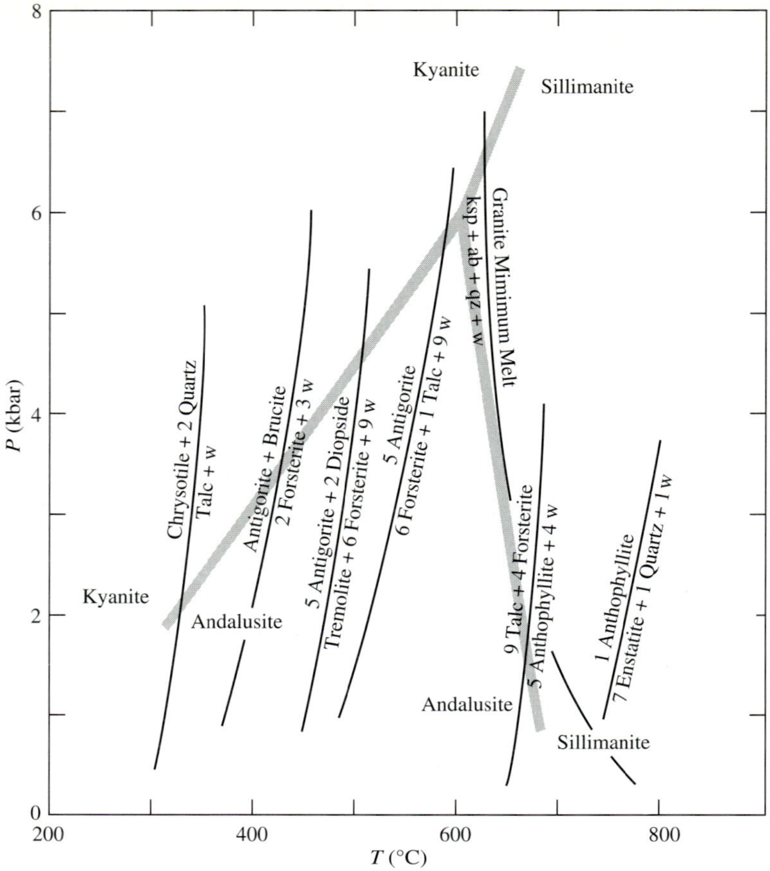

FIGURE 7-26 Petrogenetic grid for ultramafic metamorphic reactions.

Different metamorphic reactions are useful to typify metamorphosed ultramafic assemblages (Fig. 7-26). Note that olivine, a high-temperature mineral in igneous rocks, appears in these compositions at relatively low temperatures. Aluminum silicate polymorphs and the granite minimum melt curve are plotted here for reference only.

Reaction isograds appropriate for any metamorphic protolith may be plotted in a similar fashion. They represent convenient ways of analyzing mineral assemblages found in metamorphic rocks. Note that each reaction isograd is a univariant curve marking a line of stability for combined products and reactants. Thus, curve antigorite + diopside = tremolite + forsterite + water represents conditions where the assemblage antigorite + diopside + tremolite + forsterite could occur when saturated with H_2O. Furthermore, since other chemical reactions, such as CO_2

evolved during decarbonation, can cause this reaction curve to smear out in pressure-temperature space, probabilities for finding such an assemblage are not vanishingly small.

7-5 FORMATION OF MINERALS FROM AQUEOUS FLUIDS

Water is ubiquitous in the earth's crust, ranging from fractions of a percent in granulites from the lower crust to over half by weight in some recently deposited sediments. Temperatures, rates of reactions, and species of minerals formed depend on amounts and states of fluid in a rock. Previous sections on igneous, sedimentary, and metamorphic rocks allude to some roles of aqueous fluids in mineral genesis.

Water Sources Possible sources of aqueous fluids include vapor phases escaping from final crystallization of a magma, fluids driven off by dehydration of hydrous minerals during late stages of metamorphism resulting from tectonic crustal thickening or crustal subduction, connate water trapped during sediment deposition, and meteoric water circulating through pores and fractures in rocks. Actual aqueous fluid phases represent various mixtures of waters from these several sources.

Source identification for a sample of aqueous fluid is possible because oxygen isotopic composition varies with water source and history. SMOW (standard mean ocean water) contains approximately 0.2% ^{18}O. Deviations from SMOW are given as $\delta_{^{18}O}$, where

$$\delta_{^{18}O} = \left(\frac{^{18}O/^{16}O_{\text{sample}}}{^{18}O/^{16}O_{\text{SMOW}}} - 1 \right) \times 1000,$$

which gives $^{18}O/^{16}O$ enrichment or depletion, with respect to SMOW, in per mil (parts per thousand). Normal igneous rocks have $^{18}O/^{16}O$ values typically 6 to 10‰ heavier than SMOW, whereas groundwater of meteoric origin is 5–10‰ lighter. When meteoric water reacts with igneous rock, oxygen isotopes are exchanged, depleting rock while enriching water in $^{18}O/^{16}O$. Thus, oxygen-isotope analysis partially reveals sources and histories of aqueous fluids. Since fluid behavior is independent of origin, its effect on minerals and rocks may be analyzed without necessarily specifying an ultimate source.

In a discussion of hydrothermal fluids and metasomatizing solutions, water or aqueous phase does not imply a liquid as opposed to a gaseous state. Where reactions occur at temperatures and pressures above the critical end point for water (374°C and 22.5 MPa (225 bar) for pure H_2O, Fig. 7-27), any distinction between liquid and vapor is meaningless even though dissolved chemicals may substantially alter a critical end point.

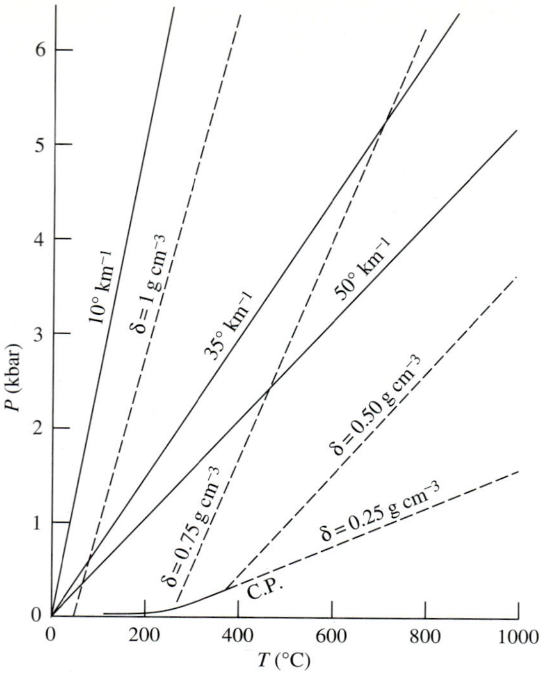

FIGURE 7-27 Density of H_2O as function of pressure and temperature. Solid lines represent geotherms. Dashed lines represent equal density. Lower curve is *LV* for water and vapor. (After F. G. Smith, *Physical Geochemistry*. Reading, MA: Addison-Wesley, 1963.)

Aqueous fluid phase means a fluid predominantly H_2O but not showing a miniscus (liquid-vapor interface).

When a fracture appears in rock in the earth's crust, it opens up an area of lower pressure and a channel for transport of aqueous fluids. When precipitated minerals fill these fractures, they become veins. Evidence from synthesis of vein minerals in laboratories, from compositions of hot springs, and from compositions of gases emanating from active and recently active volcanoes indicates that most aqueous fluids of more than 99% H_2O contain small amounts of CO_2, HCl, H_2, CH_4, SO_2, H_2S, and HF. Some analyzed fluids are one third or more CO_2, and others have several percent of various metal chlorides.

A slight increase in density of aqueous fluids results in substantial increase in solubility of most ionic species. In sedimentary and diagenetic environments, interstitial fluids may be slightly greater than 1 g cm^{-3} (Fig. 7-27). In high-temperature magmatic environments, fluid densities fall in the range 0.50 to 0.75 g cm^{-3}, substantially greater than steam as it is known at the earth's surface.

Mineral Veins Vein minerals originate mostly by deposition in free spaces within a fracture (fissure veins), by replacement of wall rock along unopened fractures (metasomatic veins), or by some combination of these two processes. Fissure veins are recognized by their locally straight boundaries and parallel walls. Metasomatic veins tend to have irregular, nonparallel boundaries. Vein minerals deposited by rising hydrothermal (aqueous) solutions are hypogene, and those from descending groundwater solutions are supergene (Table 7-6).

Water for these hydrothermal solutions may be of magmatic origin or released by dehydration of hydrous mineral phases during metamorphism. Descending solutions are generally of meteoric origin. Mineral-forming elements may be concentrated by fractional crystallization of a magma or dissolved out of rocks through which hydrothermal solutions passed. Isotopic analyses indicate a mantle source for some elements and a crustal source for others. In some cases, such as the galena-sphalerite-fluorite-barite ore veins of the Mississippi Valley, metal source remains enigmatic and controversial.

Some veins are of one generation. Tectonic movement, however, commonly reopens old fractures, brecciates prior vein minerals, permits new solutions to ascend, and causes deposition of succeeding generations of vein minerals. Successive passages of hydrothermal solutions may deposit new vein minerals on top of old ones, or they may partially or totally replace earlier generations of vein minerals.

Most veins are barren in that no economically valuable elements occur or that concentrations of these elements are too low to extract profitably. Common minerals of barren veins include pyrite, quartz, calcite, tourmaline, apatite, and micas. Ore veins contain, in addition to these gangue minerals (nonprofitable minerals removed with ore), a wide variety of metal sulfides, metal tellurides, and some native metals, such as gold or silver, in amounts sufficient to make their extraction profitable.

Pegmatites Magmas of granitic composition can dissolve up to approximately 10% by weight of H_2O and crystallization of anhydrous minerals concentrates water and other volatile elements in this magma. Even magmas initially containing less than 1% dissolved H_2O eventually reach saturation during late stages of crystallization. Crystallization beyond that point causes an aqueous phase to separate from a granitic magma. Experimental results indicate that all components of a magma occur in a newly separated aqueous phase, though not in the same proportions. Especially concentrated are volatiles such as Cl^-, F^-, and CO_2 along with B, Be, P, Li, and other elements with no structural place in feldspars and quartz.

Owing to its lesser density, an aqueous phase occupies more volume than its constituents did while dissolved in an earlier magma and is physically unstable in the earth's crust because of its buoyancy. If this aqueous phase escapes into rock fractures, carrying with it some silicate melt, crystallization due to expansion or pressure quench occurs simultaneously from both melt and vapor, because sudden removal of volatile constituents raises both liquidus and solidus. Crystallization from a vapor phase produces much larger crystals than does crystallization at the same rate from a magma. Pegmatite megacrysts grow from such aqueous vapor phases.

TABLE 7-6 Common Vein Minerals

Name	Origin*	Formula
Native elements		
Gold	H S	Au
Silver	H S	Ag
Copper	H S	Cu
Sulfides		
Chalcocite	H S	Cu_2S
Argentite	H S	Ag_2S
Bornite	H S	Cu_5FeS_4
Galena	H	PbS
Chalcopyrite	H S	$CuFeS_2$
Pyrrhotite	H G	$Fe_{1-x}S$
Pentlandite	H	(Fe,Ni)S
Covellite	H S	CuS
Cinnabar	H	HgS
Stibnite	H	Sb_2S_3
Pyrite	H S G	FeS_2
Marcasite	H S G	FeS_2
Arsenopyrite	H G	FeAsS
Molybdenite	H	MoS_2
Sulfosalt		
Enargite	H	Cu_3AsS_4
Oxides		
Cuprite	S	Cu_2O
Hematite	S G	Fe_2O_3
Pyrolusite	S	MnO_2
Cassiterite	H	SnO_2
Uraninite	H S	UO_2
Quartz	H S G	SiO_2
Magnetite	H	$FeOFe_2O_3$
Chromite	H	$CrOFe_2O_3$
Hydroxides and oxyhydroxides		
Manganite	S	MnO(OH)
Romanechite	S	$BaMn_9O_{16}(OH)_4$
Gibbsite	S G	$Al(OH)_3$
Diaspore	S G	AlO(OH)
Goethite	S G	FeO(OH)

TABLE 7-6 continued

Name	Origin*	Formula
Halides		
Chlorargyrite	S	$AgCl$
Fluorite	H G	CaF_2
Atacamite	S	$Cu_2Cl(OH)_3$
Carbonates		
Calcite	H S G	$CaCO_3$
Siderite	H S	$FeCO_3$
Rhodochrosite	H	$MnCO_3$
Smithsonite	S	$ZnCO_3$
Dolomite	H S G	$CaMg(CO_3)_2$
Cerussite	S	$PbCO_3$
Malachite	S	$Cu_2(OH)_2(CO_3)$
Azurite	S	$Cu_3(OH)_2(CO_3)_2$
Sulfates		
Barite	H G	$BaSO_4$
Anglesite	S	$PbSO_4$
Gypsum	S G	$CaSO_4 \cdot 2H_2O$
Tungstate, molybdates		
Wolframite	H	$(Fe,Mn)WO_4$
Scheelite	H	$CaWO_4$
Wulfenite	S	$PbMO_4$
Silicates		
Chrysocolla	S	$Cu_2H_2Si_2O_5(OH)_4 \cdot nH_2O$
Hemimorphite	S	$Zn_4Si_2O_7(OH)_2 \cdot H_2O$
Braunite	S	$Mn_7O_8SiO_4$
Rhodonite	H	$MnSiO_3$
Clay minerals	H S G	$Al_2Si_2O_5(OH)_4$
Chlorite group	H G	$Mg_5Al(Si_3AlO_{10})(OH)_8$
Feldspar group	H G	$(K,Na,Ca)(Si,Al)_4O_8$

*H = hypogene; S = supergene; G = gangue mineral.

A pegmatite is a body of rock, presumably of igneous origin, composed of exceptionally large crystals, ranging in size from a few centimeters to many meters. Most pegmatites have compositions very close to granite minimum melt compositions. In addition, many pegmatites have exotic minerals containing ions not tolerated in structures of major silicate minerals. Included are beryl (Be^{2+}), spodumene and lepidolite (Li^+), and tourmaline (B^{3+}).

Many pegmatites are layered (Fig. 7-28) with a top to bottom sequence of megacrysts of microcline and platy albite (cleavelandite) intergrown graphically with quartz, a massive quartz core, and a footwall soda aplite (albite and quartz with a uniform texture of grains about 2 mm in

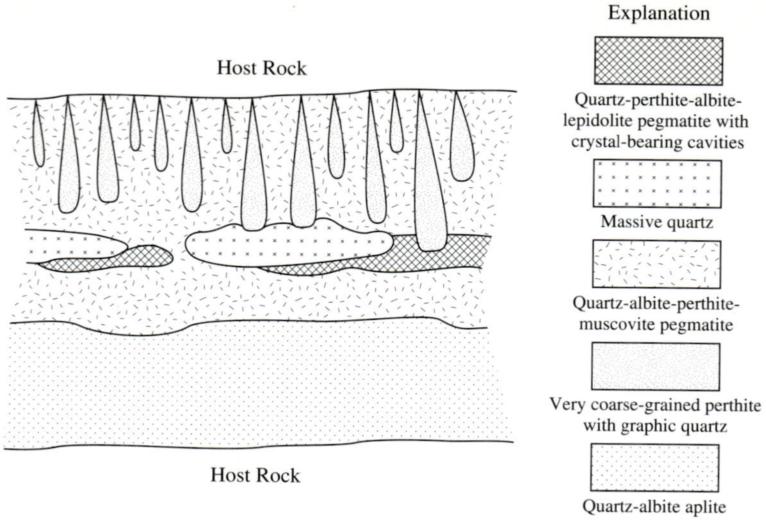

FIGURE 7-28 Pegmatite cross section.

diameter). Simultaneous crystallization of megacrysts from aqueous fluid, quartz from fluid-melt interface, and soda aplite from silicate melt keeps this system's overall composition coincident with granite minimum melt composition.

Similar reasoning may be offered for the origin of aplite veins and dikes. These aplite compositions are also very close to granite minimum melt composition. Frothing minimum-melt granite escapes into fractures in already crystallized granite or into country rock. Rapid pressure quench of a water-rich melt to a glass occurs as the aqueous phase escapes. This glass then crystallizes into a sugary-textured aplite. The close relationship between rocks as disparate in texture as pegmatite and aplite is revealed in hybrid pegmatite-aplite dikes.

Hydrothermal Alteration Hydrated silicate minerals form during low-temperature metamorphic reactions (Sec. 7-4). These same hydrated minerals may form directly from igneous minerals or from high-grade metamorphic minerals by reaction with aqueous fluids of appropriate temperature and composition. Hydration of ferromagnesian minerals can be illustrated by

$$2Mg_2SiO_4 + 2H_2O \rightleftharpoons Mg_3Si_2O_5(OH)_4 + MgO_{sol'n},$$
$$\text{forsterite} + \text{water} \rightleftharpoons \text{serpentine} + \text{magnesia},$$

or by

$$3Mg_2SiO_4 + SiO_2 + 4H_2O \rightleftharpoons 2Mg_3Si_2O_5(OH)_4,$$
$$\text{forsterite} + \text{silica} + \text{water} \rightleftharpoons \text{serpentine}.$$

Hydration of olivine to serpentine could follow either reaction, depending on compositions of aqueous fluids.

Feldspars also suffer hydrothermal alteration such as

$$3CaAl_2Si_2O_8 + 2H_2O + K_2O \rightleftharpoons 2KAl_2(AlSi_3)O_{10}(OH)_2 + 3CaO,$$
$$\text{anorthite} + \text{water} + \text{potash} \rightleftharpoons \text{muscovite} + \text{lime}$$

Alkali feldspars alter similarly. Furthermore, the end product may be kaolinite, in which case a reaction between a hydrothermal solution and a feldspar would be chemically similar to that outlined for feldspar weathering (Sec. 7-3). Indeed, in many cases effects of low-temperature hydrothermal alteration are all but indistinguishable from weathering effects. In the same way, the products of high-temperature alteration resemble the products of low-grade metamorphism.

Hydrothermal solutions need not come from afar; small amounts of water expelled by crystallization of a relatively anhydrous magma may remain in interstices of an igneous rock. During cooling below a rock's solidus, these solutions react with enclosing minerals, causing deuteric alteration or autometamorphism, which is similar to hydrothermal alteration but on a much smaller scale. Many apparently unweathered igneous rocks fresh from a quarry or roadcut show deuteric alteration to varying degrees.

FURTHER READINGS

Atherton, M. P., and J. Tarney (eds.), *Origin of Granite Batholiths, Geochemical Evidence.* Orpington, Kent, UK: Shiva, 1979.

Berner, R. A., *Principles of Chemical Sedimentology.* New York: McGraw-Hill, 1971.

Bowen, N. L., *The Evolution of the Igneous Rocks.* Princeton: Princeton University Press, 1928.

Bowes, D. R. (ed.), *The Encyclopedia of Igneous and Metamorphic Petrology.* New York: Van Nostrand Reinhold, 1989.

Colman, S. M., and D. P. Dethier (eds.), *Rates of Chemical Weathering of Rocks and Minerals.* San Diego: Academic Press, 1986.

Dietrich, R. V., and B. J. Skinner, *Rocks and Rock Minerals.* New York: Wiley, 1979.

Fairbridge, R. W., and J. Bourgeois (eds.), *The Encyclopedia of Sedimentology.* New York: Van Nostrand Reinhold, 1978.

Hyndman, D. W., *Petrology of Igneous and Metamorphic Rocks,* 2nd ed. New York: McGraw-Hill, 1985.

Krauskopf, K. B., *Introduction to Geochemistry.* New York: McGraw-Hill, 1967.

Morse, S. A., *Basalts and Phase Diagrams.* New York: Springer-Verlag, 1980.

Pettijohn, F. J., *Sedimentary Rocks,* 3rd ed. New York: Harper Collins, 1975.

Pettijohn, F. J., P. E. Potter, and R. Siever, *Sand and Sandstone,* 2nd ed. New York: Springer-Verlag, 1987.

Scarfe, C. M. (ed.), *Silicate Melts.* Toronto, Canada: Mineralogical Association of Canada, 1986.

Winkler, H. G. F., *Petrogenesis of Metamorphic Rocks,* 5th ed. New York: Springer-Verlag, 1979.

Yoder, H. S., Jr., *Generation of Basaltic Magma.* Washington, DC: National Academy of Sciences, 1976.

Yoder, H. S., Jr. (ed.), *The Evolution of the Igneous Rocks.* Princeton: Princeton University Press, 1979.

GLOSSARY

Abrasion pH The pH of intergranular water in freshly ground mineral powder.

Adatom Cluster of atomic particles that add as a group to a growing crystal face.

Allochromatic Coloration caused by impurities or defects not essential to a mineral.

Alumina saturation Chemical composition of a crystalline rock such that there is exactly enough alumina to crystallize feldspars.

Anion Any negatively charged atomic particle created from a neutral atom by gain of valence electrons.

Anisotropy, optical Condition where light velocity varies with direction through a mineral.

Antiferromagnetism A state where *d* electrons are ordered in an antiparallel array.

Aphanitic A crystalline rock texture in which individual crystals are too small to be seen with the unaided eye.

Aplite Dike of sugary-textured granite composition.

Aplite, footwall Sugary-textured rock composed predominantly of quartz and albite commonly found at the base of a pegmatite; also called soda aplite.

Aqueous fluid Crustal fluids that are predominantly water beyond its critical point.

Asymmetric unit That cluster of atomic particles associated with a lattice point.

Authigenesis In situ crystal growth before and during diagenesis.

Band gap See Energy gap.

Basal pinacoid A pinacoid intersecting only the **c** crystallographic axis; also called a base.

Bipyramid A closed form of two pyramids related by a mirror plane of symmetry.

Birefringence Maximum possible difference in refractive indices of a mineral.

Bragg angle Angle at which X-ray diffraction occurs in a mineral, the angle θ in the Bragg equation.

Bragg equation $n\lambda = 2d \sin \theta$.

Bravais lattice See Space lattice.

Cathodoluminescence Light emission resulting from electron bombardment of a mineral.

Cation Any positively charged atomic particle created from a neutral atom by loss of valence electrons.

Chain silicates Any silicate mineral composed of infinite chains of corner-sharing silica tetrahedra bound by other cations; also called inosilicates.

Characteristic radiation Monochromatic radiation caused by an inner electron falling into a vacant orbital of lower energy.

Chromophore Color-causing agent.

Circular section A section through an anisotropic indicatrix, light transmission at right angles to which appears isotropic.

Cleavage Crystallographically controlled breakage planes that occur in all samples of a mineral species.

Color center Chemical or physical imperfections that selectively absorb light in a crystal structure.

Component A constituent that can undergo independent concentration variation in different phases in a system.

Contact metamorphism See Metamorphism, contact.

Coordination number The maximum number of anions that can surround a cation while retaining cation-anion contact.

Coordination polyhedron Geometric shape of an imaginary solid created by connecting anion centers about a cation.

Cotectic A univariant curve representing low-melting liquid compositions on a liquidus surface.

Covalent bond Idealized chemical bond created by electrons shared between two or more atomic particles; also called homopolar bond.

Critical point An end to a divariant curve that is not at a junction with other divariant curves.

Crystal Any crystalline material bounded by natural planar faces that reflect internal atomic order.

Crystal class A collection of all crystal structures having the same point-group symmetry.

Crystal field Electrostatic interaction of ligand electrons acting on metal-ion electron shells.

Crystal form All faces of a crystal that have a like position relative to the elements of symmetry.

Crystalline Any material with a periodic array of its atomic constituents.

Crystalline solution Chemical variations caused by one ion replacing another in a crystal structure; also called solid solution.

Crystallization, equilibrium Process in which crystals react with melt from which they crystallize.

Crystallization, fractional Process in which, once formed, crystals no longer react with their parent melt.

Cyclosilicate Any silicate mineral composed of rings of corner-sharing silica tetrahedra bound by other cations.

Defect Any deviation from perfect periodicity in a crystal structure.

Degree of freedom See Variance.

Density Mass per unit volume; see also Specific gravity.

Diad A rotational axis of symmetry that is one half a complete rotation.

Diagenesis Cementation, crystallization, and recrystallization of a sediment following deposition but prior to metamorphism.

Diamagnetism Property of being slightly repelled by a magnetic field.

Diffraction Reinforced coherent scattered radiation from a periodic structure.

Diffraction plane Atomic layers spaced so as to cause X-ray diffraction; also called a reflection plane.

Dimorphous The capability of a single chemical composition to occur in two crystal structures.

Disorder Nonspecific distribution of two or more ions in a crystal structure.

Dispersed element An element that by virtue of its low abundance and similarity of size and charge of its ions does not crystallize as a discrete phase but substitutes in the structures of major minerals.

Dispersion Variation of refractive index with wavelength.

Disphenoid A closed form of four faces, each of which is an isosceles triangle.

Divariance A system in which two intensive variables may be changed arbitrarily without gaining or losing a phase.

Dodecahedron, pentagonal See Pyritohedron.

Dodecahedron, rhombic A closed crystal form of 12 crystal faces, each of which is a rhombus.

Dome A form of two nonparallel faces related by a mirror.

Double refraction Light split into two rays, ordinary and extraordinary, when passing through an anisotropic mineral.

Electroluminescence Quantum emission triggered by electric stimulation.

Energy gap A forbidden energy zone because two electron orbitals do not overlap.

Epitaxy Nucleation and growth of one crystal upon a different species with crystallographic orientation of the growing crystal determined by the substrate.

Equilibrium, heterogeneous A multiphase system with uniform temperature, pressure, and chemical potential for each constituent in each phase.

Equilibrium, homogeneous A one-phase system with uniform temperature, pressure, and chemical composition.

Eutectic point Pressure, temperature, and composition of the lowest temperature at which liquid can exist in a multicomponent system.

Excited state An atom or ion with one or more electrons not in their lowest energy state.

Extraordinary Light ray(s) through a mineral that do not follow Snell's law of refraction.

Facies, metamorphic All metamorphic rocks formed under the same conditions of pressure and temperature.

Facies, sedimentary All sedimentary rocks deposited in the same depositional environment.

Fenitization Rock alteration by hydrous fluorocarbonate fluids generally associated with carbonatite crystallization.

Ferrimagnetism Strong magnetic susceptibility caused by overlap of adjacent *d* and *p* orbitals causing an unequal number of electrons to be aligned antiparallel.

Ferromagnetism Strong magnetic susceptibility caused by overlap of adjacent *d* orbitals.

First law of crystallography Interfacial angles between the equivalent two faces of a crystal are the same regardless of size or mode of origin; also called Steno's law.

Fluorescence Energy emission at a wavelength different from energizing radiation.

Forbidden zone See Energy gap.

Form, closed A collection of symmetrically related crystal faces that enclose space.

Form, open A collection of symmetrically related crystal faces that do not by themselves enclose space.

Fracture Breakage in a crystalline material that is not crystallographically controlled; also breakage of any solid.

Framework silicate Silicate structure in which all four corners of each silica tetrahedron are shared with other tetrahedra; also called tektosilicate.

Geochronology The science of using radioactive isotopes and their daughter isotopes to determine radiometric age.

Glide A symmetry element that combines translation with a mirror plane parallel to that translation.

Goniometer Optical or mechanical device for measuring interfacial angles of crystals.

Ground state An atom or ion with all electrons at their lowest possible energy.

Group, mineral See Mineral group.

Group, symmetry See Symmetry group.

Habit The form or combination of forms typically exhibited by a mineral species.

Haplobasalt Simplified synthetic basalt consisting of components albite, anorthite, and diopside only.

Haplogranite Simplified synthetic granite consisting of components albite, orthoclase, quartz, and water only.

Hardness For brittle minerals, resistance to scratching. For malleable minerals, resistance to deformation.

Heterogeneous equilibria See Equilibrium, heterogeneous.

Heterogeneous nucleation See Nucleation, heterogeneous.

Hexad A rotational axis of symmetry that is one sixth of a complete rotation.

Holohedral The crystal class having the highest symmetry of its crystal system.

Homogeneous equilibria See Equilibrium, homogeneous.

Homogeneous nucleation See Nucleation, homogeneous.

Homopolar bond See Covalent bond.

Hydrothermal fluid Predominantly aqueous fluids in the earth's crust causing mineral crystallization and recrystallization.

Idiochromatic Coloration caused by an essential constituent of a mineral.

Igneous A rock crystallized from a magma, a process leading to magmatically formed rocks.

Improper Any symmetry element indicating change in chirality of its object.

Index, Miller and Bravais-Miller Reciprocals of axial intercepts cleared of fractions and factors.

Index, refractive The quotient of the velocity of light in a transparent medium divided into the velocity of light in a vacuum.

Indicatrix Surface of an ellipsoid constructed such that its radius in each direction is proportional to the velocity of light with its electric vector in that direction.

Indices Mineralogical plural of index.

Inosilicates See Chain silicates.

Invariance A condition of a system such that no intensive variable may be changed without losing a phase.

Inversion An element of symmetry relating two points that are equally and oppositely distant from a center.

Ion Any atomic particle with an electronic charge by virtue of having gained or lost one or more electrons.

Ionic bond Idealized attraction between oppositely charged ions.

Ionic potential The quotient of ionic charge divided by ionic radius used to predict element solubility during weathering.

Isomorphous Two or more minerals having the same crystal form.

Isotropy, optical Condition where light velocity is independent of crystallographic direction in a mineral.

Kink A reentrant angle on a step of a growing crystal face.

Ligand Atomic particle or group of atoms, typically an anion, capable of binding to a metal ion.

Liquidus Locus of all points in pressure-temperature-composition space at which crystals coexist with melt.

Luminescence Light emission resulting from an electron dropping from an excited state to a lower-energy state.

Luster Quantity and quality of light reflected from a mineral surface.

Magma Molten rock, a liquid that crystallizes to a solid of essentially the same chemical composition.

Magnetic domain That portion of a crystal with magnetic symmetry orientation different from adjacent portions.

Megacryst Large crystal surrounded by smaller ones in a crystalline rock, irrespective of genesis.

Melting, congruent A mineral melts to a liquid of the same composition.

Melting, equilibrium A rock melts but stays in equilibrium contact with its protolith.

Melting, fractional Rock melts escape from contact with their protolith.

Melting, incongruent A mineral dissociates to a liquid of one composition and new compound of another.

Merohedral A crystal class having less than the highest symmetry of its crystal system.

Metallic bond Idealized attraction between cations and an enveloping electron cloud.

Metamict A state resulting from destruction of crystallinity by nuclear radiation.

Metamorphic grade Relative intensity of pressure and temperature divided into very low, low, medium, and high grades.

Metamorphism Crystallization and recrystallization of minerals resulting from heat and pressure due to burial in the earth's crust

Metamorphism, contact Mineral recrystallization resulting from proximity to an igneous intrusion.

Metamorphism, prograde Mineral changes resulting from rising temperature and pressure.

Metamorphism, regional Mineral recrystallization resulting from burial beneath an overthrust sheet.

Metamorphism, retrograde Mineral changes resulting from falling temperature and pressure.

Metasomatism Metamorphic recrystallization involving chemical changes brought about by fluid passage through the rock.

Migmatite Rock in which some components were magma but containing phases not dissolved in the host rock melt.

Mineral Any naturally occurring crystalline material of inorganic geochemical origin.

Mineral group A collection of mineral species having the same crystal structure.

Mineraloid Any naturally occurring noncrystalline solid.

Mirror A plane of symmetry across which two halves of a crystal structure are mirror images.

Molecular orbital A formalized chemical bond model with electron orbitals extending to two or more nuclei.

Monad A rotational axis of symmetry that is a complete rotation.

Native Any mineral that is an element or alloy.

Nucleation Formation of an embryonic cluster of atomic particles from which a crystal may grow.

Nucleation, heterogeneous Formation of a crystal nucleus on a preexisting particle or substrate.

Nucleation, homogeneous Nucleation by statistical fluctuations in a parent fluid.

Octahedral site Any point in a crystal structure that will accept a cation of coordination number 6.

Octahedron A closed crystal form of eight crystal faces that are equilateral triangles.

Optic axis Direction normal to a circular section in anisotropic minerals.

Optic sign One of two velocity relationships in all anisotropic minerals between ray velocity and crystallographic directions.

Ordinary Light that follows Snell's law of refraction when passing through an anisotropic mineral.

Orthosilicate Any silicate mineral consisting of independent silica tetrahedra bonded by other cations.

Paramagnetism The property of being slightly attracted to a strong magnetic field.

Paramorphism Internal rearrangement of internal atomic order while retaining the old external shape.

Parting Planar breakage along twin planes or other crystallographic planes of weakness caused by alteration that may or may not appear on all specimens of a species.

Pedion A form consisting of a single crystal face symmetrically unrelated to any other.

Pegmatite Body of rock, typically granitic in composition, characterized by exceptionally large crystals.

Peritectic Inflection on a liquidus marking the appearance of incongruently formed melt.

Phaneritic A crystalline rock texture in which individual crystals are visible to the unaided eye.

Phase Any homogeneous and mechanically separable part of a system.

Phenocryst Large crystal surrounded by finer ones in a porphyry.

Phosphorescence Slowly decaying luminescence.

Phyllosilicate Any silicate mineral composed of infinite two-dimensional tetrahedral sheets bonded by interlayer cations.

Pinacoid A form consisting of two parallel crystal faces related by symmetry.

Plane-polarized Light with its electric vector restricted to one plane that contains the ray direction; its magnetic vector is similarly restricted.

Point group One of 32 symmetry groups in which one point remains invariant.

Polarization Distortion of an electron cloud such that an atomic nucleus is not centrally located.

Pole A line perpendicular to a plane.

Polymorphism Capacity for a single chemical composition to crystallize in more than one crystal structure.

Polytypy Ordered layered structures capable of more than one stacking order.

Porphyroblast Large crystal surrounded by smaller ones produced by metamorphism.

Porphyry Igneous rock texture in which large crystals (phenocrysts) are surrounded by a finer-grained ground mass.

Prism A form with crystal faces parallel to the highest-order rotational axis of symmetry.

Prograde metamorphism See Metamorphism, prograde.

Proper Any element of symmetry that does not change the handedness of its object.

Protolith The rock that existed prior to metamorphism or melting.

Pseudomorphism Replacement of one mineral composition by another while retaining the old crystal shape.

Pyramid A form with three or more crystal faces that intersect the highest-order rotational symmetry axis.

Pyritohedron A closed form of 12 crystal faces each of which is an irregular pentagon; also called pentagonal dodecahedron.

Radical A cluster of ions, with net negative charge, that does not tend to divide during geochemical reactions.

Radioactivity The property of some isotopes to change nuclear charge and mass, thereby emitting radiation.

Radius ratio A number obtained by dividing a cation radius by an anion radius.

Rare earth Any element characterized by incomplete *f* orbitals; includes lanthanides and actinides.

Reciprocal space Lattice constructed from atomic plane normals with point distances the reciprocals of the interplanar spacing.

Reflecting plane See Diffraction plane.

Refractive index See Index, refractive

Regional metamorphism See Metamorphism, regional.

Retrograde metamorphism See Metamorphism, retrograde.

Rhombohedron A closed form of six crystal faces, each of which is a rhombus.

Rotoinversion A combination of a rotational axis of symmetry with inversion through a center along that axis.

Rotoreflection A combination of a rotational axis of symmetry with reflection across a mirror parallel to that axis.

Scalenohedron A closed form with crystal faces in the shape of scalene triangles.

Screw axis A combination of translation with rotation about an axis parallel to the translation.

Screw dislocation A line defect in a crystal structure about which structure planes appear to spiral.

Sheet silicate Any silicate mineral composed of infinite sheets of corner-sharing tetrahedra; also called phyllosilicate.

Silica saturation Crystalline rock composition such that exactly enough silica is present to crystallize feldspars.

Solidus Locus of all points in pressure-temperature-composition space below which liquid cannot exist.

Solvus Locus of all points in pressure-temperature-composition space below which a homogeneous crystalline solution separates into two phases.

Sorosilicate Any silicate mineral composed of dimers of silica tetrahedra bonded by other cations.

Space group One of 230 different ways of arranging point groups in space.

Space lattice One of 14 different ways of arranging periodic arrays of points; also called Bravais lattice.

Specific gravity Ratio of the weight of a mineral to the weight of an equal volume of water at 4°C; see also Density.

Spectroscopy Composition or structural analysis performed by analysis of wavelengths of electromagnetic radiation absorbed or emitted by a substance.

Sphenoid A form of two nonparallel crystal faces related by a diad.

Steno's law See First law of crystallography.

Step Vertical atomic plane between two terraces on a growing crystal face.

Stereogram Stereographic projection of symmetry elements.

Striation Grooves of alternating crystal faces on a crystal face or alternating cleavage planes on a cleavage plane.

Symmetry group A collection of operations with the properties that the product of any two operations is itself an operation of the group, every inverse operation is an operation of the group, and there exists an identity operation.

Syntaxy Three-dimensional crystallographic control of orientation between two mineral species with similar lattice spacing.

System, crystal All point groups consistent with one of seven lattice point symmetries.

System, physicochemical Any portion of the universe that can be isolated for study.

Tektosilicate Any silicate mineral composed of a framework of corner-sharing silica tetrahedra.

Terrace Growing face bounded by steps on a crystal.

Tetrad A rotation axis of symmetry that is one quarter of a complete rotation.

Tetrahedral site Any point in a crystal structure that will accept a cation of coordination number 4.

Tetrahedron A closed form of four crystal faces in the shape of equilateral triangles.

Thermoluminescence Release of electronically trapped energy as visible light when activated by heating.

Topotaxy Control of product crystallographic orientation by parent orientation during polymorphic transformation or other solid-state transition.

Toughness Resistance to breakage.

Trapezohedron A closed form of crystal faces that are trapezia.

Triad A rotational axis of symmetry that is one third of a complete rotation.

Trimorph One of three crystal structures of a single chemical composition.

Triple point Unique temperature and pressure where three phases of one component may coexist stably.

Trivariance A system in which three intensive variables may be independently and arbitrarily changed without gaining or losing a phase.

Twinning Two or more parts of a crystal related to one another by a symmetry element not included in their point group.

Unit cell The smallest volume containing all the chemical elements and all the symmetry elements of a crystal structure.

Univariance A system in which only one intensive variable may be changed arbitrarily without losing a phase.

Variable, extensive One of those properties that are divided when a system is divided.

Variable, intensive One of those properties that are undivided when a system is divided.

Variance The number of intensive variables of a system that may be independently and arbitrarily changed without gaining or losing a phase.

Vein Tabular mineral body crystallized from hydrothermal fluids in the earth's crust.

Xenocryst Undissolved crystal carried in a magma prior to crystallization.

Xenolith Rock fragment carried in a magma prior to crystallization.

Weathering Alteration of minerals and rocks resulting from contact with the atmosphere and meteoritic water.

Wettability Ease with which a mineral surface is wetted with water.

White radiation Electromagnetic radiation that is a mixture of wavelengths.

INDEX

MINERAL MASTERY ORDER FORM

Mineral Mastery brings the computer's power and convenience to the desk top or the lap top for hobbyists and college-level geology students. It offers the means to identify over 200 mineral species by making inquiries of its information base. It displays the physical properties of various minerals with text and graphs. Mineral Mastery was a 1988 winner in the IBM/League for Innovation "Competition for Excellence."

The hardware requirements for running Mineral Mastery are:

* PC, XT, AT, PS/2, or compatible
* Color or monochrome monitor
* 512K memory
* Two 5.25″ drives, one 3.5″ drive, or hard disk
* Printer optional

To order: Send this form (no photocopies, please) and $29 to:

DataWave Software
P.O. Box 42213
Mesa, AZ 85274

Telephone: 602-820-8041

Please send a copy of Mineral Mastery (☐ 5.25 or ☐ 3.5 disk) to:

Name ______________________________

Address ______________________________

City ____________________ State ______ Zip __________